Teaching Mathematics in Primary Schools

A Handbook of Lesson Plans, Knowledge and Teaching Methods

Sue Jennings and **Richard Dunne**

Letts

EDUCATIONAL

Aldine Place
London
W12 8AW

Tel: 020 8740 2266
Fax: 020 8743 8451
e-mail: he@lettsed.co.uk

Acknowledgements

The publishers and authors would like to thank Bob Anghileri for his constructive comments on this material. Thanks are also due to Roger Trend in the School of Education, University of Exeter, for co-ordinating the QTS series and to Topics for their efficient project management.

A CIP catalogue record is available from the British Library

ISBN 1-85805-318-8
Copyright Sue Jennings and Richard Dunne © 1998
Reprinted 1999, 2000 (twice)

Designed and edited by Topics - The Creative Partnership, Exeter

Printed and bound in Great Britain by Ashford Colour Press Ltd

Contents

About the series

The Letts QTS Series offers support for all those preparing to become teachers and working towards Qualified Teacher Status (QTS). The content, teaching approaches and practical ideas are useful for trainee teachers, teacher tutors and mentors, as well as for practising teachers and teacher educators in higher education.

The Letts QTS Series addresses the new standards for QTS and the content of the Initial Teacher Training National Curriculum (ITTNC). These are central to the improvement of standards in schools. The series is specifically designed to help all trainee teachers cover the content of the ITTNC and achieve the national standards in order to be awarded QTS.

The short series handbook *QTS: A Practical Introduction* gives trainees an overview of the QTS requirement and a more detailed interpretation of each standard.

The other books in the Letts QTS Series offer trainees the chance to audit their knowledge of the content of the subjects in the ITTNC, pinpoint areas of further work, and use support materials to develop their knowledge. The first two subjects addressed are English and Mathematics for primary teachers.

There are two Letts QTS Series books for each subject:

Book 1 addresses trainees' subject knowledge at their own level by offering a systematic and comprehensive guide to the subject knowledge requirements of the ITTNC. Trainees can check their own knowledge of the subject against that specified in the ITTNC. Section one provides a comprehensive **audit** of this subject knowledge and understanding, with helpful **feedback** and follow-up set out in section two. Having identified areas of subject knowledge for attention, trainees can then use the support materials in section three to develop **key ideas** and map out their **personal learning plan**.

Book 2 for each subject is a handbook of **lesson plans**, **knowledge** and **methods**. This provides details of carefully selected lessons which illustrate effective teaching. It shows how lesson planning and classroom teaching draw on a high level of subject knowledge. It demonstrates how carefully integrated whole-class teaching and group and individual work can be designed to ensure that pupils make progress in their learning.

There is also a tutor-support pack for each subject.

The Letts QTS Series aims to break down the requirements of QTS into manageable units so that trainees can evaluate and improve their knowledge of each subject. The books in the series are written in a straightforward way by authors who are all experienced teachers, teacher educators, researchers, writers and specialists in their subject areas.

Titles on Information Technology and Science for primary teachers will follow, together with titles for trainees preparing to teach in the secondary phase of schooling.

About this book

This book is for everyone who wants to teach maths in a primary school. It is a handbook of lesson plans and teaching methods. It provides details of carefully selected lessons which illustrate effective teaching. In addition it shows how lesson planning and classroom teaching draw on a high level of subject knowledge. It also demonstrates how carefully integrated whole class teaching and group and individual work can be designed to ensure that pupils make progress in their learning.

There are two sections:

- *A framework for teaching maths*
- *Scripts, resources and discussion*

The first section, *A framework for teaching maths*, introduces the background to the second section. It sets out the essential philosophy of the later work in a discussion of *Teaching as assisted performance* as the first element of the framework. This phrase, borrowed from Tharp and Gallimore (1988),* summarizes an approach to teaching that sees the pupil as an apprentice to the teacher.

For this reason the teacher needs to have a well-established knowledge of maths, as we explained in an earlier book in this series, *Mathematics for Primary Teachers*.

In the earlier book a number of key ideas were introduced. These are further developed here in a discussion of *Key ideas* as the second element of the overall framework.

The third element, *The classroom framework*, introduces a model for planning the whole class teaching and group and individual work that contribute to effective teaching. We are grateful to David Brodie for suggesting the ideas used in the classroom framework. We have seen how he has developed this approach in Prince Albert School, Aston, Birmingham, where he is Headteacher.

The second section provides scripts, resources and discussion for six topics in maths teaching:

1. *Numbers and counting*
2. *The four operations*
3. *Extending the number system*
4. *Properties of shapes*
5. *Measurement and graphs*
6. *Handling data*

These detailed analyses of classroom work are based on the philosophy of the framework. Each topic illustrates the nature of *Teaching as assisted performance*, the centrality of the *Key ideas* and the way in which the *Classroom framework* is a crucial organizing feature.

* Tharp, R.G. and Gallimore, R. (1988) *Rousing Minds to Life*, Cambridge: Cambridge University Press.

A framework for teaching maths

Introduction

Teaching is a complex and intellectual activity. We want to provide a framework for understanding its complexity. Our *Framework for teaching maths* has three components:

- *Teaching as assisted performance*
- *Key ideas*
- *The classroom framework*

Each of these will be discussed in detail. We begin here by examining *Teaching as assisted performance*. This is followed by a detailed discussion of the *Key ideas*, then a complete review of *The classroom framework*.

Before we begin our introduction to *Teaching as assisted performance* we need to consider the nature of learning.

A framework can help us to gain a better understanding of the activity of teaching.

The nature of learning

How people learn

All teaching is based on a view of how people learn and there are many different views. We are going to contrast just two of those views which underpin much of the way in which work is planned for classrooms.

The first view is that people use their minds to make sense of the world around them. They do this by hypothesizing and testing and making adjustments to their earlier ideas. In essence, learning takes place when people analyse their experiences. The role of the teacher is to provide appropriate experiences. The teacher facilitates learning through the provision of materials. The learner acts as 'a lone scientist'.

This view of learning translates into classroom activities that focus on each individual child working at her own pace on materials that have been designed for her own personal level of achievement. The teacher's role is to facilitate the learning process and provide help when required.

The teacher as facilitator

Emphasis on language

The second view puts a greater emphasis on language. From this point of view people learn through their communication with others. The most important contribution to the learning process comes from the teacher's language. This establishes for the learner an appropriate way of thinking about experiences. The teacher's role is very important. The language she uses carries messages built up over the years so that learners gain access

The child constructs knowledge by working with appropriate materials.

to the ways in which others of the same culture have interpreted their experiences. The learner is an 'apprentice' to the teacher.

This second view of learning is enacted in the classroom when the teacher takes a proactive role in teaching the children by describing, explaining, instructing and demonstrating her expertise whilst providing maximum assistance to the learner.

Knowledge is constructed through social interaction.

The learner as apprentice

We prefer the second point of view. The approach to teaching that we have adopted is based on the idea of learners being apprentices to teachers, learning from their skills, language and attitudes.

You can think of this approach as a cognitive apprenticeship.

Looking at objects from different perspectives

This version of how people learn makes sense when we think of how school subjects differ from each other. As an example, consider what happens when you look at a flower vase. You may examine it for its aesthetic qualities, or you might look at it scientifically, focusing, perhaps, on the way it refracts light to produce a rainbow effect. You may be interested in the exact description of its curvature and this would be a mathematical viewpoint.

The vase is not in itself either a work of art, a scientific object or a mathematical object. The view depends upon the way in which the observer contemplates it. You can examine it from a particular perspective when you have the skills, language and perceptions that typify that way of looking. You are inducted into different ways of looking by being taught.

Implications for the design of teaching

The idea of learners being inducted into the language and ways of working in each subject has important implications for the design of teaching programmes. It means that classroom work in maths needs to be designed in accordance with the nature of maths. Learners must be enabled to adopt a mathematical perspective. For this reason we have provided a very full discussion of important features of maths as *Key ideas*.

See *Key ideas*.

The idea of the learner as an apprentice is an important one. We would emphasize that apprenticeship does not involve learning only a set of skills. It includes also being enabled to adopt the perceptions and ways of thinking that have become the norm for that discipline. And it means that the teacher must be very careful to demonstrate all these things. Learners need assistance in all aspects of what it means to do maths. Teaching, therefore, can be thought of as assisted performance.

Teaching as assisted performance

Assistance in cognition

If learners are to become good at maths they must learn an appropriate set of skills and understand the important ideas. They must learn how to think mathematically. Learners need assistance in **cognition**. They must be helped, for instance, to make connections between ideas, drawing on previous learning and collecting ideas together in broad categories. These are the things that good learners manage to do fairly quickly. Others need careful and detailed assistance.

Learners do not necessarily make connections between mathematical concepts. They need assistance.

Assistance in learning strategies

Children cannot learn everything whilst they are at school. They need to be able to use a powerful set of **learning strategies** so that they can continue their learning beyond what is specifically taught. Some of the most important learning strategies are exactly what is needed to

At school children should be prepared for life-long learning.

understand (making connections between ideas, drawing on previous learning and collecting ideas together in broad categories); other strategies include using mental images, repetition and memorization.

Assistance in motivation

Why should learners put any effort into learning maths? They need **motivation**. This is not a quality that learners either possess or lack from birth although we can work on their natural curiosity by choosing appropriate representations of maths. Learners need assistance in becoming motivated, and the motivation needs to be intrinsic to the teaching of maths. They need to achieve success in learning, so teachers must ensure that they do so.

> Success is the greatest motivator.

Assistance in social skills

Learning and doing mathematics are not solitary tasks. They are done in communication with other people. Mathematics teaching must include induction into what this means when doing maths. Learners need assistance in learning **social skills**. It is not a case of hoping that they will use existing social skills while doing maths. They need to be taught such skills as an intrinsic part of learning maths. These include listening to each other, responding supportively, asking questions, describing their own results and articulating their thinking processes, as well as being considerate to others.

> Assistance is given not only by the teacher but also by the children working co-operatively.

Assistance in language

The language of mathematics is precise and economical. Learners will not automatically appreciate and use the especially precise language of maths, nor will they make sense of it without communication with the teacher and others. Learners need assistance in using **language** as they learn maths. This includes interrogating text and recognizing that symbols, graphs and equations, as well as sentences and stories, are the texts of maths.

> See *Key ideas: Language*.

Summary

The five areas of assisted performance

A teaching programme that is based on the idea of learners being apprentices to the teacher will use the idea of teaching as **assisted performance**. When we teach maths the idea of 'performance' is wide ranging. We need to provide assistance in:

- *cognition*
- *learning strategies*
- *motivation*
- *social skills*
- *language*

> Performance in mathematics includes thinking mathematically, using the language of maths and providing convincing arguments.

The nature of assisted performance

Enabling children to achieve success

Assisted performance does not only mean helping pupils with things. Of course, it is a form of help, but it is of a particular type. It is based on the idea that teachers must demonstrate what kind of performance is appropriate and enable their pupils to achieve that level of performance immediately. You probably find this a surprising idea. You would be entitled to ask: *If the pupils cannot do something how can they be expected to do it successfully straight away? Surely they need to keep having a go at it, not getting it right, until they eventually manage it?*

> Failure is the greatest discouragement to learning.

It is this approach to learning that is rejected by the idea of assisted performance. The aim is that pupils will be given sufficient assistance to make sure that they can do it. If this means that the teacher is providing total assistance (because the pupil is unable to do any of the task alone) then that is part of the process. It is through doing it with assistance now that they will become able to do it without assistance later.

Is it possible to cover all aspects of assisted performance in typical school time?

Yes. The areas of learning where assistance is needed are not separate from each other. It is not necessary to devote time to each of them in turn. The approach to teaching that we will describe clarifies how in just a few minutes' teaching it is likely that many of these qualities are being assisted.

> Providing assistance to individuals becomes a realistic objective through whole class teaching.

> Assisting performance can save time.

Teaching that focuses on assisting performance can actually save time. For example, in assisting cognition connections are made between mathematical ideas which means that children have only to learn one thing well to be able to do many different things. Assisting social skills can improve the ethos of the classroom to such an extent that children do not waste time but are fully engaged in the learning process. Assisting language improves classroom communication and assisting motivation encourages children to take more responsibility for their own learning. And assisting learning strategies enables children to become independent learners.

Does assisted performance require one-to-one teaching?

No. On the contrary, there is a specific need to use a substantial amount of whole class teaching. The need for this is related to all aspects of assisted performance. We want to distinguish here between 'whole class organization' and 'whole class teaching'. Classes may be organized as whole class groups without all pupils participating. For example, the teacher may be asking questions of the whole class with only a small sub-group answering. This is not teaching. For whole class teaching the activity must be designed to involve the whole class, with the teacher explaining, instructing and demonstrating in such a way that every member of the class is helped to achieve success.

> Whole class teaching is more than just whole class organization.

> Direct questioning in a public forum can become very threatening and often leads to children developing a sense of failure.

Whole class teaching needs to be structured in such a way that the teacher provides maximum assistance during demonstration phases and reduced assistance during modelling and summarizing phases. These phases are discussed in more detail in the section on *The Classroom Framework*.

> See *The classroom framework*.

> A community of learners

The essence of the method of teaching and learning described here is of a community of learners working together in co-operation and mutual understanding to enjoy the delights of maths.

Key ideas

The nature of maths

See also *Key ideas* in *Mathematics for Primary Teachers*.

Maths provokes speculation.

The beauty of maths resides in its tendency to provoke speculation. Its essential detachment from the original problem is the key to its power and the basis for aesthetic experience.

Comparing heights

It is difficult to describe the nature of maths in a single sentence or paragraph. Instead let us explore it by means of some well-known examples. First suppose that we have two groups of five children and we want to compare their heights. (We have chosen a small sample for the purpose of illustration.) First we measure all their heights in centimetres. We collect two sets of data and record them in order in a table.

	Heights of children in centimetres				
Set A	88	101	130	159	172
Set B	88	105	118	162	172

Look at set A. We could describe it as: one child is 88cm; one child is 101cm; one child is 130cm; one child is 159cm; one child is 172cm. This is a very accurate description, but the approach would be inconvenient if we were trying to describe a very large set with, perhaps, thousands of children in it.

An artist might be more interested in the appearance of the children and a biologist in their cell structure. We are looking at the children from a mathematical perspective.

Descriptive statistics

We could try a shorthand method to communicate the general nature of the data: there are five children in the set; the shortest child is 88cm; the tallest child is 172cm. Descriptive statistics of this sort can be useful in giving an immediate idea of what a set of data is like. You can quickly see that the children surveyed were not over 200cm tall, and there were no new-born babies.

This kind of shorthand can be especially useful if we have to deal with very large sets. What we lose in detail we perhaps gain in convenience. The trouble is that, by themselves, the descriptive statistics we have used do not reveal any differences between set A and set B. If we describe set B in the same way we learn only that there are five children in the set; the shortest child is 88cm; the tallest child is 172cm. Some way is needed of summarizing the two sets that reveals the difference between them. We need to introduce some summary statistics.

Summary statistics

Look again at set A. You can see five children of different heights. When we say 'you can see ...' we are, of course, asking you to use your imagination because you cannot actually see those children. Continue working in the imagination. Imagine transforming those children you

Working in the imagination

can 'see' so that each is the same height. Imagine that to treat them fairly in terms of height you need to give each the same amount. This involves chopping off the heads of the taller ones and pasting them on to the smaller ones.

If all the children were the same height this is what they would look like.

In the imagination it is possible to do this without injury, ending up with five children of the same height. You can see that the height of each one is 130cm. If you do the same with the children in set B you find that the height of the new, imaginary children is 129cm. You can see from these summary statistics that the children in set B tend to be slightly shorter than those in set A.

Using summary statistics for comparison

How can we report our imaginary experiment? We can say:

When we think of the total height of the children in set A and imaginarily share it around so that the five children get the same amount, the height of each new child is 130cm. When we think of the total height of the children in set B and imaginarily share it around so that the five children get the same amount, the height of each new child is 129cm.

This is very long-winded. There is a shorter way of saying the same thing. We simply say:

The mean height

The mean height in set A is 130cm.
The mean height in set B is 129cm.

Mathematicians often start with real-life problems (like thinking about two sets of real people) but they enter imaginary worlds to solve the problems. It is in imaginary worlds that most of the work is done in maths.

In the present case of two sets of children, it is possible to forget the children completely now. How can we go about finding the mean of the numbers 88, 101, 130, 159, 172? Do not think about children; do not think of heights. Now you cannot cut off heads even in your imagination because there are no heads to cut off. What you can do is find the total (88 + 101 + 130 + 159 + 172 = 650) and divide by 5 (650 ÷ 5 = 130). By working only with these symbols (the numbers) we have been able to calculate the mean. This figure has nothing to do with children or with heights. It is completely imaginary. It has been achieved by working entirely with symbols (650 ÷ 5 = 130). This is the nature of maths. It takes place in imaginary worlds that are described by symbols.

Calculating the mean

We abstract the numerical data and reorganize it.

Working with symbols

We can, of course, use this method to calculate the mean height in set B. When we do this we are using the symbolic results of maths and applying them to real-life situations because they work and they make life easy. But you need to appreciate that when we deal with symbols (like numbers) we are working in an entirely imaginary world.

Working in an entirely imaginary world

Our discussion of the nature of maths reveals an important point. When children are asked to do 'sums' they are being asked to work mathematically. They are dealing with symbolic quantities that exist in the imagination. 'Five apples' exist; 'five' alone is an act of imagination.

Children are being asked to work as mathematicians in the sense which is summarized in the diagram.

The nature of maths

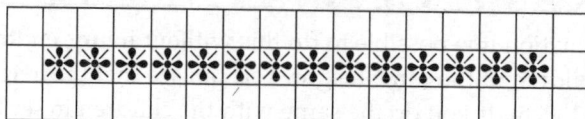

| explore objects in the real world | → | generate symbols to summarize the real world | → | use symbols to explore experience beyond the real world |

The beauty of maths lies in exploring beyond the real world.

Exploring patterns

Let's take a different example. Suppose we want to tile a bathroom using patterned and plain tiles so that we have a long row of patterned tiles surrounded by plain tiles in the following way:

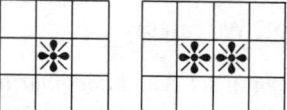

We want to work out how many of each tile to buy. We could draw several diagrams like this and make a conjecture.

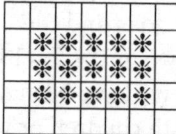 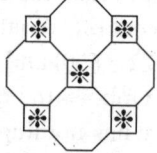 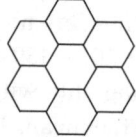

Speculation

There seems to be a pattern: the number of plain tiles increases by two each time. How can we be sure that the conjecture is correct? We could check the next one in the sequence, but what if the rule breaks down? Do we have to go to all this trouble each time we design a new pattern for the tiles? Go back to the original diagram and speculate for a moment. Inspect the diagram. For each patterned tile in the row we need two plain tiles. Then we need six more plain tiles at either end.

The clue is in the geometric structure.

The clue is in this geometric structure. It is not necessary to draw several examples. We can see from the structure that for n patterned tiles we need $2n + 6$ plain tiles. We can generate symbols to summarize the real world and then use the symbols to explore beyond the real world.

Examining the geometric structure means that we do not have to test every case.

Suppose that we now want m rows and n columns of patterned tiles surrounded by plain tiles. We shall need $2m + 2n + 4$ plain tiles. We can now go beyond the real world and ask: 'What if all the tiles were hexagonal? Or the patterned tiles square and the plain tiles octagonal? Or all the tiles were parallelograms? Or ...'

Going beyond the real world

We can explore beyond the real world. We may not be able to buy all these different shaped tiles but we can test all the cases in maths by drawing diagrams, inspecting the geometric structure and using symbols. This is the nature of maths. These cases may prove to be useful at some future date; however, in maths we do not study them for their usefulness but for completeness, elegance and beauty. We study them for the intrinsic qualities of the exploration.

Mathematical exploration does not have to take account of real-life constraints.

Studying objects for their completeness, elegance and beauty

Starting with a real-life problem

We can often start with what seems to be a simple, straightforward question in real life and find that it takes us on a journey way beyond the bounds of reality. Take, for example, the farmer's investigation of a field: 'I have 100 metres of fencing. What is the greatest grazing area I can construct with it?'

Where shall we start? Well, most fields are rectangular so let us begin by exploring all the different rectangles we can make with 100 metres. That gives an interesting result: the maximum grazing area is provided by the square. We wonder:

Speculation

> *Is there something special about a square that gives the maximum area? What happens if we try triangles? Wow! The maximum area is given by an equilateral triangle. What about pentagons? ...*

Now the first answer we found is probably all that the farmer needed to know and there are obvious reasons why pentagons are not a sensible choice (for example, they do not tessellate). However, we have travelled beyond the real world and started to explore shapes and their properties for their intrinsic value.

Exploration

Let us pursue this problem further. Once we have convinced ourselves that regular shapes give the maximum area, we might ask another question. 'Does an increase in the number of sides increase the area?' We explore this and represent the results on a graph.

Using graphs

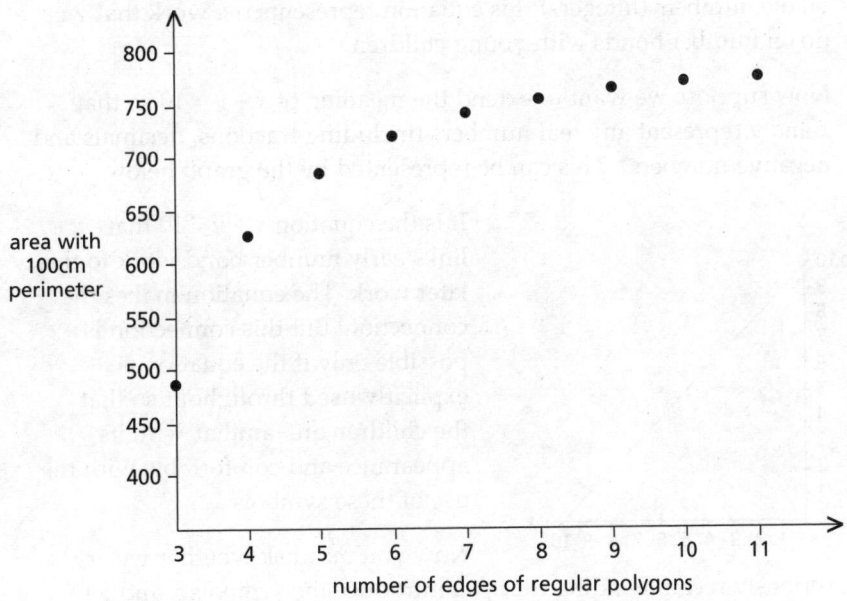

The graph shows us that the greater the number of sides the greater the area. So what happens as the number of sides continues to increase? We picture this in our imagination and we 'see' that the shape gets closer and closer to that of a circle. So what if the shape were a circle? We calculate the area. Yes. This is greater than all the others. So the maximum area using 100 metres is given by a circle.

We can consider a circle to be a polygon with an infinite number of edges.

Returning to the real world

Now we have forgotten all about that poor farmer who is waiting for our answer. What shall we tell him? We need to know more about the context so that we can interpret our results in the light of the farmer's needs. We have a range of suggestions to make as we get back to the real-life story. But to do the maths story we had to detach ourselves from real life and explore the problem in our imagination, using symbols, until we had exhausted all the possibilities.

The nature of maths

In all of these examples we started with real-life problems, generated symbols to summarize the problems, and explored the problems beyond the real world. This is the nature of maths and our first and principal key idea. It is fundamental to an understanding of all the other key ideas.

Algebra

With algebra you do less work, not more

The language of maths

Algebra is the language of maths. When we use symbols with the rules and conventions that govern their use this is algebra. Using algebra we can express important results and make links and connections within and beyond the world of maths. This gives maths its coherence and means that there is less to learn. When you learn algebra you learn a language that is used to summarize a large number of mathematical results. In school maths algebra is used to generalize results in arithmetic and geometry.

> We use algebra to summarize results and write general statements. This reduces what has to be learnt.

Algebra as generalized arithmetic

Suppose we want to discuss the sum of two numbers: we can summarize this by letting the two numbers be x and y and writing $x + y$. Now suppose we know that the sum of x and y is always 10. Then we can write $x + y = 10$. When x and y are restricted to positive whole numbers (integers) this equation represents the work that we do on number bonds with young children.

Using letters

> When we use letters we must specify what sort of numbers they represent.

Representing results as graphs

Now suppose we want to extend the meaning of $x + y = 10$ so that x and y represent any real numbers (including fractions, decimals and negative numbers). This can be represented by the graph below.

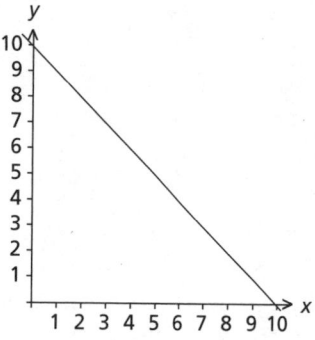

The equation makes the connection.

It is the equation $x + y = 10$ that links early number bond work to this later work. The equation makes the connection. But this connection is possible only if the equation is explicitly used throughout so that the children are familiar with its appearance and comfortable with the use of these symbols.

> Early introduction to mathematical symbols allows children to become familiar with them.

Now you may ask whether we are seriously recommending that you introduce the symbols x and y to young children. Yes, we are. Pause for a moment and consider the confusion that often arises when teachers insist on introducing one set of symbols – say, squares and triangles – to young children.

$$\square + \triangle = 10$$

Even more confusion is introduced if the teacher calls them boxes and triangles because the first symbol is a square, not a box.

When the children are a bit older these geometric symbols are sometimes replaced by question marks.

$$? + ? = 10$$

The best symbols to use

The most powerful and least confusing form

$$x + y = 10$$

is too often introduced in the later years of schooling. No wonder that algebra seems to involve more work rather than less. The children have had to cope with three different sets of symbols when they could have been using just one. Careful introduction of symbols such as x and y at an early age can assist cognition in maths by ensuring continuity and coherence.

Assisting cognition

The symbols used here have been borrowed from the alphabet. Going back to the examples at the beginning, in the first case x stands for any whole number; in the second case x stands for any real number. In both cases x is a variable.

We can inspect the equation $x + y = 10$ and look for clues to find the value of x. Suppose that y is known to be 4. Then $x + 4 = 10$. So, of all the possible values that x can take in this case it must be 6. However, we may not know the value of y. In the case where x and y are positive whole numbers our solution would be all the pairs that sum to ten: (0, 10), (1, 9), (2, 8), (3, 7), (4, 6), (5, 5).

x and y are positive whole numbers.

In the case where x and y represent real numbers we could not possibly list all those pairs because they are unlimited – ($^-$3, 13), ($^-$0.5, 10.5), (0.75, 9.25), etc. – so the best way to present the solution would be on the graph (above). But even here we cannot *see* all the pairs, we have to imagine them on a line that extends beyond the limits of the grid.

Extending the possibilities

In maths it is not only in algebra that we borrow letters from the alphabet. We also use letters to represent units of measurement, such as m for metres and h for hours. This is not algebra. Letters are used in codes, such as a = 1, b = 2. This is not algebra. Letters are used to abbreviate words, such as v for vertices, f for faces. This is not algebra. Letters are used to represent words in a sentence: for example, three apples and four apples makes seven apples or 3a + 4a = 7a. This is not algebra. It is only when the letter is a variable (can take any value from a given set of values) that it is an algebraic symbol.

Letters do not always mean algebra.

Algebra can be used to summarize geometric results. The perimeter of a rectangle with sides x and y can be written as $P = 2x + 2y$. Now the rules and conventions of arithmetic are the same as those for the algebra we are using here. The algebra we study in school is generalized arithmetic. The formula for the perimeter can be changed in appearance using the laws and conventions of arithmetic. We could use the distributive law to write it as $P = 2(x + y)$. We can also think of this as 'factorizing' the expression on the right-hand side of the equation. Alternatively, we could write $P = 2y + 2x$, again changing the appearance by noting that addition is commutative.

Using algebra to summarize

When we write the perimeter of a rectangle as $P = 2x + 2y$ we call this a 'formula'. There are many formulae that are used for perimeter, area and volume of geometric shapes. We do not use formulae only in geometry but also to summarize results in arithmetic, statistics, mechanics and so on. Using formulae can save us a lot of time and effort. We do not have to go back to square one each time but can draw on results that have been summarized symbolically in these neat and efficient formulae. *With algebra you do less work, not more.*

Formulae

Algebra means you do less work, not more.

It is not difficult to convince someone that the formula we have used for the perimeter of a rectangle is true for every case. The logic is in the geometrical structure. But it is not always so easy to win a mathematical argument. Sometimes we have to construct a watertight proof and we shall discuss this as the next *Key idea*.

It is consistency of approach that assists the children in making vital links and connections in maths.

The most common error is for children to interpret algebraic letters as objects.

When children are completely comfortable using algebra they are ready to explore maths to its full potential.

Proof

Proof is a central feature of maths. Proof is when we can convince someone that our argument is watertight; that we have covered every possibility; that there are no exceptional cases that have not been explored. Proof is based on accepted truths, i.e. the body of knowledge that already exists in maths. Look at this statement:

The exterior angles of any polygon add up to 360°.

Learning to construct a mathematical argument assists children with logical thinking.

Looking for a proof

Is this true? Can you prove it? Let us inspect this statement by looking at a triangle.

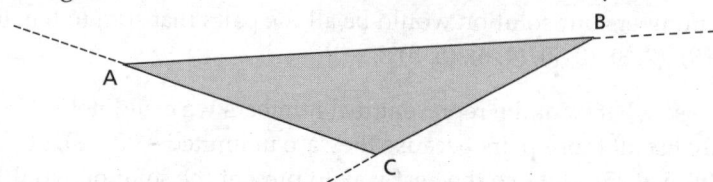

Imagine that this triangle is drawn on the floor. Stand at A and face B. Walk to B. Turn and face C. Walk to C. Turn and face A. Walk to A. Turn and face B. You are back where you started. Altogether you have done one full turn. You have turned through 360°. Try this with a quadrilateral, a pentagon and a hexagon. Do you always do exactly one full turn? Yes. Are you convinced that the statement above is true? Probably. But we have to convince others and not all will be easily persuaded. Let us try again with the triangle.

Practical work provides a visual proof. The next task is to construct a written proof.

Convincing yourself

Convincing others

Accepted facts

When we start on a proof we have to agree as to what can be accepted as fact. Here we are going to start by stating two facts. (These can both be proved.)

Some facts are frequently used to deduce further facts. They should not just be accepted as truths but rigorously proved at the outset.

1. The interior angles of a triangle add up to 180°.
2. Angles on a straight line add up to 180°.

We now draw the triangle and extend each edge as shown. The exterior angles of the triangle are marked with a double arc.

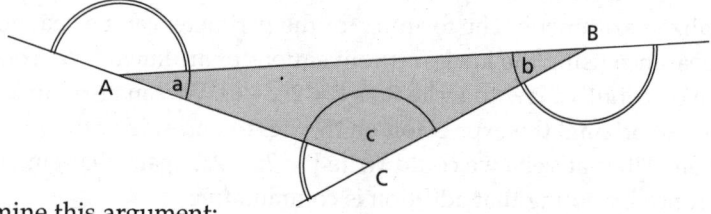

Starting with known facts and working in small steps

Examine this argument:

The sum of the interior angles a + b + c = 180 (see 1 above)

The exterior angles are (180 – a), (180 – b) and (180 – c) (see 2 above)

The sum of the exterior angles = (180 – a) + (180 – b) + (180 – c)
$$= 540 - (a + b + c)$$
$$= 360$$

Proving what seems like common sense

This is now a convincing argument for a triangle and we can use the same method to prove the statement for any polygon. We can prove what seemed like common sense.

The following example shows how we can form an argument by providing examples and, in particular, counter-examples. But if we want to cover every possibility then algebra provides us with the means to construct a convincing argument.

The sum of four even numbers is divisible by four.

Is this statement true? It seems a reasonable statement. We could try some different combinations of four even numbers.

Using examples to test a statement

$$4 + 8 + 12 + 16 = 40 \qquad \text{true}$$
$$2 + 6 + 4 + 8 = 20 \qquad \text{true}$$
$$6 + 10 + 14 + 18 = 48 \qquad \text{true}$$

The statement is certainly true for all these examples. How many examples do we need to do? If we go on we may find by chance that every example is true and we may never stumble across a counter-example. However, we may be lucky: the next example may convince us that the statement is only sometimes true.

Finding a counter-example

$$2 + 8 + 12 + 16 = 38 \qquad \text{false}$$

This is interesting. For what sorts of example is the statement true? Could we have saved some time by using algebra?

First let us look at what we mean by 'the sum of four even numbers'. How can we write this? What do we know about even numbers? We know that all even numbers are divisible by two. How do we write this? If a is any whole number then $2a$ must be an even number. Is this true? Check it. Yes, if we multiply a whole number by two then the result must be divisible by two. So if a, b, c and d are whole numbers the sum of four even numbers can be written as:

Writing the statement algebraically

$$2a + 2b + 2c + 2d$$

How does this help? Inspect the expression. What do you notice? There is a number two in every term so we can take the factor two outside a bracket:

$$2(a + b + c + d)$$

The original statement says that we want this expression to be divisible by four. Now we consider what we know about numbers that are divisible by four. Take the number 20. This is divisible by four. To divide by four we can divide by two and then divide by two again. Can we always do that with numbers that are divisible by four? Yes.

Let us do that with this expression. First divide it by two. What do we get? $(a + b + c + d)$. Now we want to divide this by two. Can we do that? We don't know. We don't have sufficient information. If we knew that the sum $(a + b + c + d)$ was an even number then we could divide it by two.

Considering known facts

We know the results of combining four numbers:

$$\text{even} + \text{even} + \text{even} + \text{even} = \text{even}$$
$$\text{even} + \text{even} + \text{odd} + \text{odd} = \text{even}$$
$$\text{odd} + \text{odd} + \text{odd} + \text{odd} = \text{even}$$
$$\text{odd} + \text{even} + \text{even} + \text{even} = \text{odd}$$
$$\text{odd} + \text{odd} + \text{odd} + \text{even} = \text{odd}$$

Three of these result in even numbers. We can now say:

Writing a concise statement

For any whole numbers a, b, c, d the sum $2a + 2b + 2c + 2d$ is divisible by four if all the numbers are odd, if all are even or if two are odd and two are even.

Are you convinced? We hope so. Follow the argument again. Is it foolproof? Yes, it is and algebra has helped to make it so.

Some statements seem to make sense, but they require closer scrutiny, as can be seen here.

The counter-example is sufficient to disprove the statement. Further examination is required to discover all the possible cases.

Make sure that you can follow the logic of this argument. Substitute numbers for the letters to test the statements.

Keep the value: change the appearance

I change my one pound coin for seventeen coins. I have the same amount of money in my purse. What are the seventeen coins?

The essence of maths

Equivalence

The phrase 'Keep the value: change the appearance' summarizes the essence of much of what we do in maths. It is a powerful tool that assists cognition. Links between concepts and ideas can be made through the mental imagery that it provides. It permeates every aspect of maths from the words, terms and symbols to the rules and conventions. It is often referred to as 'equivalence' but the rhythmic quality of the longer phrase makes it more memorable and the mere chanting of the phrase creates a pause, a time to stop and think, to inspect and look for clues.

Most of us use the idea of equivalence unconsciously by interchanging words and rearranging numbers. Regular and frequent practice has provided us with the means to become fluent and mentally agile in substituting one form for another. Children need to be taught these skills so that they too can become competent in knowing when they can apply ideas of equivalence.

> The word 'appearance' is used to denote the way that we see or speak words or symbols.

Different ways of speaking maths

Look at how many different ways we have of saying 3 + 4. We say: 'three and four'; 'three add four'; 'three plus four'; 'the sum of three and four'; 'the total of three and four'. Each of these is valid and needs to be taught explicitly. We can assist children in their learning by pointing to the phrase 'Keep the value: change the appearance' as we speak the sum in these different ways.

> What we see is the same but what we speak may be different.

Different ways of writing maths

Inspect for a moment the number $\frac{1}{5}$. We can also write this as 'one fifth', 'a fifth' (it is not immediately obvious to children that 'a' and 'one' are the same) and '⅕'. We may encounter a fifth in different forms such as: 20%, 1:5 or 1 ÷ 5. And we can write equivalent forms such as: 3:15, 6 ÷ 30, $\frac{2}{10}$ or ⁷⁄₃₅. Knowing that all of these have the same value but a different appearance means that we can decide which form suits the situation in hand. We can be flexible and move between the different forms. We can read 20% with our eyes but think a fifth or two tenths in our minds. The teacher needs to bring together these different forms and, by means of the key phrase, help the children to understand that they all have the same value but a different appearance.

> What we see may be different but what we speak is the same.

Mental maths

Now suppose I ask you to add seventeen and thirty-six in your head. What do you do? Do you say (10 + 30 + 7 + 3 + 3)? Or (17 + 30 + 3 + 3)? Maybe neither of these. There are many different ways in which you can partition the numbers so that they keep the value but change the appearance. The strategy you choose will depend upon your confidence with certain number bonds. There may be strategies that you have never thought of that are more efficient and effective than your own. Children need to see demonstrated different ways of doing mental maths so that they can choose from tried and tested methods. Whatever method is used, they need to be reminded to 'Keep the value: change the appearance'.

> Numbers can provoke mental images. These images need to be demonstrated.

The laws of arithmetic

Let us look at some of the laws of arithmetic and see how they relate to this phrase. The commutative law for addition tells us that 5 + 6 = 6 + 5. The value is the same but the appearance has changed. We know this law well; we use it all the time to make addition easier to perform.

Why do we need to consider it now? The answer is clear when we look at subtraction and see that the commutative law does not hold for this operation: $5 - 6 \neq 6 - 5$. Here the appearance has changed but so has the value. This is an important result. Often you hear children say: 'Five take six you can't do, so do six take five.' What are the implications here for teaching? Those rare yet significant results that do not comply with our well-worn phrase need specific attention and teachers need to take care over their use of language when teaching such things as subtraction to avoid common errors.

The phrase is equally applicable in geometry. Look at the two triangles below.

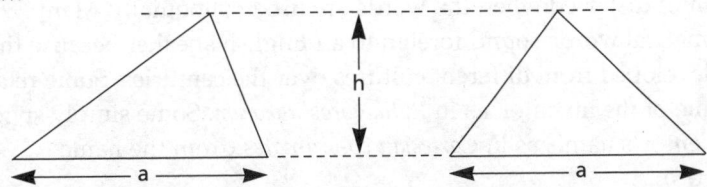

Are the two triangles the same? You should ask: 'In what way?' The same angles, the same area, the same length sides, the same colour, the same type? We need to be more specific. In fact the two triangles have the same area (the same length base and the same height) but are of a different appearance.

Now inspect these two triangles:

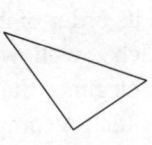 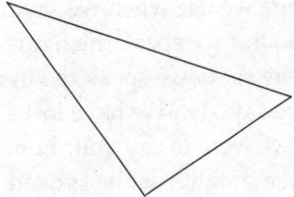

The value of the angles is the same but the triangles have a different appearance. They are what we call 'similar' triangles. Then there are triangles where all the properties have the same value *and* the triangles have the same appearance: these are called 'congruent' triangles. We could have triangles where the perimeter has the same value but they are of a different appearance. Conservation of certain properties of shape is an important aspect of geometry and the phrase 'Keep the value: change the appearance' assists cognition and provides a powerful strategy to assist learning.

Statistics is yet another area of maths where the phrase is appropriate. Look at these two sets of data:

    Data set A: 1, 3, 6, 7, 11, 12, 12, 14, 15, 16
    Data set B: 2, 2, 8, 9, 9, 10, 13, 13, 15, 16

The two sets have a different appearance but the value of their mean and the sample size is the same in each case. These summary statistics do not always provide us with sufficient information to compare sets of data. Can you construct another set of data with the same sample size and mean as sets A and B but with a different appearance? The possibilities are endless.

The phrase 'Keep the value: change the appearance' applies across all areas of maths. It encapsulates many of the significant results and assists children in their cognitive development by enabling them to make connections and be aware of continuity and coherence.

The language of maths

The language of
maths provokes mental
images.

You know the language of maths when you no longer focus on every word and symbol but start to examine how to use the mental images they provoke.

The language of maths consists of words, terms, symbols, notation and signs. It has its own syntax and style, its own conventions and laws. It borrows words from our everyday language, such as 'similar' and 'translate', and gives them a special meaning. It lends words such as 'half' and 'square' to everyday speech. The special meanings are sometimes distorted when the words are used colloquially. Many mathematical words sound foreign to an English speaker because they have developed from different cultures over the centuries. Some retain the name of the inventor, as in *Pythagoras' theorem*. Some simply suggest the inventor's name, as in *Cartesian co-ordinates* (from the name Déscartes).

Children will become familiar with the language of maths when it is used in the classroom on a regular basis.

Number notation

The number system we use today has developed from the complex notation of the ancient Babylonians and Egyptians, through the elegant decimal system derived from Arabic notation. The elegance of this system is remarkable. When we look at the number 465 we know that we are to think at once of four hundred and six tens and five ones. The position of each figure indicates its order of magnitude.

The logic of number

The language we use when we say the number 465 is helpful. When we say four *hundred* we speak the figure and attach its order of magnitude. When we say six-*ty* we speak the figure and attach ... well, we do not say 'ten', we say '-ty'. We have lost a little of the elegance that would be retained if we were to say 'four hundred and six-ten'. A completely logical system might use the spoken words 'four hundred six-ten and five-one' in response to the figures 465. So we can see that the English words used for counting are mostly logical, almost retaining the essential elegance of maths, but not quite. This is always the case in spoken language: the logic is sometimes obscured. In maths, the language is such an important aid to understanding that we need to teach the logic and the hidden logic carefully. We must do this so that the language conjures up the appropriate image. This is one of the keys to learning.

We can use the idiosyncratic way of speaking certain numbers to assist cognition.

In spoken language
the logic is sometimes
obscured.

Let us look at some of the familiar signs that we use in maths. What images do they conjure up? When we see 3 + 4 we say 'three add four' or 'three and four' or 'three plus four'. Each of these is a valid way of reading the sign, but what is the image? How best can we provide a key to learning? It is perfectly logical and correct to encourage children to see an image of three objects sitting next to four objects and then combine them to form a new set (which has seven objects). But there is another image that is equally logical and correct. This image starts with a single set of three objects which then has a 'job' done on it. The job (prompted by the + sign) is to collect some more objects. How many more? Four. So the set now has seven objects.

Some maths signs
indicate a job to be
done.

Each image is logical and correct. However, we feel strongly that the image in which a job is performed on one set is the one that should be used in teaching. This is because the image of a job performed on one set can be consistently applied for each of the four operations. Think of 5 – 3. Start with a set of five objects. The job (prompted by the minus sign) is to remove some. How many must be removed? Three. The set

It is not helpful to teach the four operations in different ways. We need to consider which representation provides a consistent approach.

Consistency of
approach

now has two objects. This consistency cannot be applied to the alternative image of five objects sitting next to three objects. Remove the three and you are still left with five.

Language should be taught in relation to mental images.

A detailed analysis such as this is necessary when considering the language we use for teaching maths. Language should be taught in relation to mental images. The precise implications of each image must be anticipated so that the most powerful selection can be made. This does not in any way imply that there is only one word (like 'add') that must be used in relation to 3 + 4. The words 'add', 'plus' and 'and' must all be used from the start so that the image is conjured up not by a single code word but by all the words that are used colloquially and interchangeably.

When children learn solely from reading they are left to interpret the signs and symbols for themselves. A classroom that is rich in oral mathematical language will assist cognitive development.

Language carries subtle messages.

It is a mistake to try to protect young children from the word 'plus' because it sounds more difficult than 'add'. It is also a mistake to try to clean up the language by insisting that 'plus' is the only acceptable term. This is not the nature of language. Language is not tidy and uncomplicated. It does, however, carry important and subtle messages if the learner is taught to inspect it for its logic. Planned and explicit use of all the different words meaning 'add' can assist children in their cognition of maths and give them sufficient confidence to improve their motivation.

Words conjure up mental images.

When we discussed 3 + 4 we emphasized that this should be taught in order to provoke a mental image that involved starting with something (three objects) and then doing a job on it. This image is applicable not only in arithmetic. In geometry the word 'transformation' generates a mental image of some shape that has a job done on it. In this case the kinds of job that can be done include: movements from the starting place to another place; turns so that the shape faces in a different direction; an alteration in the size of the shape; an alteration in the nature of the shape; or combinations of these. We refer to these as translations, reflections, rotations, enlargements, shears and so on. Each of these words conjures up a mental image of the job to be done.

Learning technical words

In geometry the language of transformation employs many words that are used in everyday contexts. Take the word 'translate', which is used in everyday speech in relation to 'translating from a foreign language'. In transformation geometry the job is to move a shape to a different position without changing its shape, size or orientation. We can help learners to notice and remember the distinctions among technical words by discussing them in relation to more everyday ideas.

When the everyday meaning is helpful to the mathematical meaning the teacher needs to draw this to the children's attention.

Seeking connections

In the case of the word 'translate' we can use the phrase 'Keep the value: change the appearance' to forge the link between its everyday use and its mathematical meaning. In both the maths and the foreign language the object changes its appearance but does not change its value. The word 'chien' in French looks different from the word 'dog' when translated into English but they both have the same meaning or the same value. Similarly a square that has been translated 10cm north may have changed its appearance (in terms of its position) but it has kept its value (in the sense of retaining its shape, size and orientation). This kind of discussion involves not only an examination of the idea of translation but also an interrogation of the phrase 'Keep the value: change the appearance'. This is the nature of learning the language of maths. Discussions that seek out connections help all of us to examine what we understand by the individual ideas.

The classroom framework

Introduction

Assisted performance

Lesson structure

Organization of
effective teaching

In *A framework for teaching maths* we described how knowledge is made accessible to children through the process of assisted performance. This means that teachers assist children to do things which they would not be able to do alone so that they gradually become able to do these things without assistance.

Assistance comes in many different forms. One of the most important aspects is the way in which schoolwork is organized. The structure of lessons (as well as the content) needs deliberate planning. It is this detailed attention to structure that constitutes the classroom framework: in short, it is the organization of effective teaching.

Lessons that have a particular structure can still provide a variety of experiences.

A structure can aid planning.

An episode of teaching

Throughout this book we use these icons to represent the phases in a teaching episode:

The **demonstration** phase: the whole class focuses on specific teaching points.

The **modelling** phase: a range of pupil responses follows the demonstration.

The **summarizing** phase: the whole class focuses on making conclusions.

A key element in such organization is the planning of teaching episodes. An episode of teaching is of no particular length but it does have a particular form. It starts with the teacher working with the whole class and it ends in the same way. It has three distinctive phases.

The first phase in any episode involves the teacher **demonstrating** the manner in which the children are expected to work. The middle phase involves the children **modelling** the teacher's initial demonstration. The final phase is devoted to **summarizing** what has been done.

In the **demonstration** and **summarizing** phases the teacher works with the whole class. During the **modelling** phase (the middle section) the teacher may continue to work with the whole class or the children may work in groups or individually.

An episode of teaching may take the whole of a timetabled lesson or it may be that the lesson contains two, three or more short episodes. In some cases an episode of teaching may even extend over more than one timetabled session. In general we would expect a session of about an hour to include two or three episodes to ensure a reasonable pace of learning.

Demonstration and summarizing are rarely seen in classrooms.

The phases describe the structure of teaching episodes and do not indicate a specific length of time.

Extended episodes require expert teaching to maintain pace and sustain interest.

The demonstration phase

Suppose we want to teach children to think flexibly, or to use a particular strategy for doing a calculation, or to use a ruler correctly. How do they know exactly what to do? How do they know what represents an appropriately accurate or economical way of doing it? We have to **demonstrate** to them what is required.

Demonstration should continue until all the children are ready to move on.

Everyday learning

School learning

In all our learning we need some kind of demonstration of what we are about to learn. In everyday learning this demonstration takes place sufficiently often for us, gradually and almost imperceptibly, to adopt it. In school learning there is no such luxury of time, nor can we be satisfied with the inevitable randomness. We have to provide demonstrations that are both visible and deliberately focused on what must be learnt.

Demonstrations need meticulous planning.

We need to attract children's interest and attention and make explanations efficient and concise. This means that we have to provide carefully thought out demonstrations, meticulously planned and prepared so that they assist the children's performance in the ways we have discussed.

It is the demonstration phase that determines the success of subsequent phases.

Children can help with demonstrations.

The teacher may choose to include some of the children to make the demonstration more effective. One or two children can be invited to the front of the class and asked to repeat the teacher's demonstration with as much assistance as is necessary. The teacher is using the child as a mouthpiece to repeat the words and actions. This anticipates the modelling phase when children will replicate the activity for themselves with appropriate assistance. However, the demonstration is distinctive and does not allow any idiosyncratic action or mistakes by the children who are participating.

The teacher insists on correct use of mathematical language and terminology during demonstrations.

Differentiation

The demonstration is conducted with all the children in the class no matter what their individual level of attainment may be. Differentiation is achieved through the level of assistance that is given to support the children's learning.

Deliberate teaching of ideas

The demonstration of a concept in this formal or schooled way is different from the way in which everyday learning takes place. At school, the teacher deals with the relevant idea very specifically, demonstrates it very deliberately (to the point of over-acting) and puts into words and actions what is being done.

Monitoring and assessment

Throughout the period of demonstration the teacher can closely monitor the progress of individuals and the whole class. In fact, the successful conduct of this phase is not possible without monitoring. Consider carefully the nature of this monitoring. Demonstration has the purpose of enabling the children to be able to do something very specific. The teacher's interest will be in the extent of the assistance that is needed for each child to achieve a level of success.

By observing the children and listening to responses the teacher is constantly adjusting pace and content.

Pace

The pace and content of the demonstration are dependent on the teacher recognizing the needs of the children by listening to their responses and observing their behaviour. Children who appear to be struggling with a particular concept may be specifically chosen to come to the front to work through a problem with assistance. This provides

A supportive atmosphere	them with individual assistance at the same time as encouraging them to articulate a mathematical process.

them with individual assistance at the same time as encouraging them to articulate a mathematical process.

It is the role of the teacher to ensure that this activity takes place in a supportive atmosphere and to provide sensitive and firm classroom management.

> A supportive atmosphere is crucial for successful whole class teaching.

The modelling phase ❖

Replicating the demonstration

The modelling phase of the episode is a requirement for each child to repeat the demonstrated process. In everyday learning this may not happen, and when the child does attempt some repetition a faulty version may be acceptable.

> Children replicate demonstrations in the modelling phase.

In the school context, each child will repeat a faultless version of the demonstrated actions. This will be achieved because the teacher will provide whatever assistance is necessary to ensure that this is done. However, it is clear that children's success in this phase is dependent on the quality of the demonstration.

Individual work in the modelling phase

Individual working

Practising problems to consolidate knowledge

In many cases the children will work individually because they can be expected to be reasonably close to this perfect performance (the teacher will make a judgement by monitoring the children's progress). They will be practising problems and exercises to consolidate their knowledge and aid memorization. Each child attempts the same problems, with differentiation being achieved through the level of assistance offered for successful completion.

> Individual work is used for problems that are straightforward replicas of demonstrations.

Assessment and recording

This individual work may be conducted in silence to allow for quiet contemplation. The teacher can circulate to check that the children are completing the work accurately and to diagnose problems. During this time she can keep informal records on the children's progress and decide which children require assistance and who will be asked to present their solutions in the summarizing phase.

> The success of individual work depends on the quality of the demonstration.

Intervention by the teacher

The teacher can intervene to provide assistance and to sustain momentum. She can ask questions to elicit responses and attempt to analyse difficulties. She can focus on challenging the children's ideas by drawing attention to and providing conflicting ideas or by asking for examples and helping children to report their thinking.

Setting targets

During the modelling phase children can be set targets to raise expectations and to keep the class working together. That is not to say that children are put under undue pressure but that they are encouraged to take responsibility for making an effort and doing their very best. This constant monitoring provides the best form of diagnostic teaching and leaves the children little time for poor behaviour.

Homework and tests

Working at home

Individual work in the modelling phase may not necessarily take place in the classroom. Following a demonstration the children may be asked to do some appropriate homework in preparation for the next lesson.

Monitoring of this work would take place in the summarizing phase that starts the subsequent classroom work. During that phase the children would take responsibility for checking and correcting their own work. The solutions would be presented by individual children (appropriately assisted by the teacher).

Recording children's progress

The teacher may collect this work in from time to time to maintain a record of the children's progress. This is important, but it ought not to detract from the responsibility given to the children for successful completion. If they become dependent on marks and grades it damages their learning of maths.

Children taking responsibility

Children, parents and teachers need to know whether the teaching and learning has been effective so testing needs to be an integral part of the programme. Tests should be thought of as an aspect of modelling and included from time to time in the modelling phase.

Regular tests

This carries an important implication. Tests (written or aural) set to assess summative knowledge should not be surprise events. They should be an opportunity to model those things that have been previously demonstrated. Of course, the full content of the test will not have been demonstrated in the minutes before the test begins. What is important is that the test paper should be distributed well in advance and be clearly related to the work children have done. This places a responsibility on the children to prepare each item and demonstrate their competence.

Preparation for tests

> Homework should be an integral part of classroom work and not a bolted-on activity set just to satisfy requirements.

> Even if children have memorized answers to test questions their successful performance in the test demonstrates learning.

Group work in the modelling phase

Children will sometimes work in groups during the modelling phase. It cannot be assumed that working in a group is easy; nor can it be assumed that group work automatically enables children to learn. They need instruction and practice, as well as continuing assistance, to work effectively as a group. Some part of this assistance can be provided by the design of the activities they do, so that children are purposely encouraged to discuss their work and to work collaboratively. For instance, they may be required to agree a solution to a problem and ensure that everyone in the group is practised in describing it (a preparation for the summarizing phase). This sort of activity employs social skills and increases confidence and motivation.

Group work

Working collaboratively

> Group work allows for peer assistance on problems that need discussion.

> Working together is an important social skill.

Whole class work in the modelling phase

The modelling phase may be conducted with the whole class. This will often involve individual children coming to the board to show their solution or offer some response. At first sight this might seem no different from the demonstration or the summarizing phase. However, there are subtle but important differences. During the demonstration phase the teacher is concerned to produce a perfect example of the work, so that when children are involved they are enabled to go through a faultless performance to show what is required uncomplicated by errors. In the summarizing phase too correct solutions are presented.

Working together on worthwhile problems

In contrast, during the modelling phase the teacher and children scrutinize the problem together and enjoy the struggle of teasing out solutions. The teacher needs to hold back and watch, respond supportively, question, describe and explain. When the class works as a whole during the modelling phase there is a need for particular sensitivity.

> When problems are intellectually challenging, working in the modelling phase is best done as a whole class.

The summarizing phase ◇

Children present their
solutions.

The summarizing phase also represents a departure from what might be expected in everyday learning. This last phase in the episode is one in which the teacher again works with the whole class. In this phase a summary is given of what has been learnt. Individual children come to the front of the class to show and explain how they completed the set problems. They are given the appropriate level of assistance to enable them to present the problem. Sometimes the teacher provides the assistance and sometimes she invites other children to do so.

Mathematics that is demonstrated in the first phase of an episode is replicated in the second and consolidated in the third.

Showing what has
been learnt

This phase is a public performance of what has been learnt. Showing and explaining their learning does not mean that children who would still struggle with the problem unaided are asked to show only the aspect they have mastered. If they can manage only a small part they are enabled to go through the complete problem even if this requires a high level of assistance.

All children are
enabled to be
successful.

We would emphasize that these presentations should take place in a supportive environment and should not be an interrogation of the children by the teacher. Presentations are part of the teaching process when children learn from each other with the assistance of the teacher. In contrast, interrogation by the teacher can be threatening and demotivating.

Monitoring progress

During the modelling phase the teacher will have monitored the children's progress and decided who to invite to present their solutions. Every child in the class is given the opportunity at some time to do so in an atmosphere of trust and respect. It is not only an opportunity to celebrate success but also a chance to discuss mistakes and jointly struggle with problems. It is the articulation of a solution, even with assistance, that aids cognition.

Summarizing may only require children to mark their own work when all have been successful in the modelling phase.

Discussing mistakes

Summarizing may be very brief if the teacher has judged in the modelling phase that all the children in the class have achieved competence. However, it may need to be more extensive in cases where some children require significant assistance.

Assessment and
recording

In addition to monitoring children in the modelling phase, the teacher is able to devote a good deal of time during the summarizing phase recording her judgement of their competence because the children are doing most of the writing and talking. She can assess their needs by listening to their presentation and observing their level of participation.

Regular monitoring is crucial to the success of this method of teaching.

Transition from one
episode to the next

The smooth transition from the summarizing phase to the demonstration phase of the next episode depends upon the ability of the teacher to judge the moment at which the whole class is ready to move on.

Planning for teaching

Summary of teaching
episode

Let us summarize what we have said so far. We have said that any episode of teaching can be represented by a series of three icons representing the three phases of **demonstration**, **modelling** and **summarizing**. Any lesson or sequence of lessons is constructed from a set of such episodes. The duration of any one episode depends upon the learning objectives and careful monitoring of the children's progress.

Starting with a scheme of work, the teacher plans sequences of lessons and then designs episodes.

A lesson does not have to start at the beginning of an episode. Children may have been set a homework task in preparation for a lesson that will start with the summarizing phase. Alternatively the children may be continuing with work in the modelling phase. Before any individual lesson can be planned it is necessary for the teacher to devise a scheme of work that consists of a sequence of episodes to provide coherence and continuity within the subject and purposely to take account of assisting the children's performance.

Planning schemes of work

The rhythmic cycle of episodes of teaching with repeated demonstrating, modelling and summarizing provides the pace and structure for a productive learning environment. The teacher can establish procedures that ensure consistency and coherence in order to reduce the stress and pressures of a working day. Children can feel more secure in a learning environment that provides a known pattern of working and a set of common expectations.

Consistency and coherence

The classroom framework described in this section provides the basis for planning lessons that are rooted in assisted performance. When we also base the lessons on the *Key ideas* in maths we can arouse children's curiosity and excitement and assist them in becoming successful at doing maths.

The basis for planning

See *Key ideas*.

Scripts, resources and discussion

The second part of this book focuses on six topics in maths teaching:

1. *Numbers and counting*
2. *The four operations*
3. *Extending the number system*
4. *Properties of shapes*
5. *Measurement and graphs*
6. *Handling data*

The six topics cover the maths curriculum for Key Stages 1 and 2.

Scripts

Lesson plans
Resources

Discussion

Our analysis of each topic begins with a number of scripts that illustrate effective teaching of aspects of the topic. The scripts are followed by an example of how a lesson can be designed to teach the topic to a particular year group. Suggestions for resources to accompany the specified lesson are given under a series of appropriate headings. The analysis is concluded with a detailed discussion which puts the scripts in context and illustrates the range of ideas that need to be taken into account when teaching the topic. The nature and purpose of all this material is described below.

Scripts

The words teachers use.

Teaching is complex and demanding. The words that teachers use, the emphasis they give to different phrases and the gestures they employ in their teaching can all make a substantial difference to the quality of learning. In *A framework for teaching maths* we discussed how teachers need to assist children's learning in very specific ways that are derived from knowledge of the subject. The scripts provided here illustrate this detailed attention.

Teachers are like actors. Actions and words have to be learnt and practised.

Some words need to be emphasized.

Learn and practise the scripts.

Each script contains examples of the exact words that can be used to teach effectively, together with an indication of what to emphasize and how to do so. You will not recognize the essential features of these scripts if you just skim through them to get a rough idea what they are about or to get a few tips for teaching. You need to learn and practise the scripts. If you learn them and use them in the classroom you will make more sense of them. You will then undoubtedly adapt them. But beware of adapting them too soon.

When you know something well and can perform it successfully you can begin to be creative.

The scripts are examples of demonstrations.

The scripts do not represent complete lessons. They are detailed examples of the way to work during the demonstration phase of an episode of teaching. This is a very important aspect to perfect because it establishes what is to be modelled by the children. What you do in the demonstration phase determines what the children understand to be the nature of the maths they have to learn.

The scripts provide examples of the demonstration phase.

Lesson plans

When you use the script you need to incorporate it into an episode of teaching that consists of demonstration, modelling and summarizing. You need to work out how much of the script you can sensibly use as a demonstration and what resources the children will need in order to model what you have done. You also need to be clear about how you will manage the summarizing phase. The suggested resources will help to provide ideas for what the children might do in the modelling phase.

An example of a lesson plan is provided for each topic. This demonstrates how you might incorporate a part of one of the scripts into your scheme of work. Notice how the structure of the lesson is meticulously planned in order to optimize the learning outcomes. You may need to deviate from this plan to respond to children's needs, and this will inform your future planning.

Resources

Suggestions for resources to accompany a specific lesson are set out under the following headings:

- *Practice*
- *Homework*
- *Using and applying maths*
- *Using information technology*
- *Tests*

Each one of these is an example of work that can be used during a modelling phase. You may be surprised to see homework and tests as 'modelling'; but in fact, this is an important aspect of the concept of teaching as assisted performance. Both homework and tests need to be purposely included as 'modelling' in episodes of teaching so that they are demonstrated and summarized as deliberately as all other work. Both must contribute to the children's learning.

Discussion

The scripts and the resources do not provide a scheme for all the teaching that is needed for the six topics. They are examples of what can be done. They need to be examined in detail so that the underlying philosophy of teaching as assisted performance can be understood and incorporated into other teaching. The discussion ranges more widely than the examples used in the scripts. It not only puts the script in a broader context of the subject matter that would be taught in a full scheme of work, but it also offers a detailed examination of the way in which the subject matter and the underlying philosophy come together. The discussion is about pedagogy.

This discussion contains numerous extracts from other scripts. These are used to clarify important points but they can also be adopted and adapted for your own classroom work. The important thing to remember is that you need first to have read thoroughly the detailed material in the *Scripts* section so that you are clear about what is meant by teaching as assisted performance. From this strong base of knowledge you can then be creative in making effective use of the extracts from scripts in the *Discussion* section.

Side notes (left margin):

The scripts are used as the basis for planning.

Examples of lesson plans

Resources to accompany a specific lesson

Resources are designed for the modelling phase.

The scripts and resources do not provide everything for a scheme of work.

The discussion is about pedagogy.

Creativity is possible when knowledge is sound.

Side notes (right margin):

Design lesson plans to suit your class.

You have to decide when it is appropriate to allow children to distract you from your main objective.

You are given ideas about how to design your own resources.

Pedagogy is the science of teaching. It has a language and a set of concepts that need to be studied by its practitioners.

❶ Numbers and counting

Introduction

The ability to count underpins much of maths.	The ability to count fluently and accurately is the basis of much in mathematics. This knowledge of counting is the key to planning lessons that specifically assist children's performance. We can capitalize on the fact that the ability to count is one of the things that children generally do very well.

As you read through the book you will see that fluency in counting is essential.

Building on the ability to count

The first script in this section shows how we build on that ability to count to make sense of the meaning of addition and how we concentrate on memorizing the addition facts. The idea is that the link between counting and addition assists cognition and serves as an example of a clear learning strategy. You will see that memorization is also assisted. The script includes the advice that a result like $7 + 3 = 10$ be put on the wall and referred to as if it were in memory. It is then covered or removed so that a mental image becomes the prompt to use the result that the teacher pretends is still there.

Assisting memorization

Instant recall requires a bank of mental images that are easily accessible.

The second script shows how to enable children to memorize results like $7 + 10 = 17$. In this case the emphasis is on assisted performance in language as a contribution to improving cognition and mental strategies. You will see how the logic of the language of number is fairly clear in 'six and ten is six-teen' but less clear in 'five and ten is fif-teen'. The script shows how our teaching can benefit from being very open about the slight lack of logic in saying 'fif-teen' rather than 'five-teen'.

The logic of number

Introducing 'take away'

The third script shows how the important process of 'take away' can be introduced. You will see that it is acted by the children as they work with everyday objects and physically take them away. In this case the logic is quite clearly in the language.

See *Key ideas: language*.

'Funny counting'

The fourth script introduces children to 'funny counting'. If you count as far as forty-five in the following fashion you begin to see things in the structure of number that are often obscured:

> ... *thirty-seven; thirty-eight; thirty-nine; thirty-ten; thirty-eleven; thirty-twelve; thirty-thirteen; thirty-fourteen; thirty-fifteen.*

The structure of the number system

This immediately illustrates the structure of the number system and introduces a flexibility in dealing with numbers that we use extensively in subsequent work. You will see that thirty-fifteen has the same value as forty-five, but a different appearance.

See *Key ideas: Keep the value: change the appearance*.

Development in teaching numbers and counting

Note that the first items in the list below involve children counting numbers until they are fluent. This is a fundamental requirement in the learning of number. They need to be able to speak the words and count in order before they start to count objects. The activities of counting in order, counting in patterns and counting to a set rhythm should not only be the first number experiences but should be repeated on a regular basis.

Number work is made so much easier when we have strategies to draw upon. The most fundamental strategy is to utilize our knowledge of the number bonds to ten. This needs to be taught specifically.

The teaching in this book has at its heart the language of maths. The teaching method includes much oral work and the success of this depends upon an early induction into this language. Children are assisted in their learning of the language of maths by working as a whole class, speaking and chanting the sounds together. Young children quickly grasp the logic in the 'funny counting' and this logic assists them in performing numerical operations.

Teachers should enable children to:

- *count fluently and accurately into hundreds and thousands*

- *count odd numbers and even numbers by alternate loud and silent counting*

- *count objects at the pace determined by the teacher*

- *memorize addition and subtraction number bonds to ten*

- *use the logic of the language of number to count in tens (starting with, say, twenty-four as well as with twenty)*

- *use the logic of the language of number to add and subtract ten*

- *use counting to do word problems*

- *use the logic of the language of number to deal with large numbers (for example, three hundred add five hundred is eight hundred)*

- *apply counting to everyday problems*

- *apply counting to collecting and handling data*

- *count vulgar fractions, decimal fractions and negative numbers*

- *apply the extended number system to real-life problems*

- *recognize the four operations (+ / − / × / ÷) as 'jobs' to be done and act these physically, counting the result to give the answer when prompted by the = sign*

- *use and apply the four operations to real-life problems*

Fluency in counting

Number bonds

The language of maths

Counting links each item in the list.

The first job in planning for teaching is to track ideas through the curriculum and note the links and connections.

The items in the list are developed throughout KS1 and KS2 and beyond.

Script 1: Teaching number bonds

Establishing number facts

This script demonstrates how the teacher establishes basic facts such as 7 + 3 = 10. Notice how there is an emphasis on memorization. It is important that children can recall number bonds such as this instantly because they provide the foundation for later number work.

Wall displays to aid memorization

Resources

- A card to be put on display throughout the lesson.

$$7 + 3 = 10$$

> For wall displays to aid learning they must be clear and uncluttered.

- Ten clear plastic beakers.

- Seven red balls; eight blue balls (or other objects that can be placed in the beakers).

Counting

The teacher demonstrates counting.

Ten plastic beakers are on display. The teacher establishes unambiguously that there are ten:

I am going to count the beakers: one, two, ... ten. There are ten beakers.

[Place seven red balls in adjacent beakers.]
If I start with seven balls in here

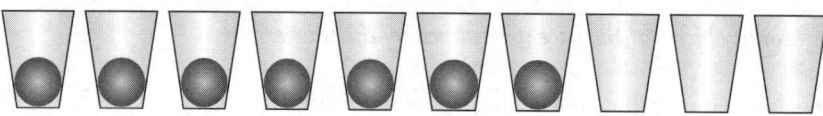

[Place three blue balls in remaining beakers.]
and put three more in here

[write on board]

$$7 + 3 = 10$$

> The deliberate and exaggerated actions by the teacher are necessary to emphasize this number fact.

The teacher assists the whole class.

I get ten. This shows us that seven add three is ten. If I ask you 'What is seven add three?' you say [gesture to encourage response from class and mouth 'ten'] *ten.* [Rub off board.]

Assisting performance

The teacher is not testing the children's knowledge but is ensuring that every child in the class can count to ten, recognize that seven objects and another three objects makes ten objects and can relate this to the symbolic equation 7 + 3 = 10.

The links are deliberately made by the teacher using every form of assistance to give confidence to the children and to ensure success. This brief introduction may not be sufficient so the teacher can continue by asking:

What is seven add three?

All the children are assisted to be successful.

She elicits responses from individual children and makes sure to include those children who she knows from previous experience may be slow to respond. All the time the answer to this question is displayed on the wall and some children may point to this. The teacher uses this response to encourage the children to memorize the answer.

Linking real images to mental images

[A child claims that the answer is on the wall and the teacher plays the game of not being able to see it.] *No, it's not. I can't see it* [looking directly at card]. *It must be in your head. You are so clever you have put it in your head. You think it is on the wall. What is seven add three? Ten. Good. It is in your head.*

Using known facts

Making connections

Developing strategies

Having established the basic fact 7 + 3 = 10 the teacher moves on to show how this one fact can be used to do other sums. The first example demonstrates how seven add five can be 'seen' to be seven add three (answer instantly known as ten) add two. This enables children to develop strategies to do mental arithmetic.

Gaining confidence

You can now see how important it is to ensure that every child in the class can do the foundation work on number bonds. Children who were already proficient in this do not suffer from the repetition but gain increased confidence in their knowledge.

First the balls are removed from the beakers and the seven red balls are replaced whilst carefully counting to establish that there are seven.

The number of beakers remains constant at ten so that any number over ten can be clearly seen.

One, two, three, ... seven. I will start with seven balls in the beakers. I am now going to add five.

The teacher places three balls in the remaining beakers to connect the previous activity with this new sum. She holds two balls in view.

Using known facts

I can see seven [indicate] *and three* [indicate] *is ten;* [nod towards each of the other two balls; count visibly but silently; then in a stage whisper say:] *eleven; twelve. There are twelve. Seven* [indicate] *and five* [indicate] *make twelve. We are going to do that again.*

Working in the head

Now the beakers are ignored as the teacher writes on the board whilst speaking.

Demonstrating how to use known facts

I am going to start with seven [writes the number 7 on the board] *then I am going to add* [writes a plus sign] *five* [writes the number 5]. *But the thing in my head* [points to 7 + 3 card on wall] *is seven add three is ten* [nods twice] *add two is twelve.*

It is crucial that the teacher makes the connection between real images and mental images.

Repetition

This exaggerated demonstration of using the number bond and counting on from ten to complete the calculation is repeated until all the children seem comfortable with the idea. It is spoken, enacted and written.

[Rewrite 7 + 5 on the board.] *It says: start with seven and add five. So I go: seven add three* [point] *is ten* [stage whisper] *eleven* [emphatically] *twelve. So I put:* [write 12 on board].

Practice

Using the same number fact to do different examples

Different examples are used to practise doing addition with this number fact using mental methods. The teacher points to 7 + 3 = 10 on the displayed card and reminds the children: *Keep in mind that seven add three is ten. Nothing else. Just seven add three is ten.* She writes on the board 7 + 4 =

Practice is essential for consolidation and memorization.

Right. Look at this [point to board] *seven add four. Stop! Say:* [point to board] *seven add three is ten* [nod; count one visibly but silently]; *eleven. The answer is eleven.*

The sum is completed on the board so that the children can connect the mental calculation with the sum written in symbols. More examples are done, occasionally returning to the beakers to remind the children of the visual representation of 'seven add three is ten'. For example, when doing seven add six:

Connecting mental and written maths

Returning to real stories

Let's do that with the beakers. [Point to seven red balls in beakers] *I start with seven; I find another six* [place three blue balls in empty beakers]. *I say seven add three is ten,* [nod and visibly count in stage whisper] *eleven, twelve, thirteen. The answer is thirteen.*

The teacher reinforces the link between real images and mental images by regularly returning to the real stories.

Children assist with demonstrations when confident.

Once the teacher has demonstrated this strategy for mental addition and judged the class to be ready she moves on to the next stage in which pupils are asked to come to the front and enact the sums to the class. They should speak and act (by nodding and so on) in the way that the teacher demonstrated to show that they are using the method taught. The selected children are assessed for the extent of the assistance they need to do this.

Script 2: Teaching the language of number

Using the language of number to assist performance

This section of the lesson concentrates on enabling children to do 'ten add six', 'ten add seven', and so on, easily and rapidly through an understanding of the language of number.

Resources
• Twenty beakers

Reading numbers in words and figures
Put ten inverted beakers on a table (using them simply as objects to count). Put seven inverted beakers on a nearby table. Confirm the total number by counting together.

Counting

One, two, three, ... seventeen. There are seventeen altogether.

The teacher is now going to demonstrate that the way we speak some numbers is not logical. The number 'twenty-seven' is written in figures with the two in front of the seven and it is spoken in the same order, as 'twenty-seven'. However, the number 'seventeen' is written logically in figures with the ten in front of the seven but it is spoken backwards. This little playlet helps the children to inspect the language of number.

Children are not confused by this play on words.

[Write seventeen in figures on the board.] | 17 |

Real stories

There is ten [count the beakers] *and seven* [count] *on this table.*

Maths stories

[Write ten and seven on the board.] | ten and seven |

That's how much I've got altogether. That's funny. That does not look right. I know. It should be:

[Write seven and ten on the board.] | seven and ten |

That's better. Oh no – it's still not right. I know:

[Write sevenandten on the board.] | sevenandten |

It's got to be one word. No! That's not right. I know:

[Write seventen on the board.] | seventen |

I have to miss out the 'and' but it's still not right.

[Compare seventen and seventeen orally.]

That's funny. It ought to be seven-ten [point to beakers] *but you say seventeen. OK. I get it. I can see seven **ten** but I say seven**teen**.*

[Write seventeen on the board.] | seventeen |

The teacher repeats this playlet with the number eighteen.

Let's try some more.

[Count out ten and eight.]

I have got ten here [count beakers] *and eight here* [count]. *I say I have got eight ten.*

[Write eight ten on the board.] | eight ten |

You say ... [gesture for response of eighteen].

[Write eighteen on the board.] | eighteen |

This is repeated with nineteen, sixteen and fourteen, which all follow the same pattern. Then the numbers fifteen and thirteen are demonstrated because these differ by not being 'fiveteen' and 'threeteen' as might be expected. Finally the numbers twelve and eleven are demonstrated.

I have got ten [count beakers] *and two* [count]. *I say I have got two ten.*

[Write two ten on the board.] | two ten |

You say ... [Whisper in a questioning tone *'twoteen?'* and shake your head. Gesture for response of twelve.]

[Write twelve on the board.] | twelve |

Then do the same for eleven.

This emphasis on language is important to establish a strategy for adding numbers to ten. Adults do this so naturally that they forget that it needs deliberate teaching.

Sidebar notes (left column):

Demonstrating how words used for numbers are constructed

Teacher as actor

Repeating with different numbers

Whispering emphasizes that twelve is different.

Sidebar notes (right column):

You can explore the construction of number words in other languages.

Script 3: Teaching subtraction

When we say 'take away' a number we mean it literally, i.e. remove it. This physical process, and its associated mental image, is then employed in rather a surprising way. Working with written word versions of large numbers (the words 'three hundred', 'sixty', 'and' and 'seven', and not the figures 367), children enact precisely the same process of 'take away'. This is a remarkably powerful approach to learning to do the same operation using figures and the algorithms that come later in school life.

Sidebar notes (left column):

Subtraction as 'take away'

The physical process of removal

Sidebar notes (right column):

When this has been done in words it can also be done in figures.

Resources
- Objects to count
- Cards

Using everyday objects

The teacher starts by placing three everyday objects, such as a ball, a box and a ruler, on the table. She is going to use the children's knowledge of the words 'take away' in their everyday language to assist them in doing subtraction.

What is on the table? [Invite the children to respond.] *Yes. A ball, a box and a ruler. Now, ...* [select someone] *come and take away the ruler. Good. What is left?* [Invite the children to respond.] *Yes. A ball and a box.*

What did we start with? [Invite response.] *A ball and a box and a ruler. We took away a ruler. We finished with a ball and a box.* [Replace the ruler]. *What is on the table?* [Invite response.] *Yes. A ball, a box and a ruler. Now, ...* [select someone] *come and take away the box. Good. What is left? Yes. A ball and a ruler.*

The teacher now gets the children to repeat the actions to demonstrate that 'take away' is something that they can all do successfully.

What did we start with? [Invite response.] *A ball and a box and a ruler. We took away a box. We finished with* [invite response] *a ball and a ruler.* [Remove all items from the table.] *This is easy isn't it? I just put some things on the table. We look at what we are starting with. I tell you what to take away. We can then say what we finish with.*

Working in the imagination

Now the teacher is going to repeat the actions with imaginary objects to encourage the children to work in their imagination.

Look. I am putting a ball, a box and a ruler on the table. [Act this out without using any objects: this is an entirely imaginary exercise.] *Look at them.* [Make exaggerated gestures to imply that you are looking at the objects.] *A box* [point to imaginary box], *a ball* [point to imaginary ball] *and a ruler* [point to imaginary ruler]. *Now, take away the ruler.* [Pick up imaginary ruler and throw it away.] *What is left on the table? Yes. A ball and a box.*

Children love to play pretend games and this activity will attract their interest and move them on from working with concrete objects to working mentally.

Working with word cards

The teacher is now going to repeat the same activity, but instead of everyday objects she is going to use cards with numbers written in words on them. She displays four cards – one each for 'four hundred', 'and', 'sixty', and 'five' – so that they can be seen by every child in the class.

I am starting with four hundred [point to the card, pause and look at the children] *and* [point, pause] *sixty* [point, pause again] *five* [point].

This slow, deliberate reading of the number demonstrates the way it should be read and reminds the children how to read the words. A child is now selected to assist the teacher.

Marginal notes (left):

Removing objects

Using real stories

The action of taking away assists cognition.

Imagining the action of taking away

Number cards in place of objects

Marginal notes (right):

All children can be successful at removing objects. Subtraction is easy!

The teacher is again helping the children to create mental images.

Number cards can be treated just like other objects.

Come and take away sixty. [The child removes the sixty card.] *Good. What are we left with?* [Invite response.] *Good. Four hundred and* [very deliberate emphatic pause to emphasize the absence of the sixty] *five.* [Write four hundred and sixty-five on the board.]

| four hundred and sixty-five |

We started with four hundred and sixty-five. Then we said, 'Take away sixty.' [Put hand over sixty.] *We then said, 'Four hundred and* [very deliberate pause to emphasize the absence of the sixty] *five.'*

Sixty is removed.

The teacher is progressing from using the cards to demonstrate 'take away' to covering up words on the board. She will now cross out the number sixty.

[Point to four hundred and sixty-five on the board.] *We started with four hundred and sixty-five. Then we said, 'Take away sixty.'* [Cross out sixty.] *We then said, 'Four hundred and* [very deliberate pause to emphasize the absence of the sixty] *five.'*

Removal by crossing out

The teacher has moved from concrete everyday objects to cards with numbers on them, to words on the board. Now she is now ready to teach the children to work in the imagination.

[Remove four hundred and sixty-five from the board.]

I am starting with four hundred [point to imaginary words] *... and ... sixty* [point] *five.*

Read what we are starting with [point to imaginary writing on board]. *Now take away sixty* [use imaginary rubbing out on board]. *What are we left with?* [Invite response.] *Good. Four hundred and* [very deliberate pause to emphasize the absence of the sixty] *five.*

Working in the imagination

Mental images formed in this way will assist the children in developing mental strategies.

This painstaking process of demonstrating subtraction first with cards and then using the imagination has established a sound knowledge base from which to progress. Some children will have made the connection early in the process but that should not deter the teacher from continuing with the whole class. Those who understand can consolidate their knowledge as each step is demonstrated. The teacher then uses monitoring to decide whether the whole process needs to be repeated with further numbers. Otherwise, additional examples should be worked through with the whole class with reduced assistance.

Do not be tempted to move on too quickly. All children can benefit from repeating these exercises.

The logic is in the language.

When sufficient examples using hundreds have been demonstrated the teacher can progress to thousands and beyond. The process is no more difficult with larger numbers because the logic is in the language.

Script 4: Teaching 'funny counting'

The language of number

We have already shown how necessary it is to demonstrate the language of number to assist children in adding numbers to ten. But the English language is not entirely consistent in the way that words for numbers have been constructed.

See *Key ideas: language* in *Mathematics for Primary Teachers: An Audit and Self-study Guide.*

The suffix 'ty' is used to denote ten: for example, 'eighty' means 'eight tens'. Some numbers, however, are abbreviated and changed in this construction process: for instance, we say 'fifty' instead of 'five-ty' and 'thirty' instead of 'three-ty'. Earlier we showed how numbers between

Improving fluency

ten and twenty are even more diverse. Not only do we now use 'teen' instead of 'ty' for ten but most of the numbers are spoken backwards, such as 'sixteen' instead of 'teensix'. The numbers eleven and twelve are a law unto themselves. Although children learn these names for numbers and become fluent in speaking them we can assist their cognition of number by making this language more easily understood. One way of doing this is to demonstrate how the numbers would sound if we were entirely consistent in our language construction. This means that the number ten should really be 'one-ty' and eleven 'one-ty-one'. We call this 'funny counting' because it always makes the children laugh. They know that the words are not real but they are being invited to think about the structure of number and particularly about place value.

The amusement is enhanced if the teacher emphasizes the 'ty' by raising the pitch of her voice and slowly speaks 'one-*ty*'. Notice that the number square we use begins with nought and if we take the logic of the language to the extreme we get 'nought-ty'. The similarity with the sound of 'naughty' makes the children laugh even more and they love to chant the numbers 'nought-ty one, nought-ty two, ...' and so on. You will see later that this funny counting helps children in learning to extend the use of multiplication tables. It is not just a distraction but a demonstration of the structure of number. The first part of this script shows how the teacher introduces this sort of counting to the children.

When we do subtraction by decomposition we often remember the steps by using a rule. Many children forget rules and make mistakes because they have not understood the underlying structure of the rule. The second part of this script illustrates how a different sort of 'funny counting' can make the rule transparent.

Using 'funny counting' makes the children laugh.

'Nought-ty' means 'no tens'.

Exploring the language of number in this way can be fun.

Rules are easily forgotten.

Resources
- 0–99 number grid.
- Poster displaying 'Keep the value: change the appearance'.

Part 1: The suffix 'ty'
The teacher uses the number square to demonstrate reading numbers. As she reads she points to the column, starting at 91 on the bottom row and moves up through 81, 71, etc., emphasizing the sound of the words and pausing each time before pronouncing the suffix 'ty'.

'ty' for 'tens'

Let us read these numbers together. [Point to 91.] *This says nine* [pause] *-ty* [high-pitched voice] *one.*

This says: eight-ty one; seven-ty one; six-ty one.

[Point again to 91.] *This says nine-tens and one; eight-tens and one; seven-tens and one; six-tens and one.*

When we say -ty we mean tens, so watch me count. Nine-ty one; eight-ty one; seven-ty one; six-ty one; five-ty one; four-ty one; three-ty one; two-ty one; one-ty one; nought-ty one.

The teacher explains the meaning of 'ty'.

At this point the teacher invites the children to join in with reading the numbers.

Read these numbers with me: nine-ty; eight-ty; seven-ty; six-ty; five-ty; four-ty; three-ty; two-ty; one-ty; nought-ty.

The class then read more of the numbers together and count objects using the 'funny counting numbers'.

Children can get very excited chanting these numbers. They soon settle down if you let them enjoy the fun for a moment.

Part 2: Language to assist subtraction

The children have already been introduced to subtraction using cards, as demonstrated in the previous script. Now they are shown a problem, such as 45 – 17, where the numbers cannot be removed in the same way.

The teacher demonstrates a method.

I want to show you a way of doing this problem:

[Write on the board.]

$$\begin{array}{r} 45 \\ -\ 17 \\ \hline \end{array}$$

Five take away seven [point] – *I can't do it.*

Examples like this can also be performed mentally. It is useful to have an alternative method to check answers when learning an algorithm.

The teacher is now going to demonstrate that forty-five has the same value as, but a different appearance from, thirty-fifteen. This is essentially what we do when we use decomposition for subtraction. We decompose the number forty-five into two parts: thirty and fifteen. This method of teaching uses the language of number rather than a rule to assist the pupils' performance.

Look at this [point to the number square]. *We can count up to forty-five* [invite the class to chant from 0 to 45]. *That's no problem. Now watch me carefully. Be careful, because sometimes I make mistakes.*

The teacher chants the numbers carefully and slowly to imply that she is struggling. This invites the children to listen and check that her counting is correct. When she gets to thirty-nine she moves on smoothly to thirty-ten, thirty-eleven and so on to attract the children's attention. At first she demonstrates by simply speaking the words, then she repeats the exercise with more explanation.

Zero; one; two, ..., thirty eight. After eight is nine. No problem. Thirty-nine; thirty-ten; thirty-eleven; thirty-twelve; thirty-thirteen; thirty-fourteen; thirty-fifteen.

Adults find this much more difficult than children.

This [point to 40] *is thirty-ten. It is thirty and ten. This* [point to 41] *is thirty and eleven. This ...*

Keep the value: change the appearance

The teacher then repeats the numbers again but this time points to the poster 'Keep the value: change the appearance'. The next step is to write 'thirty-fifteen' in figures in a way that is helpful to the subtraction problem.

Forty-five as thirty and fifteen

When we change [point] *forty-five into thirty-fifteen, we 'Keep the value but change the appearance'. It is worth the same – the same value – but it looks different. It has a different appearance. If I say, 'Is forty-five the same as thirty-fifteen?' you say, 'same value: different appearance'.*

The teacher demonstrates how to write the number 'thirty-fifteen' in figures.

[Write on the board.] 45 has the same value as 3¹5

The teacher can now demonstrate how to use this to do the subtraction that she set at the beginning of the lesson, by writing:

$$\begin{array}{r} 3^{1}5 \\ -\ 17 \\ \hline 28 \end{array}$$

Emphasis on language

She then invites children to come to the board to perform different subtraction problems whilst she assists by counting the numbers using the number square.

The emphasis on the language has provided a sound basis for understanding subtraction by decomposition. The class can now go on to do subtractions such as 801 – 26 by saying this as 'seven hundred and ninety-eleven take away twenty-six' and writing:

$$\begin{array}{r} ^{7}8\,^{9}0\,^{1}1 \\ -\ 26 \\ \hline \end{array}$$

Thinking of eight hundred and one as seven hundred and ninety-eleven helps children to understand number.

and 1004 – 37 by saying 'nine hundred and ninety-fourteen take away thirty-seven' and writing:

$$\begin{array}{r} 1\,{}^9\!0\,{}^9\!0\,{}^1\!4 \\ -\ 3\,7 \\ \hline \end{array}$$

Examples that force children to make errors

These are both well-known examples which tend to force errors, particularly when children have learnt a rule for subtraction.

Lesson plan

One lesson from a sequence of lessons

First the teacher constructs a scheme of work.

This lesson for Year 1 pupils teaches the addition of more than two numbers. It is part of the ninth topic in the following scheme of work for teaching addition and subtraction.

1. Learning how to count
2. Number bonds to ten
3. Adding two numbers
4. Memorizing number facts
5. Adding numbers to ten, twenty, etc.
6. Using known number facts to do addition
7. Funny counting
8. Subtracting one number from another
9. Adding more than two numbers
10. Using a calculator for addition and subtraction
11. Multiplication as repeated addition
12. Order of operations

Before you can design a lesson you need to know what the children have covered and what remains to be taught.

Previous work

Each lesson follows on from what has been done before.

The children have learnt that addition is a 'job' to be done. The job is to 'go to the resource table and get some more' and put them on the maths tray. They have memorized number facts and used these to do further additions. They have done subtraction and can recognize subtraction as the inverse of addition by working backwards.

Children may have been taught certain things but you cannot guarantee that they will remember them.

Lesson design

The teacher plans to make connections with previous lessons.

The children have already practised adding two numbers. They now extend that work to deal with three and more numbers. A box of counters (or other objects) is placed on the resource table and a tray is used as the 'maths tray'. The children have done a homework to revise addition of two numbers and the lesson begins with children presenting their answers and acting out the 'maths story' with counters. This is the summarizing phase of the lesson.

First the teacher makes notes on the overall structure of the lesson and then writes a detailed plan.

A maths story

Using counters to tell a real story

The teacher then writes on the board 2 + 3 + 4 = and says 'Let us read this maths story together'. A child is asked to come to the front to act out the maths story using counters. The teacher assists the actions and invites the class to give instructions. First the child gets two counters from the resource table and places them on the maths tray. They read the sign '+' as 'and go to the resource table and get', then they read '3' and the child gets three more counters and takes them to the maths tray. This is repeated for '+ 4'. They count the counters on the maths tray and write the answer 9.

The teacher then moves on to adding more numbers, such as $3 + 6 + 2 + 5 + 4$, and again a child comes to the front and acts out the story. This is the demonstration phase of the lesson. Several examples are enacted at the front of the class until the teacher is confident that all the children can do these sums with assistance. The children are given some examples to do on their own with their own set of counters. This is the modelling phase. When most of the children have completed the examples the teacher moves into the summarizing phase by inviting the children to present their answers. The next phase makes the connection that $2 + 2 + 2 + 2$ has the same value as, but a different appearance from, 2×4. This multiplication result will already have been practised.

Multiplication as repeated addition

The teacher is now ready to write a lesson plan to include learning outcomes, phases, estimated times and content.

The structure and timing of the lesson

Class	Y1	Teacher	Mrs Pearce
Date	3 April	Student	Avril Young

Lesson description	Lesson 9: Addition of more than two numbers

Learning outcomes	Read maths stories. Act maths stories with counters. Add more than two numbers together. Know the meaning of the addition sign. Make the connection between repeated addition and multiplication.

Resources	• Counters for teacher and pupils • Maths trays

Classroom framework	Time	Teacher and pupils
Summarizing ◆	5 min.	Invite children to present answers to homework on addition of two numbers and to act out the stories with counters. Emphasize addition as a 'job to be done'.
Demonstration ◆	15 min.	Invite children to assist in demonstrating how to add three and then more numbers together by acting out the maths stories with counters. Start with $2 + 3 + 4$ Interpret as 'get two counters and get three more counters and get four more counters'. Go on to $3 + 6 + 2 + 5 + 4$ and so on.
Modelling ❖	15 min.	Set questions for pupils to do individually, using their own counters and maths trays. Include a question with a number containing a zero. Set two questions with the same numbers in a different order.
Summarizing ◆	10 min.	Invite children to present answers and act out the maths stories with counters. Ensure that children do actions for 'adding a zero'. Discuss the two questions with the same numbers in a different order. Set some more questions to be rearranged to make the addition easier.
Demonstration ◆	10 min.	Invite children to assist in making the connection between repeated addition and multiplication, referring to 'Same value: different appearance'. Start with $2 + 2 + 2 + 2 = 2 \times 4$. Interpret as 'get two counters and get two more counters and ...' has the same value as but different appearance from 'get two counters four times'. Go on to $5 + 5 + 5 + 5 + 5 + 5 = 5 \times 6$ and so on.
Modelling ❖	5 min.	Set homework: first set of examples to consolidate addition of more than two numbers and second set of examples to write repeated addition as multiplication. Go over one of each to ensure that children know what they have to do.

Practice

After the demonstration phase of the lesson the children need time to practise examples on their own. The first examples should follow the demonstration exactly as it has been enacted and should include pictures of the box of counters and the maths tray. This mental image needs to be carried over into the written work. Some children will be able to work without the assistance of this imagery but others will need this support for longer. The children need to have sets of counters and their own maths trays so that they can enact the maths story each time if necessary.

You will need to decide how much practice is necessary to ensure that most children can succeed.

Children repeat questions from the demonstration phase.

The first example should replicate the demonstration in the following way:

This is a maths story. Let us read it together. $2 + 3 + 4 =$

Here is a maths tray. The tray is empty.

Here is a box. It is full of counters.

*Go to the box. Get **two** counters.* $2 + 3 + 4 =$
Take them to the maths tray.

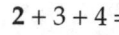

Look at the maths story again.
*Read **and*** $2 + 3 + 4 =$
*Read **three*** $2 + 3 + 4 =$
Get three more counters.
Take them to the maths tray.

Look at the maths story again.
*Read **and*** $2 + 3 + 4 =$
*Read **four*** $2 + 3 + 4 =$
Get four more counters and
take them to the maths tray.

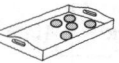

*There are **nine** counters on the maths tray.* $2 + 3 + 4 = 9$

A common mistake is to expect children to move on immediately from the demonstration examples. Children need to re-enact the demonstration examples for themselves.

Encourage children to use counters.

Act the following maths stories. Write down the answers.

1	$3 + 2 + 5 =$	4	$3 + 1 + 0 + 4 + 5 =$
2	$4 + 3 + 7 =$	5	$5 + 4 + 3 + 7 + 2 =$
3	$2 + 4 + 3 + 2 =$	6	$3 + 7 + 5 + 4 + 2 =$

When the children present their answers to these questions they should act out the stories with the counters. When question 4 is being enacted encourage the child to emphasize finding zero counters and taking them to the maths tray.

Notice that questions 5 and 6 have the same numbers in a different order. This has been set deliberately to demonstrate that numbers can be added in any order with the same result. In question 6 the numbers have been arranged so that the 3 and 7 can be added to get 10 first. This can be discussed as a strategy for doing addition. Set another question on the board and ask someone to come and rearrange it to make the addition easier. For example: $2 + 5 + 6 + 3 + 4 =$

Examples are carefully selected to teach specific ideas.

Developing strategies for addition

They may rewrite this as $6 + 4 + 5 + 3 + 2 =$ but whichever way they choose they should be encouraged to explain their choice.

Homework

Homework should be an integral part of lessons and the questions should replicate work done in class so that all children can attempt it. Examples need to be set in such a way that they provide a rich discussion point for the next lesson. Children in Year 1 can be expected to spend 15–20 minutes on a maths homework twice a week.

Following the lesson plan above, examples can be set to help children:
(a) practise adding more than two numbers;
(b) look for the best order to do addition to make it easier.

The children have already practised adding more than two numbers in class so two questions with pictures of the actions should be sufficient to remind them of this. The following examples can then be set for the children to rearrange to make the addition easier to do. You cannot expect the children to be able to read and understand the instructions on their own so you will need to spend some time explaining the homework to them. You should also write a brief explanation on the homework so that parents can help.

Write the following sums so that they are easier to do.

1	1 + 4 + 3 + 9 =	4	5 + 3 + 4 + 5 + 7 + 2 =
2	3 + 2 + 6 + 8 =	5	2 + 2 + 4 + 5 + 8 + 8 =
3	7 + 1 + 3 + 9 + 6 =	6	1 + 3 + 1 + 4 + 9 + 7 =

These examples will provide the basis for discussion in the next lesson, the whole of which can be spent in looking at the children's answers and discussing the best strategies. Each question can be acted out with the counters.

Another homework can be set to make the connection between multiplication and repeated addition. The first question should be a replication of the maths story that was acted out in class using counters.

The following questions can then be set:

The sum $4 + 4 + 4$ has the same value as 4×3.
We can write $4 + 4 + 4 = 4 \times 3$.
Complete the following.

1	2 + 2 + 2 + 2 + 2 =	4	5 + 5 + 5 + 5 + 5 + 5 + 5 =
2	7 + 7 + 7 =	5	8 + 8 =
3	3 + 3 + 3 + 3 + 3 + 3 =	6	1 + 1 + 1 + 1 + 1 + 1 + 1 =

When these questions are summarized in the next lesson they should first be acted out by the children using counters. Before writing the addition as a multiplication the class should refer to the poster 'Keep the value: change the appearance'.

The class can then be asked to act out the maths stories:

$6 \times 3 =$ $4 \times 10 =$ $2 \times 9 =$ $3 \times 6 =$

Note that we read the first one as: *Get six counters and take them to the maths tray. Do this three times.* The fourth one is: *Get three counters and take them to the maths tray. Do this six times.* You can now get the children to enact the two questions again and ask: *Is this $6 \times 3 =$ the same as this $3 \times 6 =$?* Look at the poster 'Keep the value: change the appearance' and weigh up the evidence. *Yes. Six times three is the same as three times six.* You can now ask what is the same as $4 \times 10 =$ and so on.

Margin notes:

Homework should be an integral part of lessons.

Homework as practice

Homework is summarized in the next lesson.

Making the connection between multiplication and repeated addition

Keep the value: change the appearance

It is becoming more common for young children to be set homework.

Children may be asked to study the questions for homework and complete them in class the next day.

The job of getting four is done three times.

Using and applying maths

Work in mathematics should assist children in learning to read. Throughout this book we emphasize the need for oral work and the importance of language in the learning of maths. From an early age children should be introduced to numbers in words and figures and this needs to be consolidated with written examples.

Using and applying maths requires the ability to start with a real-life problem and extract information from it, assess what the problem is about, decide what maths needs to be done, do the maths and return to the problem. We prepare children for this by introducing them to 'real-life stories', 'real stories' and 'maths stories'.

Real stories are used to provide mental images to assist children's cognition in maths. These include using counters, beakers or other concrete objects to represent the mathematical concept being taught. They are meticulously and deliberately selected for their imagery as a pedagogic tool. In contrast real-life stories have a context that needs to be interpreted before deciding what maths is to be done.

> This is a real-life story:
> *When I went to school today my teacher asked me to do some drawing with coloured pencils. I looked in my pencil case and found that I only had three pencils and one pen. When I went home I asked my mum if I could have some more coloured pencils to take to school. She said that if I was good she would go down to the shop and get me some. The shop did not have many different colours so she bought me two and ordered some more.*

> This is a real story:
> *I have three pencils and I get two more pencils*

> This is a maths story:
> *I start with three and I get two more: 3 + 2 =*

Copies of real-life stories can be given out to the children and read together as a whole class. They can then be discussed, with the teacher asking questions in order to extract the necessary information to write a maths story. It is not appropriate to give this activity to individuals or groups at this early stage. Doing this work as a whole class develops the children's skills in comprehension.

Real stories, however, can be used with the whole class and developed into individual or group work. This activity involves the children in matching cards with real stories written on them with cards that have their corresponding maths stories written on them:

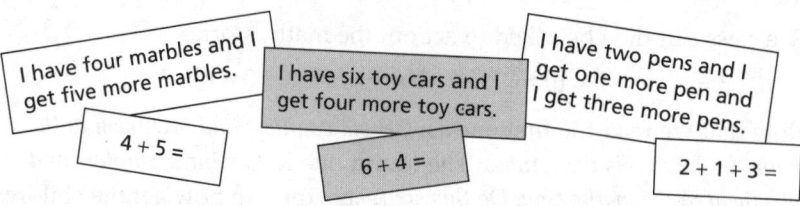

This matching activity can be replicated as individual or group work by asking the children to match cards showing real stories with cards showing maths stories and then copying them into their books.

Children need to gain confidence in maths before they can use and apply it.

Teachers need to work on real-life stories, helping the children to make sense of them.

Matching written sentences to sums helps children to read and recognize numbers in words and figures.

Using information technology

Making up real stories to match maths stories

There are various ways in which information technology can be used to assist young children in their learning of maths. The matching activity described on the previous page can be done using a word processing package. Children can improve their keyboard skills by moving blocks of words around the page and matching real stories with maths stories. These can be accompanied by pictures of the objects which the children place in a maths tray and which are then used to help them work out the answers. When the children are competent in this activity they can create their own stories by amending certain words, figures and pictures. Young children love to make up their own stories by altering given information.

> Children are often better than their teachers at using computers!

Using a computer to practise number skills

There are many software programmes on the market that give practice in counting and adding and subtracting numbers. These can be used to provide additional examples to those done orally and on paper. Using a different medium is sometimes all that is needed to attract a child's interest and provide motivation.

Should young children use calculators? There is continuing debate about this, but the important point about calculators is that children need to be taught *how* to use them and *when* to use them. Problems occur when children use a calculator inappropriately for calculations that can be done in the head and when their knowledge of number operations is insufficient to know what buttons to press.

Using a calculator to check answers

One of the first exercises using a calculator can be to check answers to the questions on the 'practice' sheet. Let us look at the processes involved here. First the child performs some questions using apparatus or working mentally. The answers are checked and the child has a set of correct answers. A calculator is used to work out the same questions. The answers are carefully checked against the known answer. The child is learning *how* to use the calculator. Any inconsistencies will immediately identify any problems with using a calculator. The order of doing these tasks is important. The children are learning that they should do a calculation mentally first and use their calculator to confirm their answer.

> Children need to realize at a young age that calculators do not always give correct answers.

Most mistakes made when using a calculator are due to a lack of understanding of the order in which calculations should be performed and how a calculator deals with conventions.

Ask the children to look at this simple calculation:

$$3 + 4 \times 5$$

Order of operations

Ask them to work it out in their head and explain how they get their answer. The correct answer is 23. This is a result of the convention: 'In the absence of brackets, multiplication and division take priority over addition and subtraction'. A common mistake is to perform the operations in the order in which they are written; in this case that would give the incorrect answer of 35.

Now ask the children to enter the calculation in their calculator as it is written. Some calculators are programmed to operate according to the convention and others are not. Ask the children to suggest ways of entering the calculation so that whatever sort of calculator they have they will get the correct answer (such as $4 \times 5 + 3$). Examples like this teach the children the importance of inspecting the calculation carefully before entering any numbers in the calculator.

Tests

What is the purpose of giving young children tests in maths? We have
discussed at length the need to assist children's performance in maths
so that every child can be successful with assistance. Our aim is to
enable children to succeed without help by providing powerful mental
images and learning strategies for them to use when working alone.
We want to know how much progress the children have made and how
successful our teaching has been. This is not achieved by setting unseen
tests as surprise events. Such tests serve only to cause stress and fear;
they do not assist performance.

First of all we need to inspect our intended learning outcomes and
select questions from those already done in class to find out what has
been learnt. We may have touched on some more challenging questions
during the course of our teaching but we are only interested here in
ensuring that all the children are capable of the core requirements.
Then we have to let the children see these questions and allow time for
preparation, such as a homework. It does not matter that the children
may have been given assistance to do this preparation. They should
be encouraged to seek help and perfect their answers. It is important
that the children take on the responsibility of becoming competent.
The questions are then given to the children to do alone.

These tests give us a picture of the kinds of things the children know and
can do well. We can diagnose problems and identify areas of weakness.
We can judge the effectiveness of our own teaching. Preparation for the
tests prompts us to summarize the work done, consolidate knowledge
and assist memorization. Success in these tests raises children's self-
esteem and encourages them to become more responsible for their own
learning. We can then use what we know the children can do well to
inform our planning and preparation of the next phase of teaching.

This system of testing should not result in children failing. First of
all the questions have all been done before in class and corrected.
Children experiencing difficulties will have received additional
assistance. Then the questions are practised again in preparation for
the test and more help is given where needed. Every opportunity is
given for children to be successful. Provision can be made for any child
experiencing severe difficulties with the subject.

The scheme of work for numbers and counting contains twelve topics.
At least four tests should be set for this scheme of work, with a final
test at the end. Some of these tests can be oral. Here is an example of
such a test. The children will have practised this activity in class on
many occasions as part of their daily routine.

Provide every child with a set of number cards that they use regularly
in class lessons. Ask questions and get the children to select the number
card with the correct answer and to hold it so that it cannot be seen.
When all the children have selected a card ask them to hold up their
cards to face you. Keep a note of those who were wrong. This activity
encourages the children to work out the answers quickly but does not
penalize those who need a little extra time. Every child can participate
and feel satisfaction in getting the correct answer. Mistakes can be dealt
with by asking the children to explain how they obtained their answers.

Numbers and counting: discussion

Introduction

The fundamental requirement for doing maths is the ability to count. All children must be enabled to do this fluently and confidently as early as possible. The performance of counting should be practised as an absolute priority. What does counting consist of? It involves:

Children learn by copying. Teachers need to demonstrate counting for children to copy.

What counting consists of

- chanting the number words in the correct order
- pointing to objects one at a time so that each object is pointed to once and only once
- co-ordinating the rate of pointing with the rate of chanting
- appreciating that the order in which the pointing takes place does not affect the counting
- appreciating that the last number in the chant reflects the number of objects involved (say, seven) and consequently how much is there (seven cups, perhaps)

Counting is a complex activity.

Speaking numbers in order

When counting is described in detail like this it becomes clear what a difficult and skilful process it is. In fact, even this description does not fully convey the complexity. For instance, when children count they must get the numbers in the right order. This is contrary to much other experience. If you tell children to fetch a bat and a ball you praise them if they fetch a ball and a bat; but when you ask them to repeat 'one, two, three' you correct them when they say 'one, three, two'. What mystery is this? Why does it matter on one occasion but not the other that the memorized order is different from the instruction? It can readily be seen that early learning can be very confusing. So how will they successfully learn to deal with the multiplicity of co-ordinated skills that we have described above? The key to this is getting the chant accurate.

Chanting the numbers

Chanting numbers accurately

Learning to chant the numbers provides a sound basis for getting other things right. You need to give children plenty of practice in chanting 'one, two, three, ... ' even before they have any idea what it might be used for. It is not unusual for children to chant things that they do not understand, so don't worry that this chanting will be damaging. Most children seem happy to chant 'Half a pound of tuppenny rice; half a pound of treacle ... Pop goes the weasel!' and so on. Do *you* know what this means? Learning the 'counting chant' can proceed in the same way with a great deal more benefit. Of course, there are other skills which must go alongside chanting numbers and these must be taught.

Children repeat advertising slogans and sing pop songs with amazing accuracy.

Teaching number vocabulary with the number chant

Reading numbers in words and figures

Children must be able to speak the numbers when they see them written as figures and written as words. Learning to read the number names (one, two, three ...) needs to be done alongside learning the figures (1, 2, 3, ...), not postponed 'until they can read'. This is part of learning to read. What does this mean in practice? Early counting involves counting along with the teacher, counting 'how many girls are here today', 'how many grown-ups are in the room' and so on. It also involves songs and rhymes like 'Ten green bottles' and 'One man went to mow'. When children are fairly well practised at these (but not

Counting activities can be done across the curriculum.

necessarily word-perfect) they can be asked to count at the speed signalled by the teacher.

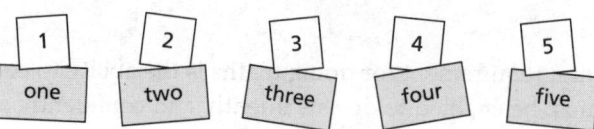

Using cards to read numbers

- Prepare two sets of cards, one set showing figures and one set showing number words.
- Hold up the cards, one by one, for the children to read and count. It does not matter if they cannot yet read the cards because they already almost know the chant. This activity will assist their reading.

Reading and chanting

Counting in rhythm

- Show the consecutive cards at different speeds. Mix the two types of cards, still showing them consecutively.

Linking the chant to visual prompts

Exercises like this enable the memorized (or nearly memorized) chant to be linked with visual prompts. While this is going on you can carefully monitor how each child responds and assist where necessary by mouthing the word, silently or in a stage whisper, so that all children can do it. The exercise itself helps with the language of maths and the visual prompts allow every child to succeed, thus aiding motivation.

Similar chanting exercises (without cards and with cards) can be done with the odd numbers and the even numbers. Introduce these by alternate speaking and whispering during the chant. For instance:

Emphasize the odd numbers.

Whisper the even numbers.

- Demonstrate counting unevenly by emphasizing the odd numbers and whispering the even numbers.
- Reduce the whispered numbers to mouthed numbers.

Speak only the odd numbers.

- Reduce the mouthed numbers to a pause and a thoughtful look that signals that something is going on in the head.
- Tell the children these are the odd numbers.
- On future occasions say: *Let us try counting the odd numbers.* You may want to say only that, or you may want to add: *You remember, we go:* **one**, *two*, **three**, *four*, **five**, ...

These skills of reading number words and figures can be used to help establish the relationship of numbers to each other. For instance:

Ordering numbers

- Assign a number to each child in the class (from 1 to whatever is needed for your class).
- Give each child a card with their own number on it (it is best to write it on both sides so they can see and show their number at the same time).
- Tell them to look at their own number and then find and stand next to the person with 'the next number'.
- Discuss the problem for the child with the highest number. Ask *How many children are in this class today?* so that the highest number is related to the number of children.
- Get the children to move around again so the numbers are 'jumbled' and ask them to find the person who is *one more than your own number* (and, later, *one less than your own number*).

What happens in the last part of this exercise, of course, is that they all stand next to the same children as they did before. They get the same result. The instructions have a different appearance but the same value.

> You can also prepare cards with patterns of dots or pictures of objects.

> You can put your hand over your mouth as you whisper the even numbers.

> You can start at any number. You can use sequences of numbers.

You need to use this activity on many different occasions so that they all carry a different card each time. You can see that a similar activity can be done with a focus on odd numbers and even numbers and later with the extended number system.

The next exercise shows how the number square can be used extensively, first to count and chant the numbers that can be seen and then to count and chant numbers in the imagination. This is going beyond the information given and assists cognition.

0	1	2	3	4	5	6	7	8	9
10	11	12	13	14	15	16	17	18	19
20	21	22	23	24	25	26	27	28	29
30	31	32	33	34	35	36	37	39	39
40	41	42	43	44	45	46	47	48	49
50	51	52	53	54	55	56	57	58	59
60	61	62	63	64	65	66	67	68	69
70	71	72	73	74	75	76	77	78	79
80	81	82	83	84	85	86	87	88	89
90	91	92	93	94	95	96	97	98	99

- Make a number square that extends from zero to ninety-nine and show it to the children.
- Chant the numbers together, pointing to each in succession.
- Miss out alternate numbers, so that either the odd or the even numbers are employed.
- Count down columns in the number square so that the children are helped to count in tens, most often counting 'ten, twenty, thirty, ...' but also counting, say, 'thirteen, twenty-three, thirty-three, ...'.
- Point to each number in the number square (one, two, three, ...) but chant 'one hundred, two hundred, three hundred, ... ten hundred, eleven hundred, ...'.
- Return to the beginning of the number square and repeat the last chant, starting with zero ('zero hundred, one hundred, ...').

> If you cover up the numbers as you go the children will see the patterns emerge.

You can work in a similar way with thousands and millions and anything you can think of. Try gillions. You've never heard of gillions? Nor have we, but you can still count in them. Continue with the number square and concentrate on odd numbers and even numbers.

Chanting to count objects

The ability to chant the numbers is of major importance. It must, of course, be enhanced by the other skills we have listed in this topic, and these need some specific assistance by the teacher. Large objects (say, plastic bottles) can be counted, with the class group doing the chanting at a rate determined by the speed at which you, or a child, walk from one to the next and point. The bottles can be placed at different distances apart, sometimes at different points at the front, back and sides of the classroom (slow counting) and sometimes on a shelf side by side (probably faster counting, depending on how quickly you actually point). You can, of course, introduce variable-speed counting so that children really have to watch carefully and moderate their chanting speed to relate to your actions.

> Counting in time with the teacher improves concentration.

This kind of practice in whole class sessions can be repeated by individual children who are asked to count groups of objects around the room or on a table. When this is done it is crucial that the teacher constantly offers the appropriate amount of assistance to ensure success. There should never be any sense that the child is being put on trial. Every child in the class should be given the opportunity, on a regular basis, to assist in the demonstration phase and present their work in the summarizing phase with the assistance of the teacher.

Children assist in demonstrations.

Children will become confident at public speaking if they can rely on assistance being given when necessary.

Matching games as an aid to learning to count

Using games to practise number facts

Further practice can be provided using cards for the games of 'snap', 'pairs', 'dominoes' and 'bingo'. Some of the children will have played these games in a different context at home but many will not have seen them before. Even when they have been played before it is unlikely that the children are aware of the strategies needed for winning.

Although all these games require matching, we will illustrate how each game develops a different skill (or set of skills). The items that have to be matched can be figures, words, pictures of objects or actual objects. The games can be designed to help children practise a wide range of mathematical skills, so it is worth outlining here the advantages of using each of these games. You will need to practise adapting them to different mathematical topics.

Select games carefully. You can maximize the learning outcomes by teaching strategies for playing the games.

Winning strategies need to be taught.

It is essential that children are taught these games so that they are able to learn from them. It is not simply a case of teaching the rules. The strategies need to be taught so that the game is elevated from requiring only guessing into one that uses clear cognitive abilities. This is extensively discussed in 'Pairs', described below.

Extend the games to include fractions, decimals and percentages.

In each of the games the content of the cards can be made as complex or as straightforward as is needed to practise whatever is being taught at the time. The games are described in this section because they are especially helpful for young children who are not only having to cope with a great deal of learning but who also benefit from practising the search/quick reaction/contemplation skills offered by each game. You can design and use any variation of them, and may find the games useful when teaching fractions, decimals, ratio and percentage.

Pairs

Matching words and symbols

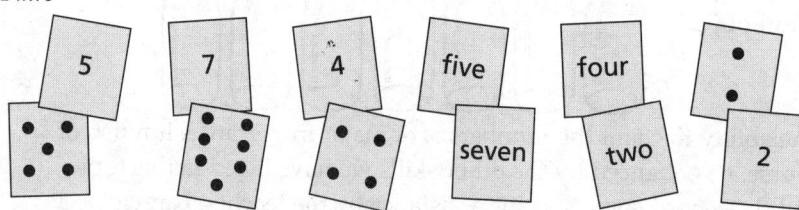

Children can handle only a small number of pairs at first.

- Design a pack of cards so that some cards carry, say, different numbers of dots and other cards carry the same value in figures or words.
- Lay all the cards separately, face down in rows, on a table.
- The players take it in turns to turn over two cards to see if they have the same value.
- If they do have the same value, the child says 'same value' and collects that pair. If not, the child says 'different value' and the cards are again turned face down ready for the next child to try.

Memorization

Obviously the beginning of the game involves only guessing where the matching cards are; after a while it depends on memorizing the position of the cards. This game is not about speedy reactions but about memorizing the positions of cards seen previously.

Demonstrating rules and strategies

The game needs to be demonstrated to the whole class in order to teach the rules of the game and the mental strategies required to win.

- Make a set of twelve very large cards and place them face down on the floor so that you know where the numbers are.
- Select two children to play the game.

Children assist the demonstration.

- Assist the first child to pick up two cards that you know are not a pair. Steer the child towards the cards you want them to select, one of which is, say, the number six.
- Finding they don't match the child replaces the cards. (Make sure they are returned to their original position; make a fuss about this by straightening them up.)

The children do not make their own choice.

- Assist the second child to pick up two cards. Again they should not be a pair but one of them should match one of the previous pair (the six again, perhaps).

At this stage the whole class will realize that you are deliberately helping the children in their selection and will begin to wonder why you are doing so. This will attract their interest and attention.

Most of the children will have noticed that the first child selected a six and the second child selected a six, but you need to ensure that every child is aware of this by demonstrating the act of thinking that is required to get the pair. Don't allow any child to tell you where the cards are.

The thinking is acted out by the teacher.

> Thinking is invisible. A teacher has to use visible actions to act the process of thinking.

- Look at the cards the second child has selected and say in a stage whisper: *You have a six.* Look puzzled, scratch your head, etc. and, looking at the class, whisper: *Did the first one have a six?* [Nods all round.]
- Assist the child in replacing the cards, deliberately noting where the six is replaced.
- Go to the first child and pointing to this second six whisper: *That is a six.* Look hard at each of the cards on the floor and show that you are trying to remember where the first six was placed.

The winning strategy is demonstrated.

It is tempting at this stage to pick up the six that has just been replaced in the hope that you can remember where the first six was placed. Attempting to find the first one (rather than the one that is definitely known) maximizes the chance of winning because, if it turns out to be wrong, there is another chance to match the mistaken card. You need to demonstrate that you make a note of where the second six is by, say, counting the number of rows along and the number up and then attempting to find the first six.

> It is worth investing the time to teach these games because they can be used later to extend number or practise matching shapes.

You can now continue either by finding the correct card or by getting it wrong, depending on the group of children and how well they are engaging in the activity. The two children go on to complete the game with the appropriate assistance and count their pairs to see who has won.

Children need to practise the rules of the game so that they become second nature. This should be done with a limited number of cards otherwise it takes a long time to finish. When the rules are causing no problems, the children need further assistance in adopting sensible strategies. You should assist them in this by explaining the thought processes. Children need to model this, also talking through what they are doing.

Snap

Number cards showing words, symbols or patterns	

- Use a pack of cards similar to that described above in the game of 'pairs'.
- Deal the cards to participating children who lay them in a pile, one by one in turn, face up.
- When two cards of the same value are showing at the same time, the quickest to react wins the cards in those piles.

> This game requires concentration and fast reactions.

Same value: different appearance

In the family game it is usual to shout '*snap*'. In the classroom it can be a rule that the children say '*same value*' instead of '*snap*' to claim the right to the cards. In a family game played for fun, calling '*snap*' is enough to win the cards. In the classroom, the game should be adapted to focus on what needs to be learnt. In this case it could be the child who is fastest in saying either 'same value, different appearance' (dots matched with figures, for example) or 'same value, same appearance' (dots matched with dots, figures matched with figures or words matched with words) who wins the cards. The snap game practises speedy reactions; in the adapted form it also practises thoughtful use of language.

Snap requires fast reactions.

The game of snap can have two or more players. Because of the speed of the game and the need for intensive concentration the children often do not listen carefully to what the other players are saying. Each group of players should appoint a referee for each game who observes the play and listens to what the players say. This can prevent arguments and is an excellent way of developing the children's listening skills.

Using a referee

Dominoes

Children need to be taught how to play dominoes.

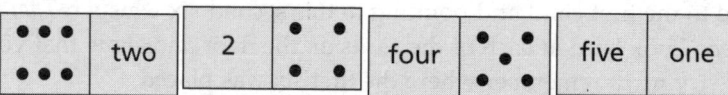

- Make a pack of cards with each card divided into two sections. In each section write a number in either dots, figures or words.
- Deal the cards to the participants. Each in turn lays a card to match the value of another to make a 'train' of cards (cards can be placed at either end).
- When a player is unable to match either end of the 'train' they miss that turn.
- When one player runs out of cards they win the game.

> This game requires concentration and contemplation. It does not depend on speed.

Time for contemplation

Again, there can be a requirement to state 'same value: different appearance' or 'same value: same appearance' or to take the card back if this is not done accurately. This game is not practising speedy reactions because there is time to contemplate, but it requires that children scan their cards for a matching pair. Although this is usually played so that each player keeps their dealt cards a secret, there is a variation in which each player lays out their cards in full view of other players. This allows each child to plan a winning strategy which maximizes their own chances of winning by using cards that benefit them and withholding cards that benefit an opponent.

Bingo

8	three	7	one
⋅⋅ ⋅⋅	12	⁚•⁚	nine

- Give each player a board (just a piece of card) with, say, eight numbers written on it in whatever form you want to practise.
- Randomly select numbered cards from a box and read or show the number to the players.
- Everyone who has that value on their board covers it with a counter.
- The first one to cover all their numbers wins.

This game is one that can be played with the whole class, the teacher acting as 'teller' or supervising a child doing so. It allows for contemplation and requires search. The same game can be played later with the numbers on the card representing the answers to addition or multiplication questions asked by the teacher.

The structure of the number system

When children can chant the numbers confidently and accurately into the hundreds (and by this time they will be reasonably good at all aspects of counting) they can be given further insights into the structure of our number system. The main ideas behind this are contained in *Key ideas: language* in *Mathematics for Primary Teachers: An Audit and Self-study Guide*, but we will describe them here to clarify their relevance to teaching young children. They are also used extensively in the scripts for this topic.

Our number system is especially powerful and economical because it uses only ten different digits (0, 1, 2, ... 8, 9) no matter how big the number we are dealing with; and it needs only these ten digits because their positions in a number contribute to its value. Compare this with Roman numerals and you will see the advantage.

In the number 495 the position of the four (third from the right) indicates its order of magnitude (we know its value is four *hundred*). Its order of magnitude is 'hundreds'. The position of the nine (second from the right) indicates that its order of magnitude is 'tens' (it indicates a value of nine *tens*). You can see how the language of number explicitly states the order of magnitude. When we say 'four thousand, eight hundred and sixty-five' we can hear that there is a four in the number (4865) whose position indicates that its order of magnitude is 'thousands'.

This wonderful system has its difficulties. Look at the number 53. We say fifty-three. This language does not make it obvious that it is five tens and three; it says fif-ty three. It does not say 'five tens and three'. It makes this number rather more difficult to understand than, say, 503 which very explicitly tells us it is five hundred and three. For people learning maths this is a complication that often denies them access to full understanding of what numbers are about.

The purpose of the earlier scripted session is to enable children to see the logic in the language that is slightly obscured by the actual words used. For this reason, they learn to speak, say, fifty-three in two ways: the normal language and the 'funny language' of 'five-ty three'. They also learn that in converting from one to the other they *keep the value but change the appearance*.

'Funny counting'

This 'funny language', used consistently, means that, for example, fifteen can be thought of as 'one-ty five'. This not only provides a link with numbers like 'six-ty five' but also means that 15 is read from left to right like the majority of our numbers. You will see that the scripted lesson also persists with the key idea 'Keep the value: change the appearance' when it shows how, say, forty-five can be spoken as 'thirty-fifteen'. This important idea makes the subtraction algorithm much easier.

Flexibility in thinking about numbers

Or 'four-ty-ty-ty'

This flexibility in thinking about numbers can be extended in different ways. When you look at the number 4000 you probably correctly say 'four thousand'. But there are many other ways of saying it that can be useful. Four thousand has the same value (different appearance) as forty hundred, four hundred tens, forty ten tens, and four ten hundreds. These different appearances need to be practised to provide confidence in thinking about numbers and place value.

> Later you will see that speaking 4000 in different ways can help in doing multiplication.

Numbers are abstractions

Numbers are abstractions.

The use of numbers like 'one, two, three, …' is very theoretical. Numbers are abstractions. When you count buttons and declare you can see seven, and count people and say you can see seven, then you are saying something about how those people are like those buttons. You have isolated a particular quality (not their colour; not their shape) that has the same value in each case. If we show you seven people and say 'How many can you see?' you correctly say 'Seven'. And you give the same answer if we show you seven buttons and ask 'How many can you see?' This is a very important idea.

> It is not only in maths that children deal with abstraction. In language, many words have an abstract or generalized meaning until qualified by other words.

We have dealt with many aspects of counting whole numbers. This level of attention is not unusual in primary schools, although we have introduced a number of novel ideas. Children usually count everyday objects (for instance, young children count beads, buttons, chairs, stairs and so on). What is less usual is to count items other than everyday objects. It is possible, however, to count other objects equally easily. If you know that what is written on the card shown

Counting fractions

is 'a half' then you can count any number of cards like it.

> Fractions are being treated here as objects to be counted.

Fluency in chanting whole numbers is used to count fractions.

Children can count 'one half; two halves; three halves; four halves; five halves; …' in the same way that they count 'one cup; two cups; three cups; …'. The same chant of 'one, two, three, …' underlies each. Counting the cards enables children to use their fluency in chanting the numbers to count in halves. They can also count the halves in cup form. This diagram

Real stories for maths stories

shows how half-cups can be counted in exactly the same language used with the cards. It also shows that when we count 'two halves' it is (*Keep the value: change the appearance*) to be thought of as one whole one.

In this way you can enable children to move flexibly between, say, 'six halves' and 'three whole ones' and understand what they are doing.

Think of halves and quarters as honorary whole numbers.

You can do similar work with quarters long before you do any formal work with fractions. Treat halves and quarters informally to begin with because they are a part of everyday language. It is quite a nice idea to think of halves and quarters as honorary whole numbers; that is, treat them with the same level of courtesy accorded to whole numbers while recognizing that they are not actually in this category.

Properties of numbers

We need to think again about odd numbers and even numbers and to introduce triangle numbers, square numbers and prime numbers into the discussion. There is no mystique about these. They are often treated with too much reverence. We want to remove some of the mystery of these numbers through an everyday scene. Let us introduce you to the staff of your new school (rather a lot of people). You talk to them happily and find your small talk concentrates on the fact that some of them teach in Key Stage One and the others in Key Stage Two. You begin to think of them as the KS1 teachers and the KS2 teachers. You have noted a particular property of each teacher and put them into categories. It helps you to think about them.

Recognizing patterns with numbers can be useful in finding generalizations. It is a precursor to algebra.

As you move around you notice that some of them are very enthusiastic and some seem rather disillusioned. You begin to think of some of them as 'enthusiastic' and some as 'tired' (although there are a couple of teachers you cannot make up your mind about). This new way of categorizing them does not divide them into the same groups as KS1 and KS2.

We need to classify people and objects to enable us to recognize common features.

We all tend to put people into categories like this. We do it because it helps us to remember them and understand them. We do the same with numbers. We notice that some numbers can be neatly put into pairs without an odd one left over. These are the even numbers. When we pair off some numbers we get an odd one left over. These are the odd numbers.

We can also see that some numbers (one, four, nine, sixteen, ...) can be arranged neatly into squares without any being left over. These are the square numbers. We are simply putting numbers into categories. It can help us to remember them and understand them.

The array of dots for square numbers provides an image of rapid growth. This is helpful later when recognizing quadratic graphs.

Now think of a number, say 15, and see if you can arrange it into a rectangle without having any spares. Putting it into pairs is no good (we get one left over), but a three by five rectangle works.

Try other numbers. Some of them resist being put into a rectangle: seven; eleven; thirteen; and many others. These are the prime numbers. 'Nine is OK (it forms a three by three rectangle). Not sure about one.' We could say it is prime because we are not allowing rectangles of width one (we do not allow a seven by one rectangle) but it seems a

We cannot find a general term for prime numbers.

Classifying people

Classifying numbers

Odd and even numbers

Square numbers

Rectangular numbers

Prime numbers

little unfair to put one in the prime category because, after all, it is square, and no other square number is prime. There is a little problem here, but it is of the same type as deciding whether this teacher is 'enthusiastic' or 'tired'. We could argue the case for either answer but for the sake of consistency in school maths we say that one is not prime.

Factors, multiples and divisors

The technical language of maths includes the words 'factorize' and 'multiple'. Children deal with factors and multiples from an early age even if they do not use the technical vocabulary. When they say $3 \times 4 = 12$, for instance, they are voicing the factors of twelve. Three is a factor of twelve. Four is a factor of twelve. Each is a 'factor' simply because it can be multiplied by a whole number to make twelve. Is six a factor of twelve? Yes. Is five? No... And so on.

You may wonder why the words 'factor' and 'multiple' are worth teaching. One reason is economy. The second is clarity. It is more economical and clearer to say 'Tell me a factor of 12' or 'Tell me all the factors of 12' than having to say 'Tell me all the numbers that multiplied by another number give the answer twelve'. But an equally important reason is prompted by where this sort of technical language is taking us. When we teach young children we are inevitably laying foundations for later work. We teach initial ideas in a sophisticated fashion so that they can be effectively utilized in subsequent work which draws on a range of previously mastered ideas. We want to discuss some of this technical language in detail.

> The technical language of maths is efficient and concise.

Factors

What exactly do we mean by the word 'factor'? Suppose we are talking only about whole numbers (sometimes called the integers). In this case we use factor to mean those numbers that will fit a whole number of times into the given number without any remainder. This means that factors exist in pairs. One factor of twelve is four. Four divides into twelve exactly three times. Three is also a factor of twelve. It divides into twelve exactly four times. Twelve can be written as three times four or as four times three. Now pause for a moment and reflect on this discussion. The fact that twelve can be written as a product of two of its factors seems quite important for later work. Perhaps we should emphasize this result and not only focus on finding lists of factors.

Study the following:

$$12 = 1 \times 12$$
$$12 = 12 \times 1$$
$$12 = 3 \times 4$$
$$12 = 4 \times 3$$
$$12 = 2 \times 6$$
$$12 = 6 \times 2$$

The factors of 12 are 1, 2, 3, 4, 6, 12. Twelve can be written as the product of factors in six different ways. The identification of factors has come from the tables, from the products rather than the list. This can be extended further by referring once again to the poster on the wall 'Keep the value: change the appearance'. From the products above let's look at the first one, $12 = 1 \times 12$, and consider how else we can write it.

> Early number work lays the foundations for algebra.

$12 = 1 \times (11 + 1)$
$12 = 1 \times (10 + 2)$

And lots more. They 'keep the value but change the appearance'.

Now inspect
$12 = 3 \times 4$
Ah yes. We can write:
$12 = (1 + 2) \times (1 + 3)$
There are many ways of doing this that 'keep the value but change the appearance'.

See *Key ideas: Keep the value: change the appearance.*

The beginnings of algebra

Now this is beginning to look a lot like algebraic work. We are factorizing twelve and laying the foundations for later work. We can develop this further:

$12 = (1.5 + 1.5) \times (0.5 + 3.5)$
or $12 = (^-5 + 8) \times (7 + ^-3)$

We can use letters for numbers. Inspect the following equation:

$12 = (x + 1) \times (y + 3)$

Twelve can be written in an infinite number of ways.

What are the possible values of x and y? Well, an obvious one would be $x = 2$ and $y = 1$. But this is not the only solution. We could have $x = 3$ and $y = 0$ or $x = 1$ and $y = 3$ or $x = 0.5$ and $y = 5$ and so on. An infinite number of solutions. What if the letters in each bracket were the same? Inspect the following equation:

$12 = (x + 1) \times (x + 2)$

How many solutions does this equation have? You may have spotted that $x = 2$ is a solution. If you multiply out the brackets you will see that in fact this is a quadratic equation with two solutions. The other solution is $x = ^-5$.

All of these ideas can be encapsulated in the algebraic equation $12 = (a + b)(c + d)$

Laying the right foundations

Just by inspecting the factors of twelve we can see how the idea can be developed right through to algebraic factorization. This demonstrates how necessary it is to lay the right foundations with young children so that later they can progress to harder maths by making connections with these simple ideas. Planning to take account of development in the subject means that the subject is presented as a body of knowledge that has links and connections. It also means that being able to use algebra implies there is less to learn.

Prime numbers

A prime number has two factors.

Two is the only even prime number.

Let us make a diversion for a moment and discuss prime numbers. What exactly is a prime number? A prime number is a positive whole number (integer) that has two and only two factors, one and itself. So three is a prime number. Its factors are just one and three. Two is a prime number. Its factors are just one and two. Two is a special sort of prime number because it is the only even prime number.

Over the centuries people have been fascinated by prime numbers. The search still goes on – now with the aim of finding the greatest prime number a computer can generate.

One is not a prime number.

What about the number one? This is not an easy question. Mathematicians themselves disagree about this. Some say that one is prime and others say it is not. Inspect it for a moment. Does it have two factors? Well, sort of: it has one and itself which is also one. We do not want to prolong the argument because the answer has been decided for us. It has been agreed that in school maths one will not be called prime.

Working out all the prime numbers between 1 and 100

Eratosthenes sieve

Finding prime factors

Writing numbers as products of prime factors

Highest common factors (HCF)

The numbers 2, 3, 5 and 7 are all prime numbers. We can find all the prime numbers below a hundred (there are twenty-five of them) by using a number square and systematically crossing out 1, then multiples of 2 except 2 itself, multiples of 3 except 3 itself, multiples of 5 except 5 itself and so on, working through the multiples of primes up to 13. We will then have all twenty-five left. This is called Eratosthenes sieve after an ancient Greek mathematician.

	2	3		5		7			
11		13				17	19		
		23					29		
31						37			
41		43				47			
		53					59		
61						67			
71		73					79		
		83					89		
						97			

Doing the activity of identifying prime numbers in this way gives practice in tables and reminds children of the patterns that can be found in a number square. If the tables are crossed off using different colours it is easy to spot numbers with common prime factors up to the factor thirteen. No one has ever found a way of generating all the prime numbers. It seems that however many prime numbers we find there is always one more. Some people have made conjectures such as 'any prime number is given by $n^2 - n + 11$' but this breaks down. Can you see why? Put $n = 11$ and then 11 is a factor of the entire expression, so the resulting number cannot be prime.

Prime factors

Let us return to factors and those special factors that are prime. To find all the prime factors of a number you could find all the factors and then identify which ones were also prime numbers. There is a neater and more efficient way of finding prime factors by successive division. Look at twelve again. You know that it is an even number so start by dividing by 2, then divide your answer again by 2 and then you can stop because the answer is a prime number.

> The prime factors of 12 can be found by repeated division because 12 can be expressed as the product of its prime factors.

$$2 \,)\, \underline{12}$$
$$2 \,)\, \underline{6}$$
$$3$$

This tells us that the prime factors of 12 are 2, 2 and 3 . Now 12 can be written as the product of these three prime factors:

$$12 = 2 \times 2 \times 3$$

Every positive whole number can be written uniquely as a product of its prime factors. This can be helpful in finding the highest common factors of a set of numbers. Suppose we want the highest common factor of 90, 315 and 495. By doing successive division we can write:

$$90 = 2 \times 3 \times 3 \times 5$$
$$315 = 3 \times 3 \times 5 \times 7$$
$$495 = 3 \times 3 \times 5 \times 11$$

Inspect each product of primes and you will see that the numbers 3, 3 and 5 are common to each. The highest common factor (HCF) is therefore

$$3 \times 3 \times 5 = 45$$

This can be particularly helpful when we want to reduce fractions or look for common properties of numbers.

Working on factors and prime factors improves number fluency.

Multiples

We say that two is a factor of twelve and twelve is a multiple of two. We have already looked at multiplication tables but let us look again at the three times table. Instead of saying 'one three is three, two threes are six, ...' you can inspect the table and say 'Two is a factor of six and three is a factor of six. Six is a multiple of two and six is a multiple of three' and so on, getting the children to chant the words with you and respond to questions. You can generalize these statements by saying if a is a factor of b then b is a multiple of a.

Using algebra to write generalizations

Lowest common multiples (LCM)

There are times when we want to find the lowest common multiple of two or more numbers. For example, when we add fractions we can only add those fractions with the same denominator. If the fractions do not have the same denominator we first have to 'keep the value but change the appearance'; in other words, we have to find equivalent fractions to each of those we wish to add with the same denominator. If we want to add thirds and halves that is easy. The lowest common multiple of three and two is six. It is straightforward and easy to spot.

The technical term 'lowest common multiple' is concise. Try explaining it and you realize how many words you need.

What about fifths and tenths? Again this is easy because ten is the lowest common multiple of five and ten. What about eighths and sixths? This is not so immediately obvious. We inspect the eight times table and the six times table and find that twenty-four is the lowest common multiple.

Is there an easier way of finding the lowest common multiple? Yes, there is. Suppose we want the lowest common multiple of 210 and 66. First write each number as a product of its prime factors.

Using prime factors to work out the LCM

$$210 = 2 \times 3 \times 5 \times 7 \quad \text{and} \quad 66 = 2 \times 3 \times 11$$

The lowest common multiple (LCM) can be found by multiplying together all the first set of prime factors by any new prime factors in the second set, giving a neat and efficient method.

$$\text{LCM} = 2 \times 3 \times 5 \times 7 \times 11$$

Once again we see the relationship between factors and multiples.

An operation is a job to be done.

Introducing the four operations

Although we consider addition, subtraction, multiplication and division in the next topic we will start this discussion here because the early work is entirely based on counting.

When we see $3 + 2$ we probably think of it as adding two numbers, which of course it is. But we want to introduce a different way of thinking about this that has many benefits in later work. Think of it as starting with the number 3 and performing the addition operation on it.

The addition operation is a job to be done.

What does this imply? It means that we have to place some additional objects next to the three we started with; that is the nature of the *add* operation, no matter what number follows the + sign. In this case, the size of the operation is 2; so in fact we add two further items, and those items are the same type as the first three.

We can now see five items collected together as a result of starting with three and performing an add operation whose size is 2. The expression 3 + 2 is best thought of not as the addition of two numbers but as starting with one number and then doing an operation on it – specifically, getting some more objects (in this case, two objects).

Consistency is crucial.

This subtle difference is important in making sense of the four operations (as we will show) because it provides a consistent approach· throughout our work in maths. The episode that follows shows how this approach to addition should be taught to children.

The maths tray story

A maths story

Young children love telling stories. This can be used to assist children in interpreting mathematical symbols and notation into words and actions. We look at the sum

Acting out a real story to match a maths story creates a mental image.

$$3 + 2 =$$

and say: *This is a maths story. Let us read it together.*

A real story

Here is a maths tray. The tray is empty.

Here is a box. It is full of counters.

*Go to the box. Get **three** counters.*
Take them to the maths tray. $3 + 2 =$

Look at the maths story.
*Read **and*** $3 + 2 =$
*Read **two*** $3 + 2 =$
*Get **two** more counters.*
Take them to the maths tray.

*There are **five** counters on the maths tray.* $3 + 2 = 5$

You can see from this that the children are becoming practised in seeing the first number as being the quantity that we start with (emphasized by being placed on the *maths tray*) with the operation 'add' being interpreted as an instruction to fetch some more – here, two more. The children can act out lots of these stories. Deliberately include examples like 4 + 0 = so that they go to the box and fetch 'zero counters' to the maths tray.

Add is the job to be done and two is the size of the job.

'Take away' is done in a similar fashion. This involves remaining at the maths tray in order to remove some from the original quantity.

Subtraction is the job of removal.

❷ The four operations

Rapid recall

It is important for children to learn their multiplication tables. They need to be able to recall multiplication facts rapidly:

> *Seven times three? Twenty-one!*

They need to use the tables to give answers to division questions:

> *Twenty-one divided by three? Seven!*

Practice in multiplication tables

They also need to use these multiplication and division facts to do long multiplication and division, and to use them appropriately in solving problems. Children learn tables successfully when teachers give them practice in doing so and show that it is important to do so. They understand and are able to apply them according to how well they are taught.

An operation is 'a job to be done'.

Multiplication is one of the four common operations taught in school maths. Each of the four operations is introduced as 'a job to be done' and this idea is used in the programme of work below. As far as multiplication is concerned, this means that 3×8 is thought of as follows:

> *I start by moving three from the resource table to the maths tray. What do I have to do now? Ah! I have to do that again, and again, and I have to do it eight times altogether.*

This important idea pervades our work with the adding, subtracting, multiplying and dividing of numbers. It is a particular way of reading an expression like 3×8. From this discussion you will see why in the recommended resources for this programme we use the three times table written as 3×1, 3×2, etc. and not 1×3, 2×3. The job is to operate on the three each time and at first the children learn to chant the table as 'three times one is three, three times two is six ...' and so on and only later abbreviate this to 'one three is three, two threes are six ...'.

Chanting the tables

Assisting problem solving with appropriate tools and representations

The scripts in this section demonstrate how the teacher utilizes the children's knowledge of the multiplication tables to extend their knowledge of number. Materials have been carefully selected to provide appropriate tools to assist in the solving of problems. Notice how much emphasis is placed on oral work before any written work is attempted.

Multiplication tables are so important that they should be memorized.

It is important to be consistent. Each operation is treated in the same way.

Using tables to develop further number skills	

Development in teaching the four operations

When the children are confident and competent with chanting the tables (but not necessarily able to recall them from memory), these can be used to develop multiplication skills with very large or very small numbers. Knowledge of one multiplication fact can lead to knowledge of an unlimited number of multiplication facts. The tables can be used to solve real-life problems involving multiplication. They provide a vivid image of the nature of maths and what it means to go beyond the information given and work in the imagination.

> The teacher assists the children in making connections between the multiplication tables and the mathematics that develops out of them.

Division as the inverse of multiplication

Tables not only provide the basis for learning about multiplication but inspection of tables allows division to be introduced. We utilize the fact that division can be seen as the inverse operation of multiplication. It is the regular reference to something that is well known, the multiplication tables, that enables children to see that knowing a little can lead to knowing a lot.

Knowing key results

Without such referencing maths can seem to be a large body of knowledge that is inaccessible to many. There are a small number of key results in maths that need to be known. They need to be committed to memory through chanting and rote learning so that they can be instantly recalled. They are the foundations for future learning and need regular attention. They include the multiplication tables which are vital for effective teaching and learning of number operations and their inverses.

Teachers should enable children to:

- *inspect number expressions containing the four operations and read each as a 'job' to be done*

- *apply memorized knowledge of the number bonds up to ten to evaluate number expressions mentally*

> Each item utilizes the knowledge of the multiplication tables.

- *use multiplication tables flexibly to evaluate expressions that include the division sign*

- *use mental algorithms that reflect the logic of number language*

- *use written algorithms for the four operations*

- *apply mental and written algorithms to solve written problems*

- *use the logic of number language to evaluate expressions in fractions, decimals, percentages and negative numbers, using the four operations*

- *evaluate algebraic expressions that use the four operations*

- *construct algebraic expressions that generalize results from investigations*

- *use formulae that utilize the four operations*

Script: Teaching multiplication and division

Inspecting

This script practises the chanting of the three times table and introduces the idea of 'inspecting'. The same approach should be used with all tables. In the script you can see how cognition in maths is carefully assisted by the device of using and over-acting the idea of 'inspecting the table'. The teacher uses exaggerated gestures such as scratching his head or putting on a quizzical look to demonstrate the act of 'thinking'. He also squeezes his eyes closed to demonstrate 'looking inside his head' and 'working in the imagination'.

> Thinking is invisible. The teacher uses gestures to demonstrate and prompt the act of thinking.

Using beads for real stories

Resources

- Transparent plastic bags each containing three large beads
- Plastic bags each containing three hundred small beads
- Twelve plastic or paper beakers that will stack
- A large display of the three times table

$$3 \times 1 = 3$$
$$3 \times 2 = 6$$
$$3 \times 3 = 9$$
$$3 \times 4 = 12$$
$$3 \times 5 = 15$$
$$3 \times 6 = 18$$
$$3 \times 7 = 21$$
$$3 \times 8 = 24$$
$$3 \times 9 = 27$$
$$3 \times 10 = 30$$

> Notice the order of the numbers. The number three is being operated on each time.

The whole class working together

The three times table

The class is arranged with every child facing the front so that they can see the board and the teacher. The teacher displays the large version of the three times table which the children will have seen before when learning to chant their tables.

> It is important that every child can see the teacher because the demonstration is very visual.

This is the three times table. You probably know it. Let's read this together. Three times one is three. Three times two is six. ... Three times ten is thirty.

Chanting together

Establishing a knowledge base

As they chant the table together the teacher monitors the class to check that every child is joining in and appears confident. This joint activity reminds the children of something that they have done before and establishes a common knowledge base. The teacher then moves on to inspect the table by picking out individual items.

Demonstrating how to inspect

If I said 'What is three times six?' you would go: umm ... [Inspect the table for 3 × 6; be very obvious about the inspection and do not go to the answer straight away.] *Notice how I am inspecting the table. Ah! It's eighteen.* [Practise several of these.]

Working backwards

Working backwards

After working forwards in this way the teacher starts to work backwards by inspecting the results of multiplying.

If I said 'What is another way of saying twenty-four?' you would go: umm ... [Inspect answers very visibly; undertake laborious inspection to emphasize the act of inspecting the table.] Notice how I am inspecting the table. Ah! It's three times eight.

This activity is repeated, with the children joining in until they are confident in working forwards and backwards with the numbers in the table. It is important that the teacher does not assume that the children will remember these facts from earlier teaching but ensures that every child is given the opportunity to gain the knowledge required to move on to the next step.

The amount of practice will depend upon the careful monitoring of the class by the teacher.

Ensuring success

The demonstration establishes a common knowledge base.

Real stories
Having worked with the figures in the table, the teacher now introduces the bags of large beads to provide a real story.

Real stories

[Show five bags of three beads.] This bag has got three beads in. This bag has got three beads in. This bag has got three beads in. This bag has got three beads in. This bag has got three beads in. What is the same about each bag? Yes, each one has got three beads. How many bags are there? Yes, five. One, two, three, four, five.

The teacher assists the children in making connections between real stories and maths stories.

I have got bags with three beads in. I have got five bags. Altogether I have got ... [Visibly think by, for example, scratching head and looking puzzled. Turn to three times table.] ... I will have to inspect the table. Ah! [point to 3 × 5] I have three in each bag [point to 3] and I have five bags [point to 5]. I have fifteen.

Non-verbal gestures

This activity has painstakingly connected the counting of beads in the bag with the figures in the table.

Making connections

[Show five bags of three beads again.] If I show you this, you can look at the table [point] and say: Hmm, he's got three in each bag; he's got five bags. He is showing that five times three is fifteen.

Real stories and maths stories

We are now reaching a vital point in the teaching episode: the teacher is going to demonstrate how the beads in the bag represent a real story and the figures in the table represent what maths is about.

*[Show five bags of three beads again.] If I wave these at you, you say: The **real** story is five bags with three beads in each. The **maths** story is [again visibly inspect three times table] 'three times five is fifteen'.*

Maths stories
The teacher then presents a range of real stories, each involving bags of three beads and encourages the children to give the maths story.

*If I show you this [wave and count seven bags of three] you say [encourage all to use the words]: I can see three in each bag; I can see seven bags. The **maths** story is 'three times seven is twenty-one'.*

The children can now move from the real stories to the maths stories so the next step is to encourage them to move from the maths story to work in the imagination. This is the nature of maths.

Working in the imagination

Reading and interpreting mathematical symbols and equations as 'stories' is the basis for understanding maths.

[Point to three times table.] If I point to that [3 × 8 = 24] you say: The maths story is 'Three times eight is twenty-four' so I can see

[demonstrate imagining something 'in the head' by, for example, closing your eyes or gazing upwards] *three beads in each bag; I can see eight bags.* [Show the real bags of beads to emphasize this.] *This is what you can see in your head. When I look at this* [point to $3 \times 8 = 24$] *I have to inspect my head to find the picture of the **real** story.*

Various results in the three times table are now used with a range of maths stories that are then translated into real stories. You will see in this introduction that the way in which the children are taught is consistent with the nature of maths. The pure figures that are in the three times table are in an imaginary world of maths that is related to the real world but separate from it. The teaching shows how the real story is one that uses the beads, objects that can be seen and touched. The maths story is entirely in figures and words. This idea is continued into the next stage of teaching.

> Children like to use their imagination to tell real stories that match the maths stories.

Extending multiplication facts

In this part the children are introduced to a way of extending the three times table so that they can do the three hundred and the three thousand times table (and more). They do this by working entirely mathematically, in a world that is imaginary because they do not need to have any bags of beads in front of them. They can work in their heads because the logic is in the language. Again they start by chanting the table as it is written and then the teacher moves them on.

Now it is my turn. I want you to listen to me and then join in when you see what I am doing.

*Three **hundred*** [emphasize 'hundred'] *times one is three **hundred*** [emphasize 'hundred']. *Three **hundred** times two is six **hundred** ... three **hundred** times ten is thirty **hundred**.* [Get the class to join in as early as possible.] *So, you can do the three hundred times table. It is not on the wall, but you can inspect it in your head.*

> The teacher demonstrates a different way of reading the multiplication tables.

*Now you can do the three **thousand** times table ...* [Start off and allow the class to join in.]

Multiplying very large numbers

Using only the three times table the teacher has shown the children that they can use their imagination to do the three hundred times table and so on. The idea is consolidated by using the three zillion times table. This requires extra concentration because 'zillions' are not in the children's common vocabulary. They realize that they are doing something special and are excited by the use of unusual words. Just getting their mouths around the word 'zillion' makes them more conscious of what they are doing. This raising of the level of consciousness is an important concept in the psychology of learning.

> Once this idea has been established the tables can be extended further.

*Now for the three **zillion** times table.* [Indicate the three times table again.] *Notice what we are doing when I say I want the three zillion times table. We are looking at* [point] *three times one ... and then we are inspecting in our heads for the word that is not written down anywhere. What is it? Ah! Zillion. Three* [point to head] ***zillion** times one is three* [point to head] ***zillion.** Three* [point to head] ***zillion** times two is six* [point to head] ***zillion.***

The language of number

The teacher has now established that the three times table can be used to get further results. But so far there has been no mention of the thirty times table. Why not? The answer lies in the language of number and the rather quirky way that we have of speaking the tens. To overcome this the teacher draws on the novel way of speaking numbers that the children have seen before to demonstrate that the table can be used for the thirty times table. The children are invited to share the teacher's 'funny' way of speaking numbers and they find this very exciting.

*Now watch me. Three-**ty** times one is three-**ty**. Three-**ty** times two is six-**ty**. Three-**ty** times three is nine-**ty**. But hold on. We don't usually say 'three-**ty**' so I have to inspect my head for what that must mean.*

The teacher then acts out the thought process of interpreting the 'three-ty' as thirty and discusses it in relation to the 'Keep the value: change the appearance' wall poster.

It is important to use the word 'three-ty' and not thirty because it is consistent with the way we say 'three hundred', 'three thousand', and so on. When we connect 'three-ty' with thirty we do it by using the phrase 'Keep the value: change the appearance' because this is used frequently in other areas of maths. It is important that children recognize that 'three-ty' is a spoken form of 30, in the same way that 'three hundred' is the spoken form of 300. Since '-ty' means tens, another way of saying 300 would be 'three-ty-ty'.

More real stories

Having established that the children can use the three times table to extend their knowledge of multiplication, the teacher relates the maths stories of the extended three times table to real stories. Connections are now made between that imaginary world of pure maths and the real world.

The teacher shows six bags each with three beads in and, as in an earlier part of the script, establishes the maths story.

This has got three beads in. [Repeat six times.] That's the real story. Where is the maths story for that? [Indicate three times table, slowly moving hand to correct line.] Yes. Three times six is eighteen.

This reminds the children of an activity that they have done before and have confidence in. The teacher now moves on to use bags with hundreds of smaller beads in them. The story is the same but the number of beads has changed.

*[Show six bags each with three hundred beads in.] This has got three hundred beads in. [Repeat six times]. That's the real story. Where is the maths story for that? [Indicate three times table, slowly moving hand to correct line.] Yes. Three **hundred** times six is eighteen **hundred**. You have to inspect the table [point] and you have to inspect your head [point].*

More maths stories

Different numbers of bags of beads are then used and the children are invited to tell the maths story. The teacher helps the children to use the right words by pointing to, say, $3 \times 6 = 18$ and doing the following step-by-step actions:

Side notes:

Interpreting thirty

Using and applying maths

The teacher demonstrates.

Making connections

Non-verbal gestures

See *Key ideas*.

The teacher demonstrates how to speak the numbers and explains the logic in the language.

The children can now apply maths to the real world.

The visual image created with beads is used to provoke a mental image.

[Point to 3; demonstrate counting the beads through the bag; mouth 'hundred'; point to times; indicate six bags; point to six; pause; move to 18 and mouth 'hundred'.] *Three hundred times six is eighteen hundred.*

Repetition to reinforce learning

The activity is repeated as many times as is necessary for all the children to become confident. The teacher then moves on to demonstrate stories for thousands. Very small beads are scooped into four beakers and the teacher asserts that each contains three thousand beads.

> *This has got three thousand beads in. This has got three thousand beads in. This has got three thousand beads in. This has got three thousand beads in. That's the real story. What is the maths story?*

Working in the imagination

The activity for hundreds is repeated for thousands and then in the imagination for millions and zillions, etc. The children can now do extended multiplication tables and apply them to real problems. They can work with the written table and they can work in their imagination. The next step introduces the idea of division as being related to multiplication. It uses the idea of 'Keep the value: change the appearance' to inspect the three times table for 'division bonds'.

> The children are now ready to replicate these problems in the modelling phase.

'How much?' and 'How many?'

In this extract the teacher repeatedly uses the words 'How much?' to elicit the answer. It is important to observe how these words are used so that you can distinguish between this and the request 'How many?' which is used later.

> Language is central to the teaching process.

Keep the value: change the appearance

> [Point to 24 in the three times table.] *How much is there? Yes, there is twenty-four.* [Point to 3 × 8] *How much is there? Yes, there is twenty-four.* [Point to 24] *How much is there? Yes, there is twenty-four. Is this* [point to 24] *the same as this?* [Point to 3 × 8]

If the children say 'yes' to this question, the teacher can say teasingly: *No, it is not. That has got a two and a four, that has got a three and a times sign and an eight.* If they say, 'It is not the same', the teacher needs to explain that it is by referring to the poster 'Keep the value: change the appearance' to help the children understand that the value is the same.

> See *Key ideas.*

> *I am keeping the value but changing the appearance. If I point to 3 × 8 and say, How much is there? your eyes move to here* [point to 24], *and you say twenty-four.*

Preparing for division

Practice to reinforce understanding

This is practised with several different examples until the teacher is confident that the children understand that the value of the multiplication and its result are the same, although their appearance is different. The idea is reinforced by using beakers and showing that whatever position a set of, say, twelve beakers is in there are always twelve of them.

> Beakers are used to provide a visual image of the maths story.

A visual image to provoke a mental image

> [Place twelve beakers randomly on the table.] *There are* [count] *twelve beakers here. How much is here? Yes, twelve beakers.* [Slide beakers around in a different random arrangement.] *There are* [do not count] *twelve beakers here. I did not remove any, so I have kept the value. But I moved them around; I have changed the appearance. How much is here? Yes, twelve beakers.*

Assisting cognition by pausing

[Very slowly stack beakers in piles of three, each time silently mouthing the counting: *one; two; three.*] *There are* [pause] *three beakers. There are* [pause] *three beakers ...* [Indicate all the twelve beakers by circling them with a hand movement.] *How much is here? Yes, twelve beakers. I did not remove any, so I have kept the value. But I moved them around; I have changed the appearance.* [Indicate all the twelve beakers by circling them with a hand movement.] *How much is here? Yes, twelve beakers.*

The teacher has established that no matter what position the beakers are in there are always twelve of them. We have now reached a vital point in the lesson where the teacher is going to shift the emphasis. Asking 'How much?' is a prompt for thinking of all the beakers together (something that is emphasized by the teacher indicating all the twelve beakers by a hand movement). Asking 'How many?' is a prompt to think of them as separate entities, and this needs to be emphasized.

Using words to prompt thinking

Repetition to reinforce learning

To do this, each pile of three beakers is indicated in turn and very slowly and deliberately they are counted in a stage whisper so that everyone knows there are four and that four is the number required when asked 'How *many* threes are there?'. Very visible up and down movements of the arm are used, pointing in turn to each pile of three whilst counting 'One, two, three, four. There are four'. The children are prevented from saying 'Four beakers' by the teacher cutting the arm movement abruptly after the word 'four'.

*Yes. There are four. How **many** threes are there? Four. How **much** is there? Wait! I'll help you.* [Unstack the beakers.] *How much is there? Yes. I can see twelve beakers* [Carefully stack the beakers again, counting 'one, two, three' in each pile]. *How many threes can you see? Yes, four. How many threes make twelve?* [Stage whisper to count so the answer is obvious.] *Four.*

Ensuring success by using a visual image

[Point to three times table.] *Hey! We knew all that without the beakers. Counting the beakers is a real story. But we have got the maths story here. We were thinking of twelve* [point to beakers, circling hand around them] *so we were thinking of ...* [inspect 'answers' in three times table] *Ah! twelve* [point]. *So we already knew* [point to 3 × 4] *that four batches of three make twelve* [unstack beakers and put them in piles of three beakers each] *and three batches of four make twelve.* [Draw their attention to the poster 'Keep the value: change the appearance'.]

[Point to 3 × 4 = 12] *How many threes make twelve? Yes, four. How many fours make twelve? Yes, three.*

Working in the imagination

This activity is practised with different numbers of beakers and then with imaginary beakers. It is then extended to hundreds and thousands of beakers.

*I am thinking of twelve **thousand** beakers.* [Emphasize the word 'thousand' but do not write anything suggestive of it: it must be 'in the head'. Rapidly pretend to distribute twelve thousand imaginary beakers.] *I am going to change the appearance by putting them in groups of four* [point to the 4 in 3 × 4 = 12]. *How many fours can you see? Yes, three thousand* [point to the space after three as 'thousand' is emphasized].

Repetition to reinforce learning

The activity is repeated with different tables until the children are fluent and able to answer questions instantly when prompted by 'How much?' or 'How many?'.

The exaggerated gestures of the teacher are used throughout as cues and prompts for the children's thinking.

The amount of practice required will depend upon careful monitoring by the teacher.

The demonstration will be followed by the children replicating the work in the modelling phase.

Lesson plan

This lesson for Year 2 pupils teaches applying multiplication to real stories. It is from the fourth topic in the sequence set out in the following scheme of work.

Using the scripts as a basis for planning

First the teacher designs the scheme of work.

1. Counting activities
2. Chanting tables
3. Inspecting the tables
4. Maths stories/real stories
5. Real-life stories
6. Extended tables
7. Inspecting the extended tables
8. Maths stories/real stories
9. Real-life stories

> The scheme of work is designed to make the connections between certain concepts transparent.

Previous work

The teacher needs to know what the children have covered.

The children have practised counting and have revised addition as 'an operation to be done'. They have learnt to chant the tables together and have used objects such as beakers to represent multiplication facts. They have also used beakers to help them inspect the tables and ask 'How many?'. They have met the idea of 'maths stories' and 'real stories' when doing addition and subtraction.

> The teacher makes connections with prior knowledge by using the same representations as before.

Lesson design

The teacher has prepared resources.

The lesson begins with the teacher pinning cards on the board. Six cards have real stories written on them in words and six others have maths stories written in figures. All the stories are multiplication problems. The aim of the demonstration is to match the real stories with their corresponding maths stories. A real story is selected and the teacher reads it with the whole class. A child is then invited to come to the board and find the corresponding maths story. The teacher assists the child to select the correct story. Three real stories are matched to maths stories in this way. The teacher then reads the remaining maths stories with the class and gets the children to match them with real stories.

Children assist the demonstration.

> The idea of 'real stories' and 'maths stories' is used again and again.

$5 \times 3 = 15$

I go to the maths table and get five counters.

I do this three times.

I now have fifteen counters.

Working in pairs

This is followed by the modelling phase in which pairs of children use sets of cards to replicate the activity. The class is brought together to present solutions in the summarizing phase.

The next demonstration involves matching real and maths stories again but this time the stories are about inspecting the numbers and asking

Moving on to division	'How many?'. They are division problems. Again the children model the activity and then present their solutions.

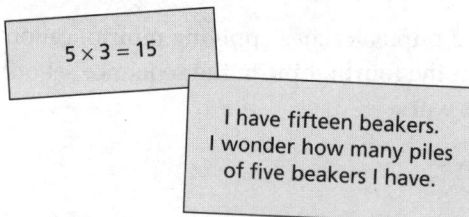

Setting homework	The teacher sets a homework. The children are given envelopes containing sticky labels with both types of matching stories written on them. They are asked to match the real stories to the maths stories and stick them in their books. In the subsequent lesson they will be asked to present their solutions.

> The multiplication tables are used to demonstrate the connection between multiplication and division.

The structure and timing of the lesson

Class	Y2	Teacher	Miss Brown
Date	24 June	Student	Mary Frost

Lesson description	Lesson 4: Real stories and maths stories based on multiplication
Learning outcomes	Match real stories and maths stories. Read word problems.
Resources	• Multiplication tables display • Large cards of stories for whole class discussion • Sets of cards for pair work • Sets of labels for homework

Classroom framework	Time	Teacher and pupils
Demonstration	10 min.	Pin to the board six cards with real stories and six cards with maths stories and read them all with the class. Remind the children which are real stories and which are maths stories. Take one story at a time. Invite children to come to the board and match maths stories to real stories (three) then real stories to maths stories (three). Assist the children in getting the correct match.
Modelling	15 min.	Give out sets of twelve cards to pairs of children and ask them to match real and maths stories. Monitor progress by asking children to read their stories and explain how they are doing the matching.
Summarizing	5 min.	Invite children to present solutions. Get them to read the stories. Put answers on the board.
Demonstration	10 min.	Put twelve more cards on the board with real stories and maths stories. This time the real stories ask 'How many?'. The division sign is not used at this stage. The children are using the multiplication tables and working backwards. Invite children to come to the board and match stories.
Modelling	10 min.	Give out sets of cards and get children to work in pairs again.
Summarizing	5 min.	Children present solutions.
Demonstration	5 min.	Give out envelopes containing sticky labels. Ask children to match the stories and stick them in their books (example on OHT).

Practice

When the teacher has demonstrated to the whole class how to match
real stories and maths stories, the children can work in pairs with sets
of cards. First they have to read the cards to each other and then each
in turn tries to match the real stories to the maths stories. It is important
to keep to the same format as in the demonstration.

The first exercises are stories about multiplication, such as:

$6 \times 2 = 12$

I go to the table and get six beakers.
I do this two times.

As the children are working it is important that the teacher moves
around the class and listens to the children read the cards. She can ask
'How much is there?' for each card to establish the fact that they have
the same value but a different appearance. The children can use sets
of beakers to act out the stories as a 'job to be done'.

The second exercises are stories about working backwards, such as:

$6 \times 2 = 12$

I go to the table and count twelve
beakers. As I look at them I wonder
how many lots of six beakers there are.

The language may seem rather difficult for such young children but
remember that they will have spoken the words many times before
and will have read them with the teacher in the demonstration. This
familiarity will help them to read the cards and the teacher can assist
them as she goes around the class.

Notice that we always write the number of objects grouped together
first and the number of times second. This is deliberate. It is consistent
with the idea of starting with a number and operating or 'doing a job'
on it. Remember that with addition and subtraction the sequence was
to start with the first number, look at the job to be done and then look
at the size of the job to be done.

An alternative way to practise this matching of real and maths stories is
to design a set of cards that match and play the game of 'pairs' or 'snap'.
This is a little more challenging because the children have to pause and
read the cards carefully. It is best if the games themselves have already
been introduced so that the children are familiar with them.

You can set questions that will introduce the idea of commutativity.
For example:

$2 \times 6 = 12$

I go to the table and get two beakers.
I do this six times.

By carefully selecting appropriate examples you can initiate discussions
in the summarizing phase, such as:

*Compare this problem with the first problem. If you get two beakers six times
how much do you have? If you get six beakers two times how much do you
have? [Use the beakers to demonstrate.] Is two times six the same as six
times two? They have the same value but a different appearance.*

Follow this with some more examples.

Homework

Homework

Children in Year 2 can be expected to do about twenty minutes of maths homework twice a week. Homework should be an integral part of the teaching programme. In many cases you will set work in preparation for the next lesson. At other times you will want the children to spend some time going over work that they have done in class. Activities such as practising and memorizing the multiplication tables can be given as homework. Whatever you set for homework the children must be properly prepared so that they can be successful. Homework is not a time to set demanding or challenging tasks that could result in failure. However, tasks do need to be carefully selected to provide the basis for an extensive discussion in the next lesson.

Homework as preparation

Helping children to achieve success

> Homework can be used to allow children time to try out questions on their own. The summarizing phase provides an opportunity for children to complete and correct this work.

A homework sheet could start with pictures showing how to act out the maths story $3 \times 4 = 12$ with counters.

> Get three counters. Take them to the maths tray. Do this four times.
> How many counters do you have? Twelve.

The sheet could continue by asking the children to act out the following maths stories and work out the answers.

> $3 \times 2 =$ $2 \times 7 =$ $5 \times 6 =$
> $2 \times 3 =$ $7 \times 2 =$ $6 \times 5 =$

Homework replicating classwork

These examples follow the work done in class so that every child can be successful. The pictures are provided to assist those who have forgotten the actions. Although the questions are straightforward the answers give some interesting results that are worth discussing.

> Assisting performance by boosting motivation through success

When the children have practised multiplying three numbers together they can be set the following questions.

> $2 \times 3 \times 4 =$ $3 \times 2 \times 4 =$ $4 \times 3 \times 2 =$
> $2 \times 12 =$ $3 \times 8 =$ $4 \times 6 =$

Developing work done as homework

When you go over these examples in the next lesson you can ask questions such as:

All these examples give the answer twenty-four. Are there any other ways that we can keep the value but change the appearance?

What about $2 \times 3 \times 2 \times 2$ or $3 \times 4 \times 2$ or ... ?

> See *Key ideas*.

Homework as practice in reading

When you have started to extend the multiplication tables you will want the children to practise reading the words out loud at home. You can ask them to go home and read the following:

> Assisting performance by providing practice in language

> Three **hundred** times two is six **hundred**.
> Three **thousand** times four is twelve **thousand**.
> Three **hundred thousand** times five is fifteen **hundred thousand**.
> Three-**ty** times three is nine-**ty**.

This can be followed by writing the numbers in words and figures and then finally getting the children to write down the answers for themselves. The emphasis at first is on reading the words because the logic is in the language of number. By the time they have to fill in the answers they will be confident and more likely to be successful.

Using and applying maths

Extracting data from real-life stories

When the children are confident in reading and working out answers to maths stories and real stories they need to learn to extract data from real-life stories. You can read the children a story and ask them questions to make sense of the context. You can then pose questions that will require them to extract data and do some calculations.

You can start with very simple stories and gradually make them more complex until the children are able to work on stories like this:

Last week I went to an athletics event in Birmingham. All the participants were under sixteen years old. I met a boy called Charlie who was running in the one hundred metre race. He told me that he had to train four days a week. On those days he ran one thousand metres and worked out in a gym. In the last month he had run a total of sixteen thousand metres in training and two thousand metres in races. This seemed like a lot of exercise to do in one month.

Making sense of real-life stories

You can ask questions like:

Where was the athletics event held?
What was the name of the boy I met?
What age were the participants?
How many days did Charlie train each week?
What event did Charlie take part in?

You can ask the children to tell you what they know about the place, the event and so on so that the context makes more sense to them. You can then ask:

How far did Charlie run each week in training?
How many days did Charlie train last month?
How many races did Charlie run last month?

Next you can provide some statements and ask the children whether they are true or false. The children have to explain and give reasons for their answers. For example:

Charlie ran eighteen thousand metres altogether last month. True or false?

Charlie ran one hundred metres a hundred and eighty times last month. True or false?

Numeracy work can improve literacy skills.

Using stories like this improves the children's skills in literacy as well as numeracy. You can also get children to apply their numeracy skills to playing games. For example, the game of bingo can be played in the following way.

Give each child a card with ten numbers written on a grid. Call out multiplication (or other operation) questions. The children cross out the number that is the result of the operation. This improves children's listening and numeracy skills.

You can make the game more interesting by allowing the children to select their own numbers from a particular range. They will soon realize that their favourite numbers such as three, seven and thirteen are not good choices for multiplication results. Before long they will start choosing numbers that have a lot of factors, such as twelve, twenty-four and so on.

> Comprehension involves inspecting text, extracting data and making sense of it.

> You can encourage children to ask their own questions about the text.

> Games are described in detail in 'Numbers and counting'.

Using information technology

Selecting the correct operation

When using a calculator to perform operations, children often have difficulty in deciding which operation to use. When the sum is written in symbols that decision has been made already and the task is to decide the order of operations. When the question is posed in words it may not be so obvious. The first task is to turn a real story or a real-life story into a maths story. Then the calculator can be used.

The most common mistake made by children is to select the wrong operation.

Before using a calculator discuss the following problems with the children and write them as maths stories.

> *On Tuesday I made some fairy cakes. I put the cake mixture into a baking tray. The tray had four rows of cakes. There were three cakes in each row. How many cakes did I make?*

> *My Dad was taking me to my Aunt's house twenty-five miles away in his car. We had gone only six miles when the car broke down. How much further did we still have to go?*

> *Last Christmas my brother gave me two toy cars. I already had six toy cars. This year he gave me three more. How many toy cars have I got altogether?*

> *I bought eighty centimetres of ribbon to make bows for my hair. I cut it into four equal pieces. How long was each piece?*

Mental calculations to check calculator results

When the class have decided how to write the maths stories they can work them all out mentally. The children then use their calculators to check their answers. The purpose of this exercise is to help the children learn how to use the correct keys on their calculators. They know what answer they should obtain and can therefore quickly check for accuracy. They can then be set questions that are more appropriate for solving with a calculator.

Training children to use a calculator means developing good habits such as estimating answers before pressing any keys.

Approximation

Work done on the extended multiplication tables prepares the children for working out approximate answers to difficult calculations. For example, when we want to calculate 63×78 we can get an approximate answer by working out 60×80. Then we can use a calculator as a way of checking whether the answer is correct. It is so easy to press the wrong keys on a calculator that we should always do a quick estimate before we begin.

The teacher makes the connections between earlier number work and using a calculator.

First the children have to decide which numbers to multiply in order to get an approximate answer. Then they use their extended multiplication knowledge to work out an approximation. And finally they use a calculator to work out the correct answer.

> To work out 32×19, first work out $30 \times 20 = 600$ then use a calculator to get $32 \times 19 = 608$. Does this seem correct? Yes. Now work out:

$43 \times 51 =$	$64 \times 28 =$	$380 \times 17 =$	$4700 \times 89 =$

Order of operations

Following on from the topic 'Numbers and counting', we need to look again at the order of operations. Children need to be reminded that, in the absence of brackets, multiplication and division take precedence over addition and subtraction. We have seen that children need to learn how to enter calculations such as $2 + 3 \times 5 =$. This needs to be extended to examples such as $60 \div \left[22 - \frac{(3 \times 4)}{6} \right] =$

Conventions in maths have to be taught.

Tests

Emphasis on oral work

Throughout this book we place an emphasis on oral work in the classroom. It follows that some assessment should also be oral in nature. Since the children have to listen carefully and do the maths in their heads, these sorts of tests are often called 'aural tests' or 'mental arithmetic tests'. However, such tests are often given to children without sufficient preparation and this results in failure. You need to plan a scheme of work that specifically teaches the children skills in mental arithmetic so that they can be successful.

Instant recall cannot be taught by testing. You have to teach children to memorize number facts before they can be expected to recall them.

Purpose of tests

You then have to decide on the purpose of the test.

- *Do you want to test instant recall, in which case speed is of the essence?*
- *Do you want the children to be able to listen to some instructions and work out a sum in their heads, taking as long as they like?*
- *Do you want the children to listen, make some notes, do a calculation and write down the answer?*
- *Are you testing skills relating to one specific concept?*
- *Are you testing a range of skills?*

Testing memorization

The learning of multiplication needs to be regularly tested and retested. First the tables should be learnt and tested with the children speaking them in order, one table at a time. Then they should be practised and tested out of order, but still one table at a time. Finally they should be practised and tested out of order and by mixing the tables so that the children can recall them at any time. Knowing the multiplication tables makes maths much easier to do.

Notice how the teacher has to make a detailed plan to ensure development and progression.

A test is a record of achievement.

A test is a child's own personal record of achievement. For this reason it is not advisable to ask children to swap tests to mark because this does not encourage a supportive ethos in the classroom. Children need to learn from their own mistakes; when the teacher goes through the test and asks children to explain their answers, errors can be corrected. By keeping their own records of test results, children can be encouraged to take on responsibility for their own learning and set targets for improvement.

These tests should not be seen as a competition between children.

Children taking responsibility

The extended multiplication tables can be tested in the same way. The teacher can decide whether the children should write their answers in words or figures. If they write the words they will need to be given sufficient time and some children may need assistance. For instance, the children could have a set of word cards each. When the teacher asks a question they can select the correct answer and, when given a cue, they can hold up the card for the teacher to see. This overcomes any difficulties with writing the words and allows the teacher to spot any errors immediately.

Using number cards to present answers

Sets of number cards written in words or figures can be used in place of the children writing in any aural test or general classroom work. The children can hold up cards in response to tables questions, word problems or puzzles. The cards should not be displayed until the teacher gives a signal so that each child has time to respond. The teacher can monitor progress and correct mistakes as they occur. This way of working also allows the teacher to adjust questions according to the speed and confidence with which the children respond.

The teacher has to be careful not to embarrass a child who holds up the wrong card.

The four operations: discussion

What are the four operations?

The four mathematical operations that we use most often in school are: add; take away; multiply by; divide by. These are often referred to as *the* four operations (or even the four rules) as if there were no more to be learnt. In fact, there are many operations used in maths, of which these are just four. In this section we will explain how these four should be taught.

We need to emphasize first that these operations are used with many kinds of numbers, not just the whole counting numbers. Any discussion of the four operations must deal with vulgar fractions, decimal fractions, negative numbers and percentages in the same style. Each of these extensions of the number system will be further discussed in the next topic.

Underpinning much of this work is the children's ability to count fluently and accurately, something that has already been discussed at some length. Here we consider how the four operations can be thought of and taught so that children can understand the processes thoroughly.

The approach to take

The approach to addition and subtraction that we described earlier uses the idea of inspecting the first number to see what to start with 'on the maths table', then looking at the nature of the operation and then the size of the operation. This procedure is continued during work with multiplication and division. It is this consistency of approach that assists children in making connections between the number operations.

In order to maintain this key idea of how to think of operations we have presented the tables in a special way. For example, in the three times table we write the three first and 'operate on it' by multiplying by the various numbers in turn. We can read this as: 'inspect the number you have to start with, look at the nature of the operation, look at the size of the operation'. Once this idea has been thoroughly established with the whole counting numbers and the four operations, it can be transferred to operations with fractions, decimals, negative numbers, percentages and ratio.

Memorizing important results

The scripted sessions outlined earlier demonstrate an approach to the operations that enables children to make sense of their meaning. We now need to ensure that children memorize important results and use those results in doing calculations that are not memorized. We will start by repeating one of the examples in the scripts that dealt with number bonds. Let us look at 7 + 3 = 10. Our earlier work has established that this requires that we:

- start with seven counters on the maths tray
- (looking at the operation) return to the resource table to get three more counters
- establish by counting that there is now a total of ten counters on the maths tray

This work has made it possible to understand the nature of addition in a way that is consistent with understanding the other operations. What

Margin notes (left)

The four rules

Fluency in counting is crucial.

Consistency of approach

Interpreting the tables

Real stories for maths stories

Margin notes (right)

Knowledge of the four operations is fundamental to developing skills in maths.

Continuity is achieved through consistency of approach.

The teacher assists cognition by making connections.

Assisting performance by assisting memorization

is now needed is to make results such as this usable, and this means that they have to be memorized.

Memorizing results

Children memorize results by using them. They cannot use these results unless they can see them. Displays of results need to be on the wall, very visible and constantly used. They should not be hidden amongst other displays but should be prominent and easily identifiable. Wall displays can make a room more attractive but the major purpose must be to assist learning.

Creating mental images

Sometimes parts of the wall display can be covered up so that children are encouraged to visualize the parts that are hidden (a first stage in memorizing). It is no good covering the whole display one day and expecting everyone magically to have committed it to memory. You need to structure your approach to assisting memorization. You may, for instance, emphasize one particular aspect and concentrate attention on it.

> When a number fact that has been seen on a regular basis is covered up the children continue to 'see' it in their minds.

$6 - 4 = 2$	$8 - 5 = 3$
$7 + 3 = 10$	$6 - 1 = 5$
$10 + 5 = 15$	$8 + 2 = 10$

Covering up results to be memorized

Today I am going to cover up six take away four is two. [Slowly cover up 6 – 4 = 2 while the children watch.] If we need to know the answer to that we will look here [point to where the numbers have been covered up] and still 'see' six take away four is two. If I say 'What is six take away four?', you will say [point to the covered position] 'Two'. You can still see it in your head. Let me test you. What is six take away four?

Pointing to hidden results prompts mental images.

For the rest of the day you should plan work that uses the answer to 'six take away four', pointing each time to the hidden result. The next day this result should be left uncovered while another one is covered up and used in the same way. Regular practice like this will help the children imprint certain results in their memory. They will be able to 'see' the results in their mind.

> Regular use of this learning strategy will assist performance.

The same sort of practice is needed to memorize addition results. The script for enabling children to memorize 7 + 3 = 10 in the topic 'Numbers and counting' illustrates the necessary attention to detail and is similar to this approach.

Using memorized results

Let us assume that some work has been done on the addition and subtraction results to ten so that some children know them well and some still rely on the visual prompt of the wall display. We can now use those results.

Deliberately choosing numbers to illustrate number facts

Suppose we have the sum 461 + 5. The numbers have been deliberately chosen to demonstrate how to use the known number fact 1 + 5 = 6 to help us answer a more difficult question.

> Number cards like this are used regularly to represent numbers.

four hundred	and	sixty	one

Number cards used as objects

*Look first at the cards on the board. We can start by putting four hundred and sixty-one on the maths tray and then get some more. We put another five on the maths tray. Altogether we have four hundred and sixty [pause; look at addition results on wall; locate 1 + 5 = 6] **six**. So four hundred and sixty-one add five is four hundred and sixty-six.*

> The teacher visibly demonstrates how to use known number facts.

You can see how this type of sum can be practised continually. You can also see that sums like four hundred and sixty-one add three hundred and five can be enacted in a similar way.

Notice that we used 'hundreds' for our first problem, not just smaller numbers. We can use thousands just as easily, and the children will succeed just as well (and with more excitement). We have deliberately avoided adding numbers with an order of magnitude of ten because they present a particular difficulty. If we need to add twenty and thirty, this is less easy to 'see' than adding two hundred and three hundred. The language obscures the logic. We have already discussed the solution to this: we use the 'funny counting' introduced in 'Numbers and counting'.

The language obscures the logic.

Assisting performance by assisting use of the language of number

Word problems

We want to concentrate now on how to enable children to use these methods when dealing with word problems. Suppose they have had some practice in, say, three hundred and sixty-four take away one hundred and sixty-two. You should now construct a word problem like:

Connecting maths stories to real-life stories

> *Duncan had three hundred and sixty-four pounds in his money box. He decided to spend one hundred and sixty-two pounds on a new bike. How much money did he have left?*

We cannot assume that children automatically see this as an invitation to do 'three hundred and sixty-four take away one hundred and sixty-two'. They need to construct a story around the problem. This is so important that we will return to this in our discussion of using algorithms for real stories. You need to practise thinking up and using questions like:

Making sense of the real-life story

> *Is that a lot of money?*
> *Do you think he has got that much in his money box?*
> *Could he buy a computer with that much money?*
> *What sort of money box is it?*
> *How does he get the money out?*
> *Would he have to ask his mum or dad before he bought the bike?*

The children can be encouraged to think up their own questions.

This questioning leads to the visual representation of the money in the box with number cards, toy money, counters and so on, so that the act of taking away can be performed in conjunction with a mental image of removal.

Using algebra

Algebra reinforces number facts.

Algebra can be used to reinforce number facts and to enable children to work forwards and backwards using subtraction as the inverse operation of addition. A table can be drawn up with numbers missing, like this:

x	7	4	2	9	5		670
y	3	6				8	
$x + y$	10		10	19	25	348	677

School algebra is generalized arithmetic. This needs to be made visible.

First the teacher invites the children to read the left-hand column and to explain the 'instructions'. When they have completed the table they explain how they calculated each missing number. This is the summarizing phase of the lesson. The choice of numbers in the table will depend upon the previous work.

Another example could be:

x	10		20				
y	6	3		5	98	493	991
$x - y$	4	7	4	35	2	7	9

Working forwards and backwards

Multiplication and division

Multiplication and division are approached in a similar way. The earlier script shows how 3×4 is thought of: *I start by putting three on the maths tray. What job do I have to do? I have to do it again and again and again until I have done it four times altogether.* You should emphasize that it is a *total* of four times that is needed (not *another* four times).

> It is crucial to maintain a consistent approach.

Four is the size of the job.

Division is read in the same way, with the division sign prompting a very specific job. The script shows how $12 \div 3$ involves starting with twelve, looking at it and wondering how many threes can be seen. Read the script carefully to see how this is acted to make it memorable.

The division sign prompts the question 'how many?'

The times tables

The consolidation of multiplication and division facts is done by learning the times tables in a particular way that involves *going beyond the information given.*

> The multiplication tables are the key to making connections.

$3 \times 1 = 3$
$3 \times 2 = 6$
$3 \times 3 = 9$
$3 \times 4 = 12$

Children who can read these multiplications can immediately say:

> *three thousand times one is three thousand*
> *three thousand times two is six thousand*

They can also say:

> *three hundred times two thousand is six hundred thousand*
> *three thousand times four million is twelve thousand million*

Extending the multiplication tables

And later they will be able to use the same logic in the language of number to say:

> *three tenths times seven tenths is twenty-one tenths tenths*
> *three hundredths times two hundredths is six hundredths hundredths*

> Assisting performance by assisting children with the language of number

The logic is in the language.

This oral approach reinforces an understanding of the structure of the way we write numbers and of place value. When we use the language of number in this way we can get answers to many questions from just one multiplication table.

Oral work can be accompanied by visual representation: here, for example, by placing sets of three beakers inside one another the appropriate number of times. Three times four can then be represented by four lots of three beakers. This may seem rather obvious but we can now use the multiplication table to demonstrate that division is the inverse of multiplication and again this uses language to emphasize the operation.

> The teacher makes the connections visible.

The teacher starts with twelve beakers and by moving them around the table establishes that whatever position they are in there are always twelve beakers. She then stacks them in threes and establishes again that there are still twelve beakers. She then says: *I look at them and wonder how many threes there are there,* and counts with the children the four stacks.

She then moves from the visual representation of the beakers to the multiplication table and pointing to the appropriate line and working backwards says: *There are twelve altogether. I look at it and wonder how many threes there are.* They all read the number four together. When the children are confident in working orally with the beakers and the tables, the teacher can move them on by writing $12 \div 3 = 4$ and saying: *There are twelve* [pointing]. *I look at it and wonder how many threes there are.* The teacher's actions demonstrate that working backwards with the tables is the same as doing division.

Using algebra

This work can now be reinforced by using algebra. A table is drawn up like this:

x	3	7	3		9	300	
y	6	3		5			4
$x \times y$			12	15	27	600	1200

Every missing number can be calculated using the three times table. When the children have completed the table the teacher invites children to come to the front and explain the process of finding the answer: this is the summarizing phase of the lesson. Later another table can be drawn up:

x	18	21		600	1500	6000	9000
y	6		3		300		
$x \div y$		7	4	200		30	300

In this second table x divided by y could alternatively be represented as $\frac{x}{y}$ to demonstrate the different ways of writing division. Again only the three times table is needed to get the answers. The same work can be repeated with all the tables and when the children are fluent with these number facts the tables can be mixed.

Conventions

Work out $7 + 6 \times 3$. What answer did you get. Did you get 25? Good, that is correct. The most common error in sums like this is to work from left to right and get 39. The arithmetic convention is that 'in the absence of brackets, multiplication and division take priority over addition and subtraction'. Now try the sum on your calculator. Not all calculators are programmed to work with this convention so you may have to enter the operations in the order in which you want to carry them out. Unfortunately this is often the case with the calculators that young children use. However, if your calculator automatically works in the correct order it is easy to forget the convention and let the machine do the work!

It is important to teach children how to use calculators properly and appropriately. At first it is essential that you give them questions that can be worked out mentally and get them to check their answers with a calculator. This will quickly throw up any discrepancies in the way their calculator works.

Using brackets	Try examples like: $32 \div (8 \div 4)$ $36 \div (4 + 2)$ $14 - 3 \times 2$ $25 - (6 - 9)$ $120 \div \left[33 - \frac{2 \times 6}{4} \right]$

Step-by-step methods

Algorithms

An algorithm is a prescribed method for dealing with a calculation. It is a kind of recipe, or a set of step-by-step instructions, that can be followed. The written maths that we do in schools involves using a number of algorithms. These algorithms include ideas like 'starting on the right' when we add a column of figures, and 'carrying' numbers. We will discuss each of the four operations in turn.

> Algorithms are efficient and economical methods for doing calculations.

Strategies for addition

Algorithm for addition

Before we discuss the addition algorithm we want you to inspect the sum $3 + 5 + 7 =$. Consider for a moment what strategies you use to do this sum. Do you work from left to right or do you look for number bonds that you can recall instantly and do them first? Most of us use strategies like this to help us to get to the answer as quickly as possible and in this case one strategy is to notice that $3 + 7 = 10$ and then add on the five to make fifteen. This strategy is only possible because addition obeys certain laws. In this case we utilize the fact that the operation of addition is commutative. That is: $5 + 7 = 7 + 5$ so we can write: $3 + 5 + 7 = 3 + 7 + 5$.

Addition is commutative.

Now inspect the sum $2 + 4 + 6 =$ and suppose that you want to combine the four and six to make ten first. The operation of addition is also associative. That is: $(2 + 4) + 6 = 2 + (4 + 6)$. Since addition is commutative you can write $2 + (4 + 6) = (4 + 6) + 2 = 10 + 2 = 12$.

> The idea of inspecting is used throughout maths. We also say that we are working like detectives.

You do not stop to consider these laws each time you do a sum in your head because you have done sums like this so often that you just know what you can and what you cannot do. Try some more sums and consider what strategies you use. What about subtraction? Do the same laws apply?

Subtraction is not commutative.

Now look at this rather more difficult sum.

```
  373
+ 235
  267
  ───
```

> This vertical method for addition requires us to start with the units column of numbers. This needs to be taught.

You may be able to do this in your head but it is hard to keep all those numbers in your memory. You may need some assistance. An algorithm is needed to help you. The steps in this algorithm are: start by adding the numbers in the right-hand column, carry any tens into the column on its left and repeat this process with each column in turn. We also inspect each column for any number bonds that make the calculation easier.

Making sense of the sum

In order to teach this so that it is understood we do rather more work with it. We need to allow pupils practice in seeing what numbers are involved in each order of magnitude. For this reason we look at sums like this in terms of:

> Notice how the numbers are spoken with the correct order of magnitude such as 'three hundred' rather than the digit 'three'.

> *What numbers can you see with the same order of magnitude as one hundred? Yes: three hundred; two hundred; two hundred.*

The same order of magnitude	*What numbers can you see with the same order of magnitude as ten? Yes: seven-ty; three-ty; six-ty.*
	What numbers can you see with the same order of magnitude as one? Yes: three; five; seven.
	Now we look at all the figures with order of magnitude one. We are going to add these together. We search the numbers and see three and seven which we know comes to ten, and we have five which makes a total of fifteen. Before we write this down consider how the number fifteen is normally written. First we write the one (order of magnitude ten) and then the five. It is confusing to some children when teachers
Writing numbers from left to right	say 'write down the five and carry the one' because this is not the usual order in which the figures are written. Many of the mistakes that children make are forced by the language used in the teaching. In this case we should write the one ten first and then write the five.

It is vital to maintain a consistency of approach.

Now we look at all the figures with magnitude of ten.

$$
\begin{array}{r}
373 \\
+235 \\
267 \\
\underline{\quad 5} \\
{\scriptstyle 1}
\end{array}
$$

Seven-ty, three-ty, six-ty and one-ty. That is seventeen-ty. Note the emphasis on reading the figures as a number of tens (using the suffix 'ty') rather than saying seven and three and six and one. Now we have to write the number seventeen carrying the ten to the next column and then writing the seven. Finally we look at all the figures with magnitude of a hundred. Three hundred, two hundred, two hundred and one hundred. That is eight hundred. The answer is eight hundred and seventy-five.

Algorithms such as this should be taught only after the children have had plenty of practice in doing mental arithmetic. Children need to see sums written horizontally and vertically and be able to move flexibly between them. They need to be taught how to select the best method for the calculation.

Flexibility is important.

Children should not be left to select any method of their choice but should be taught how to select the most appropriate method.

Algorithm for subtraction
Now look at this subtraction.

Vertical methods for subtraction

$$
\begin{array}{r}
263 \\
-26 \\
\hline
\end{array}
$$

It must be stressed to the children that we are starting with 263 and removing 26. This way of visualizing the meaning of 'take away' has been emphasized from the beginning.

The first number (in this case, the top number) is what we start with. The sign tells us what job we have to do. It is 'take away', so we must remove twenty-six. We do this by working with the figures of the same order of magnitude and immediately get stuck on 'three take away six: I cannot do it'. However, if we remember that we can 'keep the value but change the appearance', sixty-three can be written as 'five-ty thirteen'. This now allows thirteen take away six to be done.

Sixty-three as 'five-ty thirteen'

Method of decomposition

$$
\begin{array}{r}
2\overset{5}{\cancel{6}}{}^{1}3 \\
-26 \\
\hline
\end{array}
$$

This is the method of decomposition which is described in more detail in the scripts and is the most common algorithm used for subtraction today. A popular algorithm used in the past and sometimes encountered today is called the method of 'equal addition'. Consider again the subtraction 263 − 26. If we 'keep the value but change the appearance' we can write this as $(263 + 10) − (26 + 10)$. Check that this still has the same value. Now, when we write this vertically the additional ten in the first number is used to turn three into thirteen and the ten in the second number turns twenty-six into thirty-six, like this:

$$26\overset{1}{3}$$
$$-\ \overset{3}{2}6$$

Unfortunately these methods for subtraction are almost always taught as rules to be remembered and children frequently make mistakes. The most common mistake is to say: 'three take away six you can't do, so do six take away three'. It is not surprising that children do this because they frequently change the order when doing addition. However, addition obeys the commutative law but subtraction does not and this needs to be stressed when teaching these operations. One way of illustrating this is to present the children with some calculations that they are told are incorrect and ask them to identify the errors and explain them.

Mental methods leading to an algorithm for multiplication
Suppose we want to work out the product of the two numbers 43 and 20. We could do this in our heads and we could use several different strategies. For example:

$$43 \times 20 = (40 + 3) \times 20 = (40 \times 20) + (3 \times 20)$$

By doing this we 'keep the value but change the appearance'. In the first step we partition 43 into $(40 + 3)$ and in the second step we use the distributive law to multiply each number in turn.

Or we may have done this:

$$43 \times 20 = 43 \times (2 \times 10) = (43 \times 2) \times 10$$

In this we have changed the appearance of 20 to 2×10 and then used the associative law to perform the calculation. Writing it out like this makes it look very complicated but when we do it in our heads it is second nature and we do not normally stop to consider what laws we are using. We may not even have heard of the laws. How, then, do we know what to do and how can we teach children to use these strategies? Some strategies were probably demonstrated by our teachers and others we developed for ourselves because they always gave us the right answer. A lot has been left to chance and many people never work out any strategies for themselves. We want to ensure that all children have the opportunity to use mental strategies correctly.

Different strategies for mental arithmetic should be demonstrated regularly by the teacher to the whole class and by pupils as they present their results. Each time the strategies should be checked to see that they are following the laws and conventions of arithmetic and are not just a lucky find for that particular example.

When children have had plenty of practice in this we have to consider methods for working out the product of two numbers such as 43 and 27.

Before we look at an algorithm we want to pursue one of the strategies that we have already explored for mental arithmetic.

Let us 'Keep the value: change the appearance':

$$43 \times 27 = (40 + 3) \times 27 = (40 \times 27) + (3 \times 27)$$

First of all we have partitioned the 43 into (40 + 3) and then used the distributive law to multiply each number in turn. Does this help? Partly, but we still have to work out 40×27 and 3×27. We can do each of these in turn and then add the results together.

$$40 \times 27 = 40 \times (20 + 7) = (40 \times 20) + (40 \times 7) = 800 + 280$$

$$3 \times 27 = 3 \times (20 + 7) = (3 \times 20) + (3 \times 7) = 60 + 21$$

Answer: 1161

Phew! That was long-winded, wasn't it? Inspect the last two lines of working again. We had to multiply each number in turn and add the results. There must be a neater way of writing this. Look at this table:

	40		3	
20	800	60	860	
7	280	21	301	
				1161

Now that makes it look much simpler and each calculation can be done mentally. However, if we have three-digit or four-digit numbers it starts to get clumsy. The whole of this method can be captured in a neat and efficient format set out vertically like this:

```
    43
  × 27
   860
   301
  1161
```

Look back at the table and identify where each of these numbers has come from. It is important when teaching this algorithm to stress that we are multiplying first by the twenty and then by the seven (not by the two and the seven). It is also important to note that we could just as easily multiply first by the seven and then by the twenty. Look back at the table to see what adjustments you would have to make to do the multiplication in this order.

Algorithms like this are elegant and economical but are only useful when they are remembered correctly and this requires sufficient preparatory work with mental arithmetic.

Algorithm for division

Suppose we want to know how many threes there are in 452. The three times table does not go this far, but can it help us? Yes, it can. I can 'see' that 300 is in the table because 'three times one hundred is three hundred'. I can also 'see' 120 in the table because 'three times forty is twelve-ty'. And I can also 'see' 30 in the table because 'three times ten is thirty'. So by referring to the idea 'Keep the value: change the appearance' I could write 452 as (300 + 120 + 30 + 2) and I can now divide by three and get $100 + 40 + 10 + \frac{2}{3} = 150\frac{2}{3}$.

Setting out problems in tables can make maths look easier.

The vertical method is economical and efficient.

The multiplication tables help with division.

We could set this out like this:

$$3 \overline{)452} \xrightarrow[\text{change the appearance}]{\text{keep the value}} \quad 3 \begin{array}{|ll} 300 & 100 \\ 120 & 40 \\ 30 & 10 \\ 2 & 0\frac{2}{3} \\ \hline & 150\frac{2}{3} \end{array}$$

Alternatively we could partition 452 like this:

$$3 \overline{)452} \xrightarrow[\text{change the appearance}]{\text{keep the value}} \quad 3 \begin{array}{|ll} 300 & 100 \\ 150 & 50 \\ 2 & 0\frac{2}{3} \\ \hline & 150\frac{2}{3} \end{array}$$

And this is essentially the same as the long division algorithm:

$$
\begin{array}{r}
150\frac{2}{3} \\
3 \overline{)452} \\
\underline{3} \\
15 \\
\underline{15} \\
02
\end{array}
$$

Using algorithms for real stories

Using the methods we have discussed can ensure that children are able to do and understand these very complex mathematical operations. Of course it takes a lot of work on the part of the teacher. It takes just as much work to ensure that children can apply this complex maths to real or realistic problems. Young children who can do 3 + 2 quickly and accurately cannot necessarily answer the question:

There were three birds on a branch; two more birds flew on to the branch. How many were on the branch altogether?

If children are to apply their pure maths (3 + 2 = 5, which we call a maths story) to a real-life problem they need careful teaching in how to do it. We will look at a real-life problem using numbers to suit the context.

There were sixty-three children in the playground. Twenty-six went in. How many were left in the playground?

Children find it very difficult to recognize that this is a subtraction problem. Why should this be the case? They need a great deal of assistance with making sense of the word problem, and they need equal assistance in seeing how it is connected to the subtraction algorithm. For children, the word problem and the algorithm are not obviously the same thing.

What do we mean when we say that children need assistance to make sense of the word problem? They need to be able to construct a story around it, and they need prompting to do this. We will not offer a full script here, but we will suggest some questions that might be employed.

Where is the playground?
What kind of playground is it? [They usually say it is a school playground and describe how their own playground looks.]
Why should some of the children go in?

You will recall that we made this point earlier when we talked about the word problem:

Another real-life story

Much work needs
to be done before
introducing algorithms.

Writing real stories
using figures is
generalization.

Writing sums
using letters is
generalization.

x is any number and y
is any number.

x and y can stand for
the same number.

Duncan had three hundred and sixty-four pounds in his money box. He decided to spend one hundred and sixty-two pounds on a new bike. How much money did he have left?

It is worth commenting on the order in which we discussed these problems. It may be tempting to suggest that our first discussion, dealing with numbers with order of magnitude in the hundreds, was harder than the one with order of magnitude in the tens. However, we deliberately chose this sequence because children can do a great deal of work visualizing large numbers and using the logic of the language before they can easily deal with algorithms.

Generalization of number

What do we mean by generalization of number? Well, suppose every time you wanted to find out how many marbles, say, that you owned you had to go back and count them – 'one, two, three ...' – that would be very time-consuming. Now suppose we told you that you could say, 'I know I have three marbles and here are four more marbles and that makes seven marbles', you are beginning to generalize. You are learning to add.

Now suppose we forget that you are adding marbles and say $3 + 4 = 7$. Every time you have three of something and want to add four of the same thing you can refer to this sum. This is generalization of number.

Finally, suppose we do not know what numbers you are adding but want to write down what you must do every time you want to work out how much of something you have, then we can write $x + y$ where x is the number you start with and y is the number you add to x. This is generalization of number. We have used letters to represent numbers; the letters represent any numbers; the letters are generalized numbers.

The teacher makes the connection between arithmetic and algebra visible to the children.

Introducing letters for numbers

This way of writing a general rule can be introduced in the classroom in the following way:

Cards with the letters x and y written on them are stuck on the board with a plus sign between them:

$$\boxed{x} \; + \; \boxed{y}$$

We are going to do some adding. We are going to start with a number x and add a number y to it. [Repeat.] I am going to begin with x as the number 6 [lift off x and write the number 6 in its place] and y as the number 9 [lift off y and write the number 9 in its place]. [Cover the number 6 with letter x.] The letter x is the number 6 and the letter y is the number 9 [covering 9 with the letter y].

Letters in algebra should be introduced as variables and not as objects.

A child comes to the front and calculates the answer and writes it on the board.

Examples are varied as the children are introduced to different operations and different sorts of numbers. At least one example should give x and y the same value to show that x is any number and y is any number and in some cases those numbers may be the same. This work allows the children to become familiar with the idea of using letters for numbers in a well-known context: that of simple number operations.

Using and applying maths

Now let us look at a different problem. Suppose that pencils cost 8 pence each and pens 12 pence. If you buy three pencils and five pens you have to work out 8×3 and 12×5 and add the results together. You have to work out $8 \times 3 + 12 \times 5$. Suppose you buy pencils and pens on a regular basis, although you may buy different quantities each time. You work out the total cost of x pencils and y pens by calculating $8x + 12y$. This is generalization of number.

But wait a minute. This doesn't look the same. Shouldn't it be $8 \times x + 12 \times y$? Let's look at this more closely. Where have the multiplication signs gone? This is just a convention. When we use letters for numbers and we want to indicate multiplication we write the letters and numbers next to each other without the symbol for 'multiply'. Instead of writing $8 \times x$ we write $8x$. This is a useful convention. Because the 8 and the x are written close together it is sufficient to remind us that multiplication is performed before other operations in the absence of brackets. We now have a simple rule to help us with our calculation.

Let us summarize this. We have an everyday problem. We know how to calculate the answer. We want to write a general rule for calculating problems like it. We use letters to represent numbers. We write the calculation as a generalized expression. We use the laws and conventions of arithmetic to simplify the expression. This is the nature of maths.

What letters to use

It is important to select letters for use in algebra that do not represent the beginnings of words. For example, if you want to represent the number of pens then it is best not to choose the letter p. This is because the letter p could be mistaken for an abbreviation for the word pen rather than 'the number of pens'. This leads to errors such as $12p$ meaning twelve pens instead of twelve times the number of pens or even a confusion with twelve pence. The letters x, y and z are the best to use on a regular basis because they then act as a prompt or cue for 'this letter stands for any number', but other letters should be used as well to afford flexibility and familiarity with the general idea of letters standing for numbers.

Generalization of number in geometry

Look at the rectangle below:

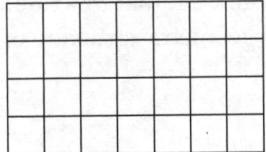

Notice that the array of squares gives us a pattern. The number of squares (the area of the rectangle) can be calculated by multiplying the number of squares in each row by the number of rows. Does this work for other rectangles? Yes. This is beginning to look like a generalization. We can say the generalization in words. Can we also say the generalization in symbols?

Suppose there are x squares in each row and there are y rows, then there are xy squares altogether. This is a geometric formula. This is generalization of number.

Margin notes (left):

An algebraic expression is economical and concise.

Algebraic conventions

The nature of maths

Abbreviation is not algebra.

Algebra to describe patterns

Margin notes (right):

Conventions in algebra have to be taught and practised.

Algebra is elegant and concise.

Algebra can be used to describe geometric patterns elegantly.

Let us summarize this. We explore the geometric structure of a
shape. We calculate its area, say. We use letters to represent certain
measurements. Using letters, we construct a general formula for the
area, writing it as simply as possible. We use the formula whenever we
want to calculate the area of that shape.

Generalization of patterns

We have looked at generalization of number operations and geometric
formulae. Now let us look at generalizations that arise from recognizing
certain patterns. Suppose a child has been putting rods together to
make a pattern as in (a) and then builds a second shape, repeating the
pattern, as in (b)

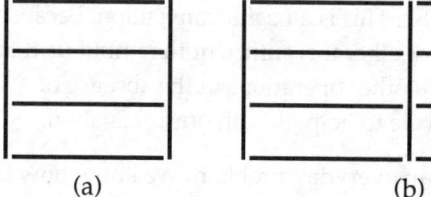

(a)   (b)

The first pattern requires six rods and the second pattern requires
eleven rods. If the child continues building in the same way how many
rods will be needed for the next pattern? Well, each step means the
child adds on five more rods. We can work out how many rods are in
the next few patterns. There will be sixteen, then twenty-one, then
twenty-six and so on. What if we wanted to know how many rods were
in the two-hundred-and-fiftieth pattern? This would take a long time.
We would have to add five, then add five, then add five, and so on
until we reached the required term. Surely there must be a quicker way.

Go back and inspect the structure of the pattern. The first pattern takes
one rod at the front and a set of five rods to complete it. The second
pattern takes the one rod at the front and a set of five rods times two to
complete it. The seventh pattern takes one rod at the front and a set of
five rods times seven to complete it. The tenth pattern takes one rod at
the front and a set of five rods times ten to complete it. The two-
hundred-and-fiftieth pattern takes one rod at the front and a set of five
rods times two hundred and fifty to complete it.

We can generalize the pattern. The nth pattern will need one rod at the
front and a set of 5 rods times n to complete it. That is $1 + 5 \times n$ rods,
which we can write as $1 + 5n$ rods. We can be confident that this rule
works because we have constructed it from the geometric structure of
the pattern.

Sequences

Suppose we had not constructed the pattern but instead we had been
given a sequence of numbers 6, 11, 16, 21, 26, ... and were told that it
continued by successively adding five. We call each number in the
sequence a 'term' so that 6 is the first term, 11 is the second term and so
on. The difference between each term is five. We want to generalize the
sequence. We want the nth term. We do not have the geometric structure
to refer to so we have to inspect the numbers. Each term in the sequence
is one more than a number in the five times table. The nth term will be
the nth number in the five times table add one. That is $5n + 1$.

❸ Extending the number system

Introduction

Echoes of earlier phrases

We have shown in our discussion in the previous section how the four operations carried out on whole numbers need to be presented and practised in particular ways. The importance of this approach becomes clearer as we discuss the teaching of fractions, decimals and negative numbers. The following scripts reiterate phrases that have been used in the earlier teaching: this is deliberate and of the utmost importance.

In this work the methods for teaching whole numbers are used again and are prompted in the memory by the use of repeated phrases. It is now a matter of not only recalling from memory but of recalling from memory at the same time as applying the established ideas in a new context. This is what makes learning especially effective. It is the confidence that children have achieved in their learning with whole numbers that we want to utilize when teaching fractions, decimals and negative numbers. These numbers are an extension of the number system; they obey the same rules, laws and conventions as the whole numbers. These links are made visible through the common methods and phrases employed.

The teacher makes the connections between the counting numbers and the extended number system.

Links made visible

The specific representations of fractions and negative numbers in the scripts have been chosen to assist cognition and use of language in maths. Fractions are represented on cards and counted in exactly the same way as the counting numbers. This script shows how careful selection of the representation of fractions can help later development.

Choice of representation to assist cognition

Ways of representing mathematical concepts must be selected for their power of assisting cognition.

A bizarre story to assist cognition

In the script for negative numbers you will see that a story has been constructed to provide a representation that assists cognition. Using the picture of lumps of earth and holes in a garden may seem bizarre but it provides a powerful mental picture that enables the children to operate with negative numbers with ease. At the same time the story attracts the children's interest and ensures that the introduction of some complex concepts is an enjoyable experience.

Continuity with everyday life can cause misconceptions.

Curriculum documents imply that children should first be taught about halves and quarters. The words for these fractions are in our everyday language and are well known by most children in certain contexts. However, they are not always used as mathematicians would like. You hear people talk about 'the bigger half' or 'cutting a pizza into quarters', neither of which is exact. This continuity with everyday life can bring about misconceptions. Our script, therefore, begins by counting fifths because they are not in such common use.

Development in learning fractions, decimals and negative numbers

This order of teaching the extended number system has been carefully selected to develop fluency in counting and familiarity with the symbols and words before moving on to operations. Although it is vital to start with an emphasis on reading and counting numbers you can change the order of some items. For example, you may wish to move straight on to multiplying and dividing fractions before introducing decimals. You will want to adapt to the children you are teaching and take into consideration what they have previously been taught. However, do not assume that because they have met fractions before they will necessarily be able to retrieve that knowledge easily.

Teachers should enable children to:

- *read fractions as symbols and words*
- *count fractions fluently*
- *convert improper fractions to proper fractions*
- *add fractions*
- *apply fractions to word problems*
- *read decimals as decimal fractions, numbers after the decimal point and words*
- *count decimals*
- *add decimals*
- *convert decimal fractions to decimal numbers using the decimal point*
- *apply decimals to word problems*
- *multiply fractions and divide fractions*
- *use the results obtained with fractions to multiply and divide decimals*
- *read and count negative numbers*
- *add negative numbers*
- *multiply and divide negative numbers*
- *apply negative numbers to word problems*
- *read percentages*
- *connect percentages to fractions and decimals*
- *apply percentages to word problems*
- *know and use the terms 'factor' and 'multiple'*

Reading, recognizing and counting before learning the four rules

The order in which you teach topics must allow for continuity and progression.

Script 1: Counting, adding and subtracting fractions

In this first script the teacher demonstrates how to speak fractions and how to associate the spoken word with fractions written as symbols and words. The children are explicitly told that the number on the cards being used is a fifth. This helps them learn the language of maths. At first they are asked only to confirm this fact and can therefore be confident of success, an important factor in increasing motivation.

When the children have practised speaking fractions they move on to counting them with the teacher. The continued assistance of the teacher again brings success and reduces any threat associated with the introduction of new ideas. The activity of speaking and counting fractions can be rehearsed as often as necessary before moving on to converting vulgar fractions to mixed numbers, etc. The teacher assesses the children's needs by careful and continuous monitoring and through her knowledge of the class.

Resources

- A set of cards like playing cards, each with a fifth written on it in either words or symbols: one fifth, a fifth, ⅕ and $\frac{1}{5}$

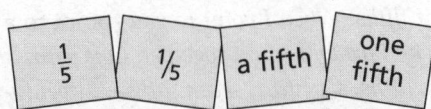

(It is important to establish the interchangeability of the various ways of saying and writing 'a fifth'. It may seem fairly obvious to an adult that *a fifth* and *one fifth* are the same thing, but a child has no way of knowing which minor difference is important and which is within the realms of the normal variation in language. It may be interesting to note that there is a real difficulty for children when teachers do not emphasize that the distinction between *one fifth* and *a fifth* is accidental. The set of cards can be extended later by other equivalent forms such as percentages, equivalent fractions, ratio and decimals, and the activity repeated.)

- Poster: 'Keep the value: change the appearance'

Counting fifths

The teacher puts one of each type of card on the board.

This is the number one fifth [point to the first card]. [Point to the second card and at the same time point to the poster and quietly read the words on it, *Keep the value: change the appearance*, encouraging the children to join in.] *And this is one fifth. And* [point to the next card] *this is one fifth. And this is one fifth ...*

I am going to give each of you a card with a fifth written on it and when I ask you 'Have you got one fifth?' you say 'Yes'.

[Take enough sets of cards and distribute them randomly.]

Have you got one fifth? Yes. Have you got one fifth? Yes ...

Every child is given a card and answers 'Yes'. This guarantees that every child is successful. The activity establishes that a fifth can be written in

Sidebar notes

Learning to speak the words for fractions

Children need help in speaking mathematical words and symbols.

Learning to count fractions

Fraction cards as objects

Later you can do the same activity using 20%, 0.2, ²⁄₁₀ and so on.

Keep the value: change the appearance

Establishing the different ways of writing 'a fifth'

Maximum assistance is given to ensure success.

Guaranteeing success

different forms, so while its appearance might change its value stays the same. The teacher collects the cards in, shuffles them, gives them out again, then points to the number one fifth on the board, saying:

Responding to the word 'much'

If I ask you [select a child] *if you have this much, you say 'Yes' and you* [selecting another child] *say 'Yes' and you* [another child] *say 'Yes'...*

This is not merely repeating what has been said before but is establishing that the children are familiar with the word 'much' so that fifths can be considered as a quantity.

The exercise is repeated but this time the teacher asks *How much have you got?* and the children are asked to say the words 'one fifth' to give them practice in speaking the words associated with the symbols or words on the card. The teacher emphasizes the sound 'fi-f-th' so that the children do not pronounce it 'one fith'. This is assisting the children with the language of maths.

Learning to speak the word 'fifth'

Counting fifths

> Repetition builds up the confidence of the children.

The teacher is now going to get the children to count the fifths. She again distributes the cards. To emphasize the counting she asks the children to put their card on the table as they count. This careful counting establishes that the fraction is a number that can be counted just like other numbers. The teacher can gain the attention of the children by varying the speed of counting.

Now we are going to count fifths. When I point to you [point to a child] *put your card on the table and we will count together. One fifth, two fifths, three fifths, four fifths, five fifths, six fifths, seven fifths, ... twenty-nine fifths* [point to each child in turn until all the children in the class have put their cards on the table].

Improper fractions and mixed numbers

That was easy. Now pick up your cards. We are going to count them again.

One fifth, two fifths, three fifths, four fifths ...

[When the fifth card is placed on the table, pause, raise a finger to indicate some thinking is required and use your hands to mimic weighing one thing against another. This should be accompanied by an appropriate puzzled expression. Then whisper:]

> Gestures are used to demonstrate an act of thinking. In this case the act is of weighing evidence.

Five fifths?

[Use hands to draw an exaggerated circle round the five cards.]

Five fifths is one whole one.

One whole one?

[Point to the poster and again appear to weigh up the evidence. Then, appearing to make a decision, go on counting.]

One whole one, one whole one and one fifth, one whole one and two fifths ...

Alternating between improper fractions and mixed numbers

The teacher carefully establishes that every child in the class is confident in speaking the words and counting the numbers, alternating between improper fractions and mixed numbers. The counting may be repeated if necessary to ensure that every child is confident with this early preparatory work.

Practice to reinforce understanding

The teacher now reinforces this counting with sets of cards. Alternatively she can invite children to come and place cards on the table.

Now I will collect the cards. If I put this much on the table [place seven of the cards on the table] *and I say 'How much is there?' you can say* [assists child to answer] *seven fifths or you can say* [helps another child to utter] *one whole one and two fifths.* **You are right and you are right.**

What if I put this much on the table [place eleven cards]? *What do you say when I ask how much is there? Eleven fifths* [one child] *two and one fifth* [another child]. *When I put this much ...* [Continue with different numbers of cards.]

Let us summarize what the children can do at this stage. They can recognize a fifth written in different ways in words and symbols. They can say the word 'fifth' and they can count fifths. They can count using vulgar fractions or mixed numbers.

Addition and subtraction of fractions
The teacher is now going to build on this knowledge to teach the children to add and subtract fractions with the same denominator. Subtraction resulting in negative answers will be avoided until negative numbers have been taught.

The teacher gives the pack of cards to a child.

Put three fifths on the table [child puts three cards on the table]. *Good. And then put another four fifths on the table* [child puts another four cards on the table]. *Good. Now tell me what there is on the table altogether.* [Child gives one form of answer.] *Yes: seven fifths, that's right, and what is another way of saying that? Right, one and two fifths.* [Accept either answer as correct and elicit the other.]

Take the cards back, and I will tell you to do exactly the same thing all over again.

[Repeat in exactly the same way.]

Put three fifths on the table – good – and then put another four fifths on the table – good – and tell me what there is on the table altogether. Seven fifths or one and two fifths. Good. Take the cards back, and I will tell you to do exactly the same thing all over again.

[Repeat, but this time write the sum on the board in both forms as it is being done.]

$$\frac{3}{5} + \frac{4}{5} = \frac{7}{5} \qquad \frac{3}{5} + \frac{4}{5} = 1\frac{2}{5}$$

You look at this [point to $\frac{3}{5}$] *because it tells you what to put on the table first, then you look at this* [point to +] *because it tells you to get some more, and you look at this* [point to $\frac{4}{5}$] *because it tells you how much more to get; and this* [point to =] *asks you to say what is now on the table.*

The teacher ensures that the children can work out how much there is altogether by repeating the process of placing first three and then four cards on the table and counting them. First they count them all, starting with 'one fifth, two fifths, ...' at the same time demonstrating how this addition is written using the correct symbols and signs. Then they count them by placing the first three cards on the table and counting on 'four fifths, five fifths, ...' and again demonstrating how this is written. Each detail is carefully explained.

Using counting to learn addition

Adding fractions like adding objects

Relating spoken maths to written maths

See Key ideas: Keep the value: change the appearance.

Assisting performance by helping children learn the language of maths

The teacher makes connections with earlier work.

Assisting performance through repetition

The teacher makes the connections between the written and spoken maths.

Good explanations are the key to understanding maths.

The exercise is then repeated with different numbers of cards until the children are confident with the process. The same activity is then used for subtraction. The children complete practice exercises at appropriate points on their own so that the teacher can assess how well they have understood the work.

Finally the whole activity is repeated with different fractions. Each time the words and actions are used until the children are confident and competent at adding and subtracting fractions with the same denominator.

Working in the imagination

As the children become confident, instead of using cards the teacher asks the children to use their imagination. The teacher pretends to give out cards, says what is written on them, and the children come to the board and write what is written on the imaginary cards. Once a set of cards has been designated the children count the numbers on the imaginary cards and continue by doing addition and subtraction.

Every child in the class has now been enabled to count, add and subtract fractions with the same denominator. The shift to working with fractions with different denominators requires work on equivalent fractions using the poster 'Keep the value: change the appearance'.

Script 2: Adding and subtracting negative numbers

Resources
- Pens for drawing pictures on the board

Telling a story

Preparatory work on negative numbers will have taken place before this work that is similar to the work on counting and adding fractions using cards. This script extends the work on negative numbers to include the important notion of $1 + {}^-1 = 0$ on which the combination of positive and negative numbers depends. The representation in this script has been selected to provide a powerful mental image of this notion to assist cognition.

The teacher uses the pedagogic tool of story-telling to introduce this idea. She plays the role of an eccentric mathematician who is more interested in maths than the state of her garden. The first part of the story utilizes counting and adding numbers which the children are familiar with.

I am going to tell you a story about my garden.

A

This is my garden: a lovely flat lawn and this is me. [Draw diagram A on the board, to some amusement.]

Side notes (left margin):

Repetition to reinforce cognition

Replication with different sized fractions

Creating mental images

Children count negative numbers using cards.

Teacher as story-teller

Teacher uses humour.

Side notes (right margin):

Concrete materials are used as the basis for developing mental images to assist cognition.

It is essential that children are given plenty of practice combining negative numbers before moving on to combining positive and negative numbers.

Stories are powerful tools for learning that are often neglected in the maths classroom.

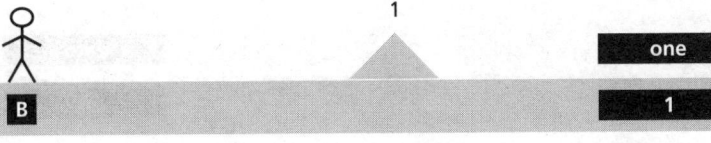

Sometimes I come out in the morning and I see that someone has left a
lump of earth in my garden. I see this [draw diagram B].

Some people would say, 'This is a nuisance: somebody has left a lump
of earth in my garden.'

But I don't and you don't. Instead I rush indoors and get my maths
book and in it write about the lump of earth. I write **1** [convey great
excitement about this].

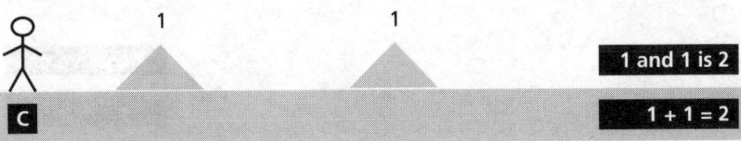

Sometimes I come out and I see this [draw one lump] and this [draw
second lump]. So I say: I can see one lump here and one lump here; that
is two. I write **1 and 1 is 2** [write on board while speaking].

I write **1 and 1 is 2** [write 1 + 1 = 2 while speaking]. I say **1 plus 1 = 2**
[pointing to 1 and 1 is 2 while speaking to emphasize the
interchangeable language].

So I rush into the house and write it down in my maths book [continue
with humour.]

The teacher helps the children's understanding of mathematical
language by emphasizing that 'and' and 'plus' are the same here and
demonstrates the correct use of the equals sign. The children will have
seen this before but the teacher uses every opportunity to reinforce
these ideas.

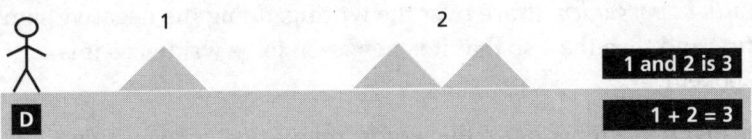

Sometimes I come out in the morning and I see this [draw one lump] and
over here I see this [draw two lumps]. So I say I can see one lump here
and I can see two lumps here; and I write **1 and 2 is 3**. I write 1 + 2 = 3
[emphasize the interchangeable language and writing as before].

So I rush into the house and put this in my maths book. This is really
exciting [continue with self-mockery].

The teacher has now established that lumps of earth can be
represented by the counting numbers and added. She monitors the
children's responses to judge how many examples of this type are
required. Where counting has been well established the children can be
successful in something they know well. This increases motivation.
The teacher then moves on to introduce zero.

Sidebar (left):

Matching the maths
story to the real story

Using known number
facts to establish the
context

Reinforcing the correct
use of signs and
symbols

Continuing with
humour

Sidebar (right):

It is important to
establish the meaning
of the visual
representation
through something
that is well known.

The teacher makes the
connection between
the written and
spoken maths.

Assisting performance
by helping children
learn the language of
maths

Zero lumps of earth

Sometimes I come out of the house and I see this [indicate level ground]. Some people would say, 'There are no lumps of earth', but I would say 'I can see zero lumps of earth'. You know I would be so excited by what I have seen that I would rush into the house shouting 'This is wonderful' and write 0 in my maths book.

> In maths the absence of something is established as a zero quantity.

It is vitally important to emphasize that zero lumps of earth *can be seen*, rather than it being the act of not seeing. This is an aspect of maths operating in imaginary worlds. The teacher then moves on to introduce the representation of negative one as a hole.

Introducing 'negative one'

Now you must be finding this all rather exciting. But wait! Sometimes I come out of the house and I see this.

Some people would say, 'Someone has dug a hole in my garden and stolen a lump of earth. There is a hole in my garden.' And they would be very upset.

> The abstract concept of negative numbers can be visualized by the concrete image of holes in the ground.

I am different. I would say, 'This is very interesting. I can see one [write 1 next to the hole, then pause] missing [carefully and deliberately write the negative sign to the left of the 1, then pause again] in my garden.

Demonstrating how to write 'negative one' in figures

*I say, 'I can see negative one' [write the words 'negative one'] in my garden. I write ⁻1. So of course I write in my maths book ⁻1 because I can **see** negative one lumps of earth in my garden.*

You know that some people say [stage whisper] 'There is a hole in the garden'. We say [in ordinary speech] 'I can see negative one lumps of earth in my garden' [trace over the writing, doing the negative sign first and then the 1 so that it is now seen to be written as it is spoken].

Using 'negative' rather than 'minus'

Note that it is wrong to use the words 'minus one' when writing '⁻1'. The correct words are 'negative one'. 'Minus' is an instruction to remove something; 'negative one' is the name of the particular kind of number being introduced here.

> A negative number is an object, a noun, and not an operator.

Notice how a pause is used twice as a cue for thinking. The first pause links the word 'missing' with the negative sign and the second pause gives the children time to contemplate this sign before the statement is repeated using the words 'negative one'.

Addition of negative numbers

Sometimes I see this [draw first hole] and I see this [draw second hole].

<table>
</table>

I see negative one here [write ⁻1] *and* [write and] *I see negative one here* [write ⁻1]. *I say* ⁻1 *and* ⁻1 *is* [pause, then in stage whisper] *a hole and a hole is two holes* [normal speech] ⁻2 [write ⁻2].

In my maths book I write ⁻1 + ⁻1 = ⁻2. *This reminds me that I saw* ⁻1 *lumps of earth in my garden and I also saw* ⁻1 *lumps somewhere else in my garden, so I saw* ⁻2 *lumps of earth altogether.*

The whisper is used conspiratorially to remind the children that although they can see holes this is a maths lesson so they are going to call them negative ones.

The teacher continues with examples that combine negative numbers until the children are confident. She judges how many are needed by monitoring the children's responses.

So if you saw that I had written ⁻2 + ⁻1 = ⁻3 *in my maths book you know that I saw ... What did I see?* [Help the children to recognize that it was two holes and one hole, but we actually say, 'I saw ⁻2 lumps of earth and ⁻1 lumps of earth so I saw ⁻3 lumps of earth altogether'.]

The children are now being expected to interpret the symbols and explain what they might see. The teacher gradually moves into working in the imagination.

And we can do sums. If I write [write ⁻5 + ⁻3] *it means think of* ⁻5 *lumps of earth* [draw a diagram in the air: level ground with 5 holes; stage whisper 'one hole; two holes; ... five holes'] *and think of* ⁻3 [draw a diagram in the air: level ground with 3 holes; stage whisper 'one hole; two holes; three holes']. *Then if I write* [put equals sign] ⁻5 + ⁻3 = *it means that I have to put down how much it is altogether* [count imaginary holes that have been drawn in the air]. [Write ⁻5 + ⁻3 = ⁻8] *It comes to negative eight.*

Once the children are confident in combining ordinary numbers and negative numbers they are ready to move on to the idea that one add negative one is zero.

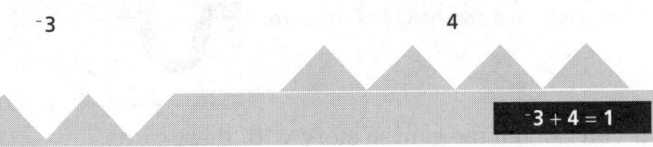

If I come out and see this [draw hole] *and this* [draw lump] *then I say I can see negative one* [point to hole] *and I can see one* [point to lump]. *I write* ⁻1 + 1 = *and then I see that the lump could be used to fill the hole, and it would make level ground, so I write* ⁻1 + 1 = 0 [point to lump and slide finger to show how it could be moved into the hole].

Once this important fact has been established the teacher can move on to combine any number of positive and negative numbers.

Creating a mental image

Confidence in combining negative numbers

Working in the imagination

Introducing 'one add negative one'

The story provides a mental image.

Practice to reinforce cognition

The children have already practised counting and adding negative numbers using cards.

Understanding that 'one add negative one is zero' is the key to combining positive and negative numbers.

⁻3

4

⁻3 + 4 = 1

> *If I come out and see this* [draw three holes] *and this* [draw four lumps] *then I say that I can see negative three* [point to three holes] *and I can see four* [point to four lumps]. *I write* $^{-}3 + 4 =$ *and then I see that three of the lumps can fill the three holes and I still have one lump, so I write* $^{-}3 + 4 = 1$ [make exaggerated gestures to demonstrate filling the holes].

The physical gestures are used to provide mental images for combining positive and negative numbers.

After sufficient practice at adding small numbers of holes and lumps the teacher goes on to add large numbers, using gestures only.

Working in the imagination

> *If I come out and see this* [count ninety-nine holes in a stage whisper] *and this* [count one hundred lumps in a stage whisper] *I can see that I have negative ninety-nine and one hundred.*
>
> *I write* $^{-}99 + 100 =$ *and then I see that ninety-nine of the lumps can fill the holes and I still have one lump so I write* $^{-}99 + 100 = 1$ [make exaggerated gestures to demonstrate filling all the holes].

Creating mental images

Using large numbers like these encourages the children to work mentally.

This demonstration can now be followed by the children doing a practice exercise where the first questions use pictures and the rest have to be imagined. When the children have completed the exercise the teacher summarizes by asking the children to present their solutions and enact the stories.

It is important that the story is not only used to introduce the idea but is referred to regularly when doing work with negative numbers. The visual image provides a mental image to assist cognition. We often see concrete materials being used to introduce ideas and then being forgotten in subsequent lessons. Some children will need this visual image to assist their thinking for some time.

Real stories to maths stories and back to real stories

In the discussion section we describe how we move from the garden story to a card representation for subtraction. We could go on with the story but it loses its credibility when we try to subtract negative lumps of earth. We have to be very careful with representations that are close to everyday life. We do not, however, use a completely new representation but move carefully from the garden to cards that represent the garden. We abstract the story so that we can move on.

The teacher makes the connection between the garden story and the cards.

Moving towards abstraction

Materials are made that fit into each other like this:

Lumps and holes represented by cards

Card In the top half draw the top half of a zero, in the bottom half a complete 1.

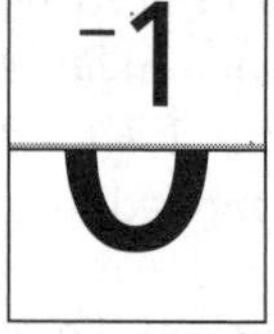

Pocket with backing card Make the pocket half the height of its backing card. On the pocket draw the bottom half of a zero, on the backing card a complete $^{-}1$.

Placing the card in the pocket combines 1 with $^{-}1$ and joins the two halves of the zero.

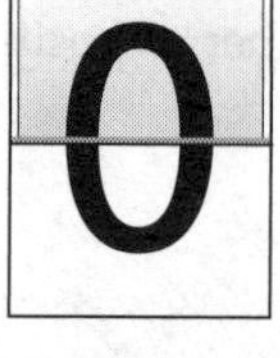

See if you can tell the garden story with these cards.

Lesson plan

Planning for progression

This lesson for Year 5 pupils teaches addition of negative numbers. It is the second in a sequence of lessons which cover the following scheme of work.

1. Addition and subtraction of negative numbers using cards (see Script 1 for use of cards)
2. Addition of negative numbers using garden story
3. Combining positive and negative numbers using garden story
4. Combining positive and negative numbers using cards in place of garden story
5. Using a calculator to add and subtract negative numbers
6. Problems involving negative numbers

> The scheme of work is designed to make connections visible.

Planning for continuity

Planning to make connections

Previous work
The children in this class have regularly used cards for counting. They have counted whole numbers and fractions with cards. In the previous lesson they counted and added negative numbers with cards. They did not combine positive and negative numbers. Adding negative numbers has been seen to be similar to adding fractions with the same denominator. They were set a homework to practise adding negative numbers.

> Continuity of approach is essential to link topics in maths.

Lesson design
The lesson begins by the teacher summarizing the homework and ensuring that all the children are confident at adding negative numbers.

Ensuring a common knowledge base

The teacher then checks that all the pupils are facing the front and that they can all see the board. At first she explains to the class what they are going to learn. Then she begins by telling the garden story as in the script. She acts the part of an eccentric maths teacher who is more interested in writing down sums in her book than worrying about her garden. The story is designed to attract the children's interest and attention and to provide a powerful visual representation to assist cognition.

> Class organization is an important detail for successful whole class teaching.

Attracting children's interest and attention

From the previous lesson the teacher knows that there are three children who were not fully confident in using cards to add negative numbers. She decides to use the garden story to reinforce this work and so she plans to do some extra examples on simple questions before moving on to combining positive and negative numbers. She plans to get these three children to assist her in telling the story.

> Assisting performance by building confidence

Adapting the lesson to suit the class

By extending the demonstration part of the lesson the teacher knows that the children will have to continue with the practice exercise for homework in preparation for the next lesson. She decides to include

**Ensuring that all
children are challenged**

some challenging questions at the end of the exercise for those children who need to move on. These will not involve new concepts but questions will be designed to get the children to describe and explain their answers.

Monitoring progress

At the end of the lesson the teacher will check through the first few questions on the practice sheet to ensure that the children know what to do. She will record the children's progress in preparation for the next lesson.

The structure and timing of the lesson

Class	Y5	Teacher	Mrs Smith
Date	6 February	Student	Anne Miles

Lesson description	Lesson 2: Negative numbers
Learning outcomes	Add negative numbers using garden story.
Resources	• Coloured pens or chalk

Classroom framework	Time	Teacher and pupils
Summarizing ◆	10 min.	Go over the homework sheet and invite children to tell the story of adding negative numbers using cards.
Demonstration ◆	35 min.	Check that all the pupils are facing the front and can see the board. Explain to the children what they are going to learn.
		Tell the garden story and draw garden pictures neatly on the board.
		Get the children to join in with the story and invite some to come to the front and tell their own stories. Remember to write down the sums in both words and figures to reinforce language.
		Set questions with large numbers that cannot be drawn and get children to enact the story with exaggerated gestures.
Modelling ◈	10 min.	Move into the modelling phase, with the whole class doing questions on the board and then hand out a practice exercise.
Summarizing ◆	5 min.	Briefly summarize the first questions on the practice sheet to ensure that the children know how to do their homework.
Modelling ◈	30 min.	Set the practice sheet to be continued for a half-hour homework in preparation for the next lesson. Explain that the last three questions are challenge questions that will be explored in the next lesson and let the children decide whether they can attempt them.
		Record the children's progress.

Practice

After the demonstration phase of the lesson the children need to practise examples of adding positive and negative numbers. It is important to set identical questions to those that have been demonstrated, including pictures of the garden, as the first examples to ensure that the children can be successful. This building of confidence improves the children's motivation. Practice and reinforcement assist learning strategies and provide a firm base for cognition. Some children will find these examples very easy at this stage but they will be able to complete them quickly and reaffirm their success. Through careful classroom organization and management these children can be encouraged to assist their peers who may be struggling.

Start with questions such as $3 + 2 =$ using small numbers accompanied by diagrams of a garden. These are followed by questions such as $24 + 15 =$ and $100 + 99 =$ using larger numbers without diagrams. This moves the children on to working in the imagination. Garden diagrams are again used for questions of the type $^-4 + ^-2 =$ followed by questions without diagrams such as $^-100 + ^-99 =$. Finally questions are set that combine positive and negative numbers of the type $^-3 + 4 =$ and $7 + ^-5 =$ with diagrams, and then examples such as $^-50 + 60 =$ and $^-79 + 81 =$ without diagrams. The practice questions have, so far, followed the format of the lesson, allowing the children to re-enact the garden story as they complete the examples.

The next set of examples in the practice exercise provides a variety of these questions given in any order. These will be completed by the children who have successfully done the earlier examples and are ready for the challenge. These examples will be discussed in the summarizing phase of the lesson and this will also provide the demonstration for a similar set of questions set as homework. Notice the tabular formation and the use of algebra. Regular use of this format will help to show the connections between the counting numbers and the extended number system.

x	14	$^-7$	13	$^-20$	200	$^-200$	$^-7$	49
y	32	$^-11$	$^-6$	$^-19$	$^-1$	$^-1$	12	37
$x + y$								

In this first table the children work forwards adding positive and negative numbers. You can make the questions more challenging by leaving the x or y numbers blank so that the children will have to ask questions such as:

'There are six holes in the garden. How many more holes must there be to make thirteen holes?'

'There are four holes in the garden. How many lumps must there be to end up with seven lumps?'

x	$^-6$			$^-999$	250	$^-45$		$^-685$
y		$^-4$	$^-200$				$^-876$	
$x - y$	$^-13$	7	400	1	199	$^-90$	0	0

Practice to assist learning strategies

Replicating the demonstration phase

The tabular format can be used for all number operations.

Algebra to reinforce number facts

Assisting performance by using the learning strategies of repetition and practice

Design questions to move children on from using concrete representations to working in the imagination.

Algebra helps to make links with earlier work with positive numbers.

Homework

Homework as preparation

Children in Year 5 can be expected to spend 30–45 minutes on a maths homework twice a week. They should attempt all the questions in preparation for the next lesson and they are asked to discuss the work with their parents. Although the children must have attempted the homework there is no shame in making mistakes or struggling with a question. The first part of the next lesson will summarize the homework and provide an opportunity for the children to ask questions and get assistance. The homework described follows the lesson on the addition of negative numbers and prepares the children for the next stage.

> Homework can be completed in pencil and corrected if necessary when it is discussed in class.

The tabular format is one that is frequently used. The children have to look at the algebra for the instructions. Similar tables will have been used with the counting numbers, fractions and decimals. It is the familiarity with the format that allows the children to make the connections between the various types of numbers. The letters x and y are used deliberately to get the children accustomed to using these letters as generalized numbers.

Letters as generalized numbers

> This is consistent with the idea of letters as 'variables'.

The first table sets out questions that are straightforward additions. The examples are no more difficult than those covered in the lesson. The second table provides more challenging questions. The children have to work backwards as they solve simple equations mentally. They are being prepared for the subtraction lesson.

x	5	$^-9$	7	1000	$^-100$	$^-99$	$^-25$	$^-87$
y	8	$^-4$	$^-3$	$^-999$	99	$^-99$	30	$^-93$
$x+y$								

x	14	$^-6$			$^-60$	$^-25$		$^-63$
y			$^-4$	$^-48$			40	
$x+y$	20	$^-16$	4	2	1	$^-50$	5	$^-100$

Children taking on responsibility for their own learning

Instead of handing this work in the children use it to present their answers to the class. Each child is responsible for marking his own work and correcting mistakes. The teacher monitors the work by checking as she walks around the class during the presentations. She may deliberately select a child who has made mistakes to do a presentation so that errors can be corrected and common mistakes discussed. By demonstration the teacher shows that it is acceptable to make mistakes but that it is important to discuss and correct them.

> Children need to be encouraged not to be embarrassed about making mistakes.

Maintaining pace and sustaining interest

It is not necessary to go over every question in class. The teacher has to decide by careful monitoring the needs of the group and move the children on appropriately. It is important to maintain a good pace to sustain interest and attention. Should one or two children need additional assistance this can be dealt with at the appropriate time rather than painstakingly going through every detail and slowing down the rate of work. The teacher needs to sense the rhythm of work that suits the class. Some of the questions towards the end of the exercise are particularly difficult but all the children in the class can gain from an explanation from another child. All too often differentiation means that some children are consigned to only ever seeing simple questions and are never given the opportunity to appreciate the complexity of maths.

> All children are entitled to try questions even if they find them difficult.

Using and applying maths

Fluency in combining negative numbers

Children need to be fluent in combining negative numbers before they move on to apply them to real-life situations. We sometimes assume that children are familiar with the contexts that we provide but that is rarely the case. Not many children will have experienced temperatures of ⁻10, for example, yet we often expect them to work with such an idea.

We do not use these contexts to teach negative numbers but children need to see real-life examples of where such numbers are used.

Making sense of the context

We need to work within the context to help the children interpret the words into a maths question and write it in symbols. Suppose, for example, that we say that the temperature one morning is 19°C and by lunchtime it has risen by five degrees. We can discuss with the children what time of year it may be and what country we could be in. We can ask whether it is hot in the morning and what it may be like by lunchtime. The purpose of this is to demonstrate to the children that when they encounter a word problem they have to make sense of it first before they decide what maths to do. We ask what we have to do to work out the temperature at lunchtime. We decide that we have to do an addition sum and finally we work out 19 + 5 = 24.

Working like detectives

Problems like this can be demonstrated and then the children can be given a story with blanks where they have to insert missing words. These stories are more powerful if the children have to do some detective work and look for clues in the text. The beginning of a story is given in the example below.

Read the following story through to the end and then choose the appropriate words and symbols from the list and insert in the correct places.

frozen, warm, cold, ⁻10, ⁻14, ⁻15, December, six

Children inspect the text for clues.

It was a ____ day in _____. Charlie was staying at his gran's in Newcastle for Christmas. When Charlie woke up he heard the man on the radio say that the temperature in the night had been a record low of __ degrees Celsius. It was now __ degrees Celsius, a rise of four degrees. The man said that with a wind chill of five degrees that would mean that it would feel more like __ degrees outside. The maximum temperature during the day was expected to be ⁻5 degrees Celsius with a drop of __ degrees to ⁻11 degrees the following night. Charlie was excited. This would mean that the lake had been _____ over for five days and there would be supervised skating that day. His gran made him wear lots of ____ clothes and off he went with his friend Joe.

Looking for clues

This sort of exercise assists the use of language and encourages children to make sense of the context. They can follow this by writing their own story using a set of words given by the teacher.

There are few contexts involving negative numbers that make sense to young children. They are not familiar with high finance of course, but a simple story of a child borrowing money from a parent reveals how the maths story can be told in different ways.

Interpreting real-life stories

Tim owed his mum £10. He paid her 20p each week. How much does he owe after twelve weeks?

Questions like this encourage discussion and debate.

This could be represented mathematically in three different ways:
1000 − 240 = 760 or ⁻1000 + 240 = ⁻760 or ⁻1000 − ⁻240 = ⁻760 Each needs to be discussed and the answers interpreted in the original context.

Using information technology

Using a calculator

Understanding that
calculators vary

Children need to learn how to use a calculator when dealing with negative numbers. This is one of the most difficult areas to deal with because calculators differ considerably in the way they handle these numbers. Some older calculators refuse to accept negative numbers at all and give an error message for a negative result. Most calculators have a key, pressed after entering the number, that changes a positive number to a negative number. Thus negative three requires the following procedure:

> You can see the importance of differentiating between negative and minus when you come to use a calculator.

| enter the number 3 | ⟶ | press the +/– key |

This does not always result in a negative number being displayed on the screen so children have to remember what procedures they have followed. More sophisticated calculators have a negative key that you press before the number and some will allow you to press the subtraction key to obtain a negative. Children are likely to use a variety of calculators at school and at home and they need to be aware of the different procedures and have practice in using different types. Teachers often make the mistake of giving hard sums, that the children find difficult to check, to be done on a calculator. We are suggesting that you give children questions that they have already worked out mentally in order to learn the correct procedures. In this case the children should use the practice questions on negative numbers described earlier.

Re-working questions
on a calculator

> Children need to be fluent at working mentally with negative numbers before attempting to use a calculator.

The teacher will need to provide a variety of calculators in sufficient quantity for one per child. The subtraction practice sheet is given out, without answers, to the whole class. The children work through the first three questions using a calculator and check their answers against their previous work. Provided the first three are correct they continue with the questions and check their answers as before. The teacher assists those children who are having problems. After a set time the whole class stop work and children are invited to present their answers and explain how they obtained those answers on the calculator. Alternative procedures are explained and compared.

Explaining methods

When the children are confident in using the calculator for negative numbers they need to be given examples that are suited to calculator use. The important point here is to ensure that the children go through certain mental procedures before pressing any keys. This needs careful teaching by example.

> Developing good habits for working with a calculator

Demonstrating
thinking

Suppose I want to work out $^-4271 + ^-9265$
Will the answer be positive or negative?

Let me imagine that I see over 4000 holes in my garden. I see over negative 4000 holes. Then I see even more holes. I see about 9000 more holes. I see about negative 9000 more holes.

About how big will the answer be? I have negative 4000 and another negative 9000. The answer will be about negative 13 000.

The class then work out the subtraction and check their answer. They follow this with some examples of their own. Each time they predict the answer. This exercise instils good practice when using a calculator.

Tests

Tests are not surprise
events.

Working without
assistance

Learning outcomes

Selecting appropriate
examples

Real stories to maths
stories

As we have said before, tests should be a regular feature of your
programme of work. These tests are not surprise events but are expected
as a normal part of classroom life. The questions should mirror the work
that has been done in class so that the children have every opportunity
for success. The aim is not merely to test memory but to see whether the
children can do the questions on their own without assistance. We have
stressed that teaching means providing assistance, even total assistance
where necessary, until the children can manage without it. Then they
have learnt. Teachers and children need to know when that moment has
arrived in order to plan for future work.

When you write a test you first need to decide exactly what knowledge
you want to test. The questions in this test are designed to find out
whether the children can:

- add negative numbers with the assistance of a diagram
- add negative numbers without the assistance of a diagram
- work out the missing numbers in an addition sum
- subtract negative numbers with the assistance of a diagram
- subtract negative numbers without the assistance of a diagram
- work out the missing numbers in a subtraction sum
- interpret questions written in words into questions written in
  symbols

Having decided what you want to find out you have to decide how
many questions to set for each required outcome. The test is not a
practice exercise so you do not want to repeat questions but you need
to ensure that you have covered all the possible types of addition and
subtraction of negative numbers. Let us look first at just the addition of
negative numbers without a diagram. You need to select numbers that
are too big to be represented by diagrams and they need to include
such examples as:

$$57 + 21 = \qquad ^-56 + 52 = \qquad 69 + {}^-71 = \qquad ^-44 + {}^-23 =$$

These are sufficient to test addition. Notice that although the numbers
cannot be drawn as diagrams they are not difficult to handle mentally.
There are rather more examples required to test subtraction:

$$83 - 61 = \qquad 30 - 32 = \qquad 45 - {}^-10 = \qquad ^-72 - {}^-5 =$$
$$^-34 - 4 = \qquad ^-27 - {}^-20 =$$

Before going on to teach the application of negative numbers to real-life
problems such as temperature, you need to ensure that the children can
interpret questions written as words into questions written as symbols.
This needs to be practised in a lesson and test questions may look like this:

When I come into my garden one morning I see three lumps of earth
and four holes. I run into the house and write in my maths book ...

When I come into my garden one morning I see five holes in the
garden. My neighbour is very helpful and he says that he has four
lumps. I go inside and write in my maths book ...

When you mark the tests you will know whether the children are ready
to move on and which children continue to need assistance.

Tests help you to know
how well you have
taught something.

Questions have to
be carefully matched
to the purpose of
the test.

Extending the number system: discussion

Introduction

Building on what we know

In everyday life we accumulate knowledge by building on what we already know. Consider the essential knowledge of how to cook. When we look up a recipe for a cake that we have never baked before we follow the instructions carefully. These instructions do not give us every little detail because it is expected that we will already have a certain basic knowledge of cooking. We know how to mix eggs and fat together so that they do not curdle and how to add the flour to keep the cake mixture light and airy.

Having confidence in the basics

It is the confidence that we have in these basic skills that allows us to experiment and try out new ideas. We employ the same principle when we design an instructional method for teaching maths. In this discussion we look at how we use the children's confidence and knowledge of the ordinary counting numbers to extend the number system to fractions, decimals and negative numbers.

Children are good at counting.

Young children become very good at counting whole numbers. They enjoy chanting numbers in sequence detached from any association with objects. They like to show how they can count to very big numbers. Then they learn to associate the symbols and words with the numbers they speak and they learn to count objects.

> Although we know that most children can count fluently, we must plan to establish this knowledge base at the beginning of a set of teaching episodes.

Making links

It is this confidence and knowledge that we want to utilize in extending their knowledge to fractions, decimals and negative numbers. We want to make those vital links between something that they know so well and something new.

Rational numbers

When we count 'one, two, three, ...' we are using whole numbers. Think about the number 3. It can be written in other ways, for instance, $\frac{6}{2}$, $\frac{24}{8}$. If we write it in the form $\frac{a}{b}$ we are expressing it as a rational number. It has the same value as 3, but a different appearance. Other rational numbers are, for example, $\frac{7}{10}$ and $\frac{1}{5}$.

Vulgar fractions, decimals and percentages

We also call these numbers vulgar fractions. They are vulgar because they are in the most basic form for a fraction. There are other forms. The vulgar fraction $\frac{7}{10}$ can be written as .7 or 0.7. This is then a decimal fraction. And the same fraction can be written as a percentage (70%), or a ratio (7:10).

> The phrase 'keep the value: change the appearance' is used to make the links between these different forms of numbers.

Numerators and denominators

When a decimal is expressed in the vulgar form $\frac{a}{b}$ we call a the numerator and b the denominator. These words make sense if you just think of the ordinary language of money. What denomination coins have you got? Ten pence pieces. How many (what number) have you got? Four. We give the number (the numeral, the numerator) of the type (the denomination, the value) of the object. This is the same as in the vulgar fraction $\frac{7}{10}$. We are dealing with a particular denomination (tenths); we have seven of them (our numeral is seven).

Proper and improper fractions

There are proper fractions ($\frac{4}{7}$ for example) where the numerator is less then the denominator. Proper fractions represent numbers that lie between nought and one. Then there are improper fractions ($\frac{13}{7}$ for example) where the numerator is greater than the denominator. Improper fractions represent numbers greater than one and they can always be turned into mixed numbers (in this case $1\frac{6}{7}$). That is, they can be turned into numbers that have a whole number part and a fractional number part.

Whatever type of fraction we have, the essential feature to remember is that they are numbers and numbers can be counted. Once we can count numbers we can add, subtract, multiply and divide them.

Fractions in everyday life

Children meet fractions in everyday life. They become familiar with quarters and halves when telling the time or cutting up objects such as cakes or pizzas. They know them so well that they count them and use them with the same confidence as whole numbers (they can be thought of as honorary whole numbers).

When we are teaching maths concepts that go beyond everyday life we want to raise the level of consciousness and awaken the mind to do some higher-level thinking. For this reason we choose a fraction that is used less frequently in everyday life to introduce the notion of fractions. We start with fifths.

What you hear and what you see

Suppose you close your eyes and I read any of the following: *one fifth*, ⅕, $\frac{1}{5}$. Each time you will hear the same sounds but if you open your eyes you will see three different representations of those sounds. We want children to recognize all those representations and to be able to read them. And later we want them to recognize the same value but the different appearance of 20%, $\frac{5}{25}$ and so on.

This recognition is made easier by designing cards, like playing cards, with the different representations of a fifth written clearly on them. The choice of representations depends upon the purpose and learning objectives of the teaching episode.

Teaching children to count, add and subtract fractions

In the fractions script you can see how the children count fifths with the teacher. The teacher assists their performance by counting *'one fifth, two fifths, three fifths, ...'* with the children. The shift from counting whole numbers to counting fractions is hardly noticeable. The teacher is using the children's confidence in counting whole numbers to teach them to count fractions with the same denominator. This is no different from counting beakers or counters.

Same value: different appearance

Raising the level of consciousness

Same value: different appearance

Fraction cards

Counting fractions like objects

Colloquial use of fraction words often lacks the rigour that we expect in maths.

The numbers change their visual appearance but not the way they sound.

When the children are confident in counting fifths the teacher moves on to count other fractions, such as thirds, but now gets the children to 'imagine the cards' and to come to the board and show everyone what is written on their (imaginary) card. In this way the teacher can establish that the children have understood that fractions may sound the same but can look different. The same exaggerated counting using pauses and gestures also ensures that by demonstration the children understand the notion that three thirds is the same as one whole one, in exactly the same way that five fifths is a whole one.

By repeating this activity with sevenths and tenths, etc. the teacher helps the children to recognize how many of a particular fraction make a whole one. Cards are used only to introduce the counting of fifths, with the children doing the rest in their imagination (unless the teacher has judged through monitoring that the children require greater assistance with another set of cards).

Children need to be given practice in counting, adding and subtracting fractions with the same denominator until they are completely confident and competent. This activity is often neglected because it seems too easy or too trivial yet it is the key to later work because, of course, fractions can only be added and subtracted when they have the same denominator. To add or subtract fractions with different denominators requires us to find equivalent fractions to those given so that they have the same denominator. We can immediately see that the phrase 'keep the value: change the appearance' is once again applicable here.

Algorithms for addition and subtraction

At no time have we had to resort to teaching addition or subtraction with the use of an algorithm. Addition of fractions has been an extension of addition of whole numbers. That is not to say that the algorithm itself is rejected. Algorithms provide neat and economical ways of setting out more complex problems but they are best remembered when the underlying concepts are fully understood.

It is easy to identify children who have been taught how to add fractions using an algorithm through the common errors they make. The most common error is to 'add tops, add bottoms' and this is an indication of a lack of understanding of the problem. They are merely following a rule that has been incorrectly memorized and this error becomes even more frequent as the children learn rules for multiplication and division.

Multiplying and dividing fractions

You have seen how children can become confident and competent at counting, adding and subtracting fractions with the same denominator and moving between vulgar fractions and mixed numbers. Let us look at this again.

- Count out twelve fifths. *How much is there? Twelve fifths? That is, twelve times a fifth is twelve fifths.*
  $\frac{1}{5} \times 12 = \frac{12}{5}$.

Multiplication is a way of generalizing addition. It is repeated addition. Note the careful and considered use of 'How much?'. This language implies the need to think about the totality of the items.

Side notes (left margin):

Working in the imagination

Practice

Adding fractions with the same denominator

Common errors

Counting assists multiplication.

Side notes (right margin):

The teacher has to represent the act of thinking with verbal and non-verbal gestures.

The algorithm for adding and subtracting fractions is essential when moving on to generalization using algebra.

- Count out the cards two at a time. Do this eight times. *How much is there? Eight times two fifths. There are sixteen fifths.*
$\frac{2}{5} \times 8 = \frac{16}{5}$

- Count out the cards four at a time. Do this six times. *How much is there? Four fifths times six. There are twenty-four fifths.*
$\frac{4}{5} \times 6 = \frac{24}{5}$

Continue this activity with different groupings and then with different fractions. Move on to work in the imagination. The careful use of 'How much?' to indicate the totality of items contrasts with 'How many?' which prompts consideration of the number of items.

Look at this counting again.

- Count out twelve fifths. **How many** *fifths are there? Twelve. That is, twelve fifths divided by a fifth is twelve.*
$\frac{12}{5} \div \frac{1}{5} = 12$.

- Count out cards in groups of three. Count thirty fifths. *How many three fifths are there? Ten. Thirty fifths divided by three fifths is ten.*
$\frac{30}{5} \div \frac{3}{5} = 10$

We have not had to teach algorithms or rules. We have simply used the children's confidence in counting, adding and subtracting to extend their thinking to multiplying and dividing. This mirrors the way in which the children have been working with whole numbers and it is this continuity that assists the children's learning. Here, as in the earlier number work, the logic is in the language.

Going beyond fractions as objects
The consideration of fractions as objects does not tell the full maths story of fractions. Using cards to represent fractions has allowed us to consider fractions as objects that can be counted. This in turn leads us to addition and subtraction of fractions and to the multiplication of fractions by whole numbers.

Fractions can also be considered as 'operators'. For example, we can multiply by one fifth. That is we can find one fifth of something. The distinction between a fraction as object and fraction as operator is important. We believe that the idea of a fraction as object should be introduced to children first so that fractions can be counted and added. This mirrors the introduction of whole numbers to young children. When the children are confident in this counting they can proceed to the idea of a fraction as an operator.

Many published schemes use the idea of fraction as operator to introduce fractions with colouring-in activities. Children are asked to find, for example, a fifth of a circle or rectangle and colour it in. Although this activity appears to bring some immediate success because most children are good at colouring it does not provide a good knowledge base for developing an understanding of fractions. We recommend that children first do counting activities like those described above and then move on to look at equivalent fractions.

Equivalent fractions
We want to emphasize the need for continuity with ideas developed when teaching whole numbers. Plastic cups were used to provide real

Side notes:

Working in the imagination

Counting assists division.

Fractions as operators

The need for continuity

Notice the order in which we have written this multiplication. It is consistent with our work with whole numbers.

Consistency of approach provides continuity and helps to make those vital connections between mathematical concepts.

Real stories for maths stories

stories to match the maths stories employed in teaching counting and the four rules. We shall use these cups again now to introduce the idea of equivalent fractions.

- Cut the cups into halves (and later into quarters, eighths, fifths, etc.) like this:

The visual image of parts of cups is more powerful than colouring in parts of shapes.

- Count the half cups in exactly the same way as you have been counting the cards. Count out seven halves. Demonstrate how these are equivalent to three and a half. Point to the poster 'Keep the value: change the appearance' and write $\frac{7}{2} = 3\frac{1}{2}$. You can also write $\frac{1}{2} \times 7 = \frac{7}{2} = 3\frac{1}{2}$. Look at the seven halves and ask: *How many halves can you see?* Look at three whole ones and a half and ask: *How many halves can you see?*

Keep the value: change the appearance

You can repeat this exercise with different numbers of halves and then with different fractions.

When the children are confident working with fractions of cups in this way you can move on to look at the equivalence of, say, six quarters and three halves. Children need lots of practice in these activities before they are ready to move on to adding and subtracting fractions with different denominators.

Practice

Using multiplication tables

We are going to show how the multiplication tables can be used to extend multiplication facts to multiplying fractions.

Again it is the consistency of approach that aids learning.

We have shown earlier that the three times table can be used to go beyond the information given. We can say:

three **hundred** times four is twelve **hundred**
$300 \times 4 = 1200$

We can also say:

three **hundred** times five **thousand** is three **hundred thousand**
$300 \times 5000 = 300\,000$

The logic in the language

We can use the same logic in the language to extend this idea to fractions. We can say:

three **tenths** times seven is twenty-one **tenths**
$\frac{3}{10} \times 7 = \frac{21}{10}$

and

three **hundredths** times nine is twenty-seven **hundredths**
$\frac{3}{100} \times 9 = \frac{27}{100}$

We can extend this to:

three **tenths** times four **hundredths** is twelve **tenths hundredths**
$\frac{3}{10} \times \frac{4}{100} = \frac{12}{1000}$

'Tenths hundredths' are the same as thousandths.

and

three **thousandths** times five **hundredths** is fifteen **thousandths hundredths**
$\frac{3}{1000} \times \frac{5}{100} = \frac{15}{100000}$

The language of number is too often neglected in the teaching process.

Now we can extend this to any fractions:

*three **fifths** times four **sevenths** is twelve **fifths sevenths***

$$\frac{3}{5} \times \frac{4}{7} = \frac{12}{35}$$

By demonstration we can show that 'fifths sevenths' are 'thirty-fifths'. This is acceptable if the children have had lots of practice using the tables to extend their multiplication facts. You may prefer to start with the one times table and do the following:

*one **tenth** times one **hundredth** is one **tenth hundredth***

$$\frac{1}{10} \times \frac{1}{100} = \frac{1}{1000}$$

Notice that we have not had to teach any rules or algorithms. The logic is in the language. We have based all of this work on a sound knowledge of the multiplication tables. The success of this method depends upon the teacher preparing the groundwork by doing lots of oral work with whole numbers.

Extending the fraction script to decimals

The continuity that we have achieved with the teaching of fractions as numbers can be followed through with the introduction of decimals or, to give them their full name, 'decimal fractions'. After all, these are not really new numbers to be studied but a different form of writing a particular fraction using the position of digits to denote the size or value of the denominator.

Start by using cards showing different representations of a tenth: one tenth, $\frac{1}{10}$, ¹⁄₁₀, 0.1, 0.10, 10% and so on, using forms suited to the class you are working with. The counting activity is repeated using hundredths, then thousandths and so on with imaginary cards. Teachers need to exaggerate the pronunciation of these words to distinguish between, say, 'hundreds' and 'hundredths'. When the children are familiar with counting they can move on to addition using decimals.

- Count out seven tenths on the table. Count out a further five tenths. Give the answer as 'twelve tenths' and 'one and two tenths'.

Write on the board: | 0.7 + 0.5 = 1.2 |

Note that in the decimal form there is only one way of writing this answer.

It is important in this work that children can alternate between reading 0.7 as 'nought point seven', 'seven tenths' and 'seventy hundredths' and so on (and, of course, seventy per cent). Making the connection between fractions and decimals can assist children in their learning of decimals.

Using multiplication tables again

Look back at the way we extended the three times table to multiplying fractions. Notice how we can multiply tenths, hundredths and thousandths, etc. We can say:

*three **tenths** times two **tenths** is six **tenths tenths***

$$\frac{3}{10} \times \frac{2}{10} = \frac{6}{100}$$

$$0.3 \times 0.2 = 0.06$$

A sound knowledge of fractions is the key to a better understanding of decimals. We sometimes think that because measurement and money

Sidebar notes:

Extending to any fractions

The logic is in the language.

Using cards

Writing tenths as decimals

Speaking decimal numbers

Connecting fractions and decimals

You cannot use these ideas in isolation. It is the consistent and persistent use of language that is needed to aid learning.

Once again it is the consistency of approach that helps to make the connections.

The multiplication tables are fundamental to multiplication and division of all numbers.

A decimal is a form of fraction.	are decimalized there is no need to know about fractions, but remember that decimals are just another form of fractions.

Recurring and infinite decimals

All rational numbers $\frac{a}{b}$ can be written in decimal form. Numbers such as $\frac{1}{2}$ or $\frac{1}{8}$ convert to 'finite decimals', in this case 0.5 and 0.125. That is, they have a fixed number of digits.

Finite decimals

However, numbers such as $\frac{1}{3}$ or $\frac{1}{11}$ convert to 'infinite decimals' (0.333333... and 0.090909...) with repeating digits and these are also called 'recurring decimals'. The set of digits that repeat (or recur) are denoted by a dot above the first and last digits in the set, such as $0.\dot{3}$ or $0.\dot{0}\dot{9}$.

Recurring decimals

> Exploration of the extended number system takes us into an imaginary world beyond everyday life.

Children need to be taught how to convert from fractions to decimals and vice versa. This can be an ideal opportunity to use computers because generally the number of digits in the decimal part can be extensive enough for the children to search for patterns. Calculators are less helpful because the displays are smaller and the last digit may be rounded up.

Irrational numbers cannot be written in the form $\frac{a}{b}$. They are infinite decimals without any repeating patterns. Examples of irrational numbers are $\sqrt{2}$ and π. When we write these as decimals we have to decide how many decimal places to show. Suppose we write each to five decimal places then we get 1.41421 and 3.14159 respectively. Each of these is an approximation.

Infinite non-recurring decimals

Normally children first meet irrational numbers when they are doing work on the circle. They are often confused by instructions to use 3 or 3.1 or 3.14 and so on as the value for π. They need to be introduced to the idea of π as an infinite decimal and to understand that the number of decimal places selected depends upon how much accuracy is needed.

Percentages

Making connections

We mention percentages here to remind you that the connection needs to be made between fractions, decimals and percentages. Percentages are simply another form of writing hundredths, and operating with percentages is the same as operating with fractions and decimals. The value is the same; it is only the appearance that has changed.

> Connections between the various forms of number must be made visible to children.

It is when we start working with percentages that we immediately see the importance of learning about fractions as 'operators'. We normally want to calculate a 'percentage of' something and this requires a fraction or decimal multiplication. It is important to inspect the number we are operating on. A 10 per cent pay rise may be significant for the managing director of a company but a less significant amount for someone on the production line.

Calculating percentages

Using games

The games of snap, pairs and dominoes, as described in the first topic, are ideal to practise matching fractions, decimals and percentages. The children should state either 'same value: same appearance' or 'same value: different appearance' to win a point.

Increasing and decreasing

There are some key words associated with percentage, such as 'increase' and 'decrease', that cause children to make errors. Suppose a video is increased in price by 10 per cent. Now we could calculate 10 per cent of the original price and add it on. This takes two operations, the first a multiplication and the second an addition, but it gives an impression that 'increase' is an additive operation. In fact 'increase' is a multiplicative operation.

'Increase' is a
multiplicative process.

When we introduce an idea to young children we sometimes choose methods that cause problems later on.

To calculate the increase by doing just one calculation you have to *multiply* the original price by 1.1. (The one whole one stands for the original price and the 0.1 or tenth stands for the 10 per cent.)

Suppose the price is increased by a further 10 per cent. Is this an overall increase of 20 per cent? No. But this is the most common error made by children. You have to multiply the original price by 1.1 and then by 1.1 again. This repeated multiplication is the same as multiplying by 1.21 ($1.1 \times 1.1 = 1.21$) and this indicates an overall increase of 21 per cent.

Repeated
multiplication

The word 'increase' is also used in connection with the enlargement of shapes. We increase the lengths of the edges of a shape by multiplying by a scale factor. This is exactly the same process as a percentage increase or decrease, except that in percentages you have to work out the scale factor first. For example, an increase of 35 per cent gives a scale factor of 1.35. A decrease of 15 per cent gives a scale factor of 0.85. An increase of 25 per cent followed by a decrease of 8 per cent gives a scale factor of $1.25 \times 0.92 = 1.15$.

Making connections

It is the role of the teacher to assist the children in making these connections. The connections help us to see that there is less to learn. Percentage increase and enlargement are merely applications of fraction and decimal multiplication. This is why a sound knowledge of operations and their inverses is the key to developing maths beyond Key Stage 2.

Negative numbers

We complete the story of numbers with the negative numbers. We have shown how cards and counting can be used to introduce whole numbers, fractions and decimals. This theme can be continued with the negative numbers. Cards with the words 'negative one' or the symbol '⁻1' are counted and added until the children are confident in using the language and competent at adding negative numbers.

Negative numbers as
objects to be counted

Negative numbers are purely a figment of the imagination.

Combining positive and
negative numbers

Combining positive and negative numbers requires the children to understand the notion that positive one add negative one is zero. This is the key to more advanced work with negative numbers and so we have constructed a story (as in the script) to provide mental imagery to assist cognition. Stories can be powerful tools in teaching maths but they must adhere to the underlying concepts. In this case the lumps of earth represent the positive numbers and the holes in the ground the negative numbers.

This is a mathematical result that needs to be taught.

⁻3 + 5 = 2

It is not difficult to visualize a lump of earth filling up a hole in the ground to leave a flat surface or a zero. This filling of holes can be enacted by the teacher and pupils using exaggerated actions and these provide a lasting image that helps prevent the common errors we so often see.

The story creates mental images.

Using cards to represent the story

Abstract concepts are better understood when the teacher uses an appropriate representation.

The story of the garden can be represented by cards that fit together. The card with a pocket represents the 'hole' or negative one and the card that fits into the pocket represents the 'heap of earth' or positive one. When the two cards are fitted together they represent zero because one and negative one make zero. This means that we can have many cards fitted together in this way and still have zero. We now have a better representation to help the children subtract negative numbers.

$1 + {}^-1 = 0$ $1 + {}^-1 = 0$ $1 + {}^-1 = 0$ $1 + {}^-1 = 0$ $1 + {}^-1 = 0$

The cards can be used in the following way:

- Set out the maths table with lots of cards fitted together so that there is the equivalent of zero on the table, just like the flat garden.

- Set out lots of separated cards on the resource table so that there are lots of ones and negative ones available.

Doing the job of addition

This activity is consistent with the approach used with whole numbers.

- Get the children to come out and collect cards from the resource table to perform $2 + 3$, ${}^-3 + {}^-4$, $5 + {}^-2$, $1 + {}^-7$ and so on by moving the appropriate cards from the resource table to the maths table. This is exactly like the activity with beakers that the children did to add whole positive numbers.

  Two add three [collect two ones and then three ones]: *easy, five. Negative three add negative four* [collect cards]: *easy, negative seven. Five add negative two* [collect five ones and two negative ones]: *well, two of these ones fit together with two of these negative ones, leaving me with three. One add negative seven* [collect one and seven negative ones]: *well, one and negative one fit together, leaving me with negative six.*

Doing the job of subtraction

- Get the children to come out and perform $4 - 3$, ${}^-6 - {}^-4$ and so on. This time the child gets the first number of cards from the resource table and puts them on the maths table, then takes the appropriate number of cards away from the maths table.

- Now set the question $2 - 5$. A child collects two cards representing positive two from the resource table and puts them on the maths table. Five now have to be taken away. The child removes the two she has just placed on the table. She needs to remove three more. She goes to the pile of zeros and picks up three of them. She takes out the positive ones from each and removes them from the table. Now what is left on the maths table? Negative three.

Getting negative answers

- Set questions like ${}^-4 - {}^-7$ and then get the children to set some questions of their own.

The whole range of addition and subtraction of negative numbers can now be achieved and the children have a useful mental image to work with. You can now set questions involving large numbers to encourage the children to work in their imagination. The actions can be mimed with imaginary cards until all the children are confident.

Working in the imagination

Notice that at no time have we suggested that you refer to such things as temperature to teach negative numbers. Temperature is a specific application of negative numbers and research has shown that any number line representation used in the teaching of these numbers forces children to make errors in their calculations. Consider what meaning can be attached to addition and subtraction operations. A temperature may rise but we do not add two temperatures together. How can you explain subtracting a negative temperature? Mathematics goes beyond real life and is all the more exciting because of that fact. However, once we have taught the maths concepts we shall want to show how they can be applied to everyday situations.

> When the children are fluent in operating with negative numbers they can be introduced to real-life applications such as temperature.

Applying maths concepts once they are known

Multiplication and division of negative numbers

Using the cards as described above, the children can enact multiplication as follows:

$3 \times 5 =$

I move three ones from the resource table and put them on the maths table. I do this five times. I now have fifteen on the maths table.

$^-3 \times 5 =$

I move three negative ones from the resource table and put them on the maths table. I do this five times. I now have negative fifteen on the maths table.

$15 \div 3 =$

I move fifteen ones from the resource table to the maths table. I look at them and wonder how many threes I can see. [Put cards in piles of three.] I can see five.

$^-15 \div ^-3 =$

I move fifteen negative ones from the resource table to the maths table. I look at them and wonder how many negative threes I can see. [Put cards in piles of three.] I can see five.

Real stories to represent maths stories

The children can now do any addition or subtraction with positive and negative numbers and they can multiply negative numbers by positive numbers and divide negative numbers by negative numbers. These can all be enacted with the cards. Can we do multiplication of any number by a negative number? What does this mean? We cannot collect cards a negative number of times. It does not make sense. Maths cannot always be represented with concrete materials in this way. Maths goes beyond everyday life into the imagination.

> The beauty of maths is that it takes us into an imaginary world where so much is possible.

Maths goes beyond everyday life.

We know that $3 \times 5 = 15$ and $^-3 \times 5 = ^-15$. Because multiplication is commutative we also know that $3 \times ^-5 = ^-15$. When we inspect these results we can see that the only remaining multiplication is $^-3 \times ^-5 =$. This is especially difficult for mathematicians to explain. The answer is 15. But a convincing explanation needs to be postponed. It cannot be explained using the cards and the visualization that we have introduced. It goes beyond the information given. That is the nature of maths.

The nature of maths

4 Properties of shapes

Introduction

Deductive logic

It is in geometry that we find some of the most exciting examples of maths. Geometry makes visible the deductive logic that is an important part of maths. To get the most out of doing geometry you need to be able to think like a mathematician. You have to look at shapes and speculate, to look at the evidence before your eyes and search for clues. You have to know what language to use to describe what you see, to argue the case and to convince someone else of what you see. You have to be able to use your imagination, to go beyond the information given.

Going beyond the information given

> In our pursuit of improving numeracy we must not forget this branch of maths that is such a delight to teach and learn.

Lines drawn on a page do not end but go beyond the edges of the page to infinity. Points beyond the limits of a graph and hidden faces of polyhedra have to be imagined. Children can be taught to work and think like mathematicians through well-planned and purposeful activities.

Defining a square

Consider one of the most common shapes that you know, the square. Write down all that you know about a square's angles, edges, diagonals, symmetry, etc. All that information is conveyed in its name which distinguishes it from other shapes. We want children to build up the knowledge that is contained in that information.

Working like detectives

We also want children to be able to work like detectives, to inspect diagrams or pictures, look for clues and make deductions. We want them to feel the excitement of discovery as they use known facts to prove a result. We want them to be able to follow and construct an argument with successive statements following on logically from each other: 'If this ... then this....'

> Deductive logic is a skill that can be applied to other disciplines.

Constructing an argument

Properties of shape

Children need to be able to calculate perimeters, areas and volumes of the most common 2D and 3D shapes; to construct plane shapes and to make polyhedra; to know when shapes are similar or congruent and to understand the effect of transformations on shapes.

Demonstrating skills

The role of the teacher is to demonstrate these skills and help children make connections between algebra and geometry using formulae and graphical representation. This includes representing and interpreting relationships by plotting points (called Cartesian co-ordinates) on rectangular axes and recognizing that in mathematics we can go beyond the information given.

Development in learning properties of shapes

Having taken a look at what we want children to achieve in geometry, we need to think about where to start and how we can best develop that knowledge and understanding. If we look at all the information that is conveyed by the word 'square' then it is obvious that we cannot introduce all of these ideas to children at once but need to plan a scheme of work that develops the ideas gradually. The first script in this section describes how teachers can assist children to name shapes and know their properties. Careful introduction of mathematical language and terminology in the early years provides the necessary foundation for later work.

> Spatial awareness is not just something people are born with, it can be taught.

Teachers should enable children to:

- *speak and write the names of common shapes: triangles, rectangles, squares, circles, hexagons, pentagons, cubes, cuboids, cylinders and spheres*

> Language is a key feature of geometry.

- *identify a specific shape from a selection of shapes by its name*

- *know the number of edges, faces and angles of common shapes*

- *use the edge and angle properties of shapes to identify and describe them*

- *know the meaning of the word 'regular'*

- *deduce the names of shapes from their edge and angle properties*

- *draw shapes accurately*

- *know that angle is a measure of turn and recognize fractions of a turn*

- *speak and write the names and properties of special types of triangles: scalene, isosceles, equilateral and quadrilaterals: rectangle, square, rhombus, trapezium, parallelogram, kite*

- *use properties of shapes, including symmetry properties, to recognize, visualize and describe them*

- *deduce the names of shapes from their properties*

> Classifying shapes using their properties helps children develop convincing mathematical arguments.

- *measure and draw angles*

- *construct 2D and 3D shapes*

- *identify triangles by angle properties: right-angled, acute-angled, obtuse-angled*

- *use properties of shapes to compare them*

- *know the properties of diagonals of quadrilaterals*

- *know the mathematical terms 'similar' and 'congruent'*

- *solve problems using properties of shapes*

- *transform 2D shapes (reflection, rotation, translation, enlargement) and know the effect on shapes of the transformations*

- *work out the perimeter, area and volume of shapes*

Developing knowledge of shapes

Script 1: Teaching the names and properties of common shapes

Learning maths words

This first script demonstrates how the teacher helps the children to associate the word 'triangle' with the shape. They are told that the shapes are triangles. They do not have to guess or hope that they are correct: they know because they are told. All the children in the class then speak the word together until they are confident as a group. This is followed by each individual child saying the word. It is not sufficient to say the word once and hope that the children will remember it. The teacher must ensure that every child can speak the word fluently. It is crucial to establish this common knowledge base right at the beginning so that all children can participate in the lesson.

Establishing a common knowledge base

Resources

* A set of card triangles – one for each member of the class (Ensure that the triangles are different in size and type, avoiding too many equilateral or isosceles triangles.)

Preparing resources

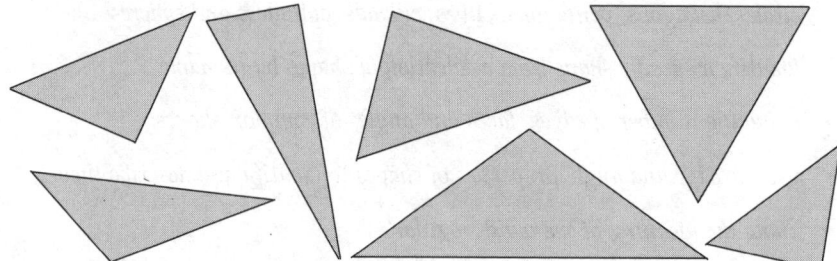

Most people associate the word triangle with an equilateral triangle. This exercise reminds us of the different sorts of triangles that exist.

* A table full of shapes including: a variety of triangles, some made from card or plastic and some made with wooden rods or straws; a variety of other polygons, some made from card or plastic and some made with wooden rods or straws; open boxes; solid shapes; some shapes with curved edges; and some rods making shapes that are not closed

Naming triangles

The teacher begins by holding up the triangular cards one at a time and saying:

This is a triangle and this is a triangle and this is a triangle and ...
When I give you one of these and say 'Is this a triangle?' you say 'Yes'.

Confirming knowledge

Each child is given a triangle and asked the question: *Is this a triangle?*

Associating words and images

This initial introduction to the word associated with the visual image of a triangle allows the children to link the name of the shape with its image. Every child can be successful right from the start as they can all say the word 'Yes'. They all receive a triangle that they can examine more closely and feel. The cards are then collected in and shuffled so that the children receive a different triangle the next time. The teacher says:

Assisting performance through success

Learning to speak maths

This time when I give you one of these and ask 'What is this shape?' you say 'This shape is a triangle'. What do you say?

All together:

This shape is a triangle.

Each child is again given a triangle and asked the question: *What is this shape?*

The teacher mouths the words along with the children to encourage and remind them what to say. Again they can all be successful in saying the words as the teacher provides assistance.

So far the children have been asked to associate the name 'triangle' with its visual image. The teacher now moves on to demonstrate some of the properties of a triangle.

Learning properties

> *A triangle is a flat shape* [pointing]. *It has three angles and three straight edges.*

During this demonstration the teacher points in an exaggerated way at each feature as it is described and writes the spoken words on the board. She then moves to the table and selects a shape (this is a triangle but different in appearance from the first).

> *Is this a triangle?* [Points to the poster 'Keep the value: change the appearance'.]

Demonstrating the process of thinking

The teacher is now going to demonstrate the process of deduction by making gestures and asking questions. This may seem a rather trivial example but this careful introduction to deductive thinking is vital to prepare children for more complex cases.

Non-verbal gestures

Three gestures prompt the children to pause and think. The teacher shrugs her shoulders at the question and puts on a puzzled look. She uses her hands to indicate weighing up the evidence as if her hands were the arms of a balance. Then she asks:

Inspecting

> *Is this shape flat?*
> [Lifts it up and looks at it from several angles.]
> *Yes.*
> *Does it have three angles?*
> [Points to each in turn and counts silently 'one, two three'.]
> *Yes.*
> *Does it have three straight edges?*
> [Traces out each in turn and counts silently 'one, two three'.]
> *Yes.*
> *Is it a triangle?*
> [Nods and gets all the class to join in.]
> *Yes.*

Deduction

The activity is then repeated by the whole class. Individual children are invited to come to the table and select a shape. They mimic the teacher by shrugging, looking puzzled and using their hands to weigh up the evidence. They ask the class the questions and together the class deduce whether the shape is a triangle. Each time the process is repeated in an exaggerated fashion so that the idea of pausing and asking questions and weighing up the evidence can be fully appreciated. There is a tendency in classrooms to rush on to the next step before all the children are ready, whereas here you can see that concepts are established with every member of the class before moving on. Each child is offered the opportunity to participate in this collaborative activity.

Weighing the evidence

Over a period of time this episode is repeated with rectangles, squares and so on until the children have a repertoire of shapes, along with their names and properties, to work with.

Assisting performance through assisting with the language of maths

The teacher represents the act of thinking with verbal and non-verbal gestures.

The initial activity was enacted with a familiar shape to establish a common knowledge base.

Script 2: Classifying shapes

Looking for clues

Homework as preparation

In this script the children use their knowledge of the properties of shapes to look for clues and deduce the name of a shape from its properties. The teacher may need to repeat some of the first script before starting this lesson. Children are prepared for this work in a homework task that reminds them of the language associated with shape and revises the process of deductive logic. The teacher begins by going over the homework with the whole class.

Resources

- A set of shapes (for use by the teacher and kept out of sight of the children) and a bag large enough to hold one shape at a time for a child to feel. The selection of shapes can be varied according to the teacher's intentions for the lesson.

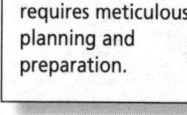

Work in geometry requires meticulous planning and preparation.

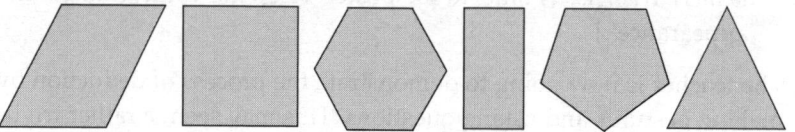

- A table of shapes to provide variety and choice

- A set of words on cards that can be used to describe shapes

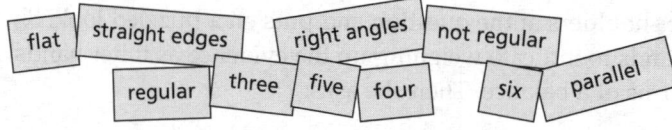

Working like detectives

Looking for clues

The teacher invites two children to come to the front and asks one to feel inside the bag containing one of the shapes (say, a rectangle). The child is asked to describe the shape in the bag without using its name. The child gives a response such as:

The shape is flat. It has four straight edges. It has four right angles. It is not regular.

As the child describes the shape the teacher and class help the other child to find the appropriate words on cards and put them on the board.

Matching objects to their descriptions

The teacher invites a third child to go to the table of shapes and select a shape with the same properties as those described. The description and the words are being used to create a mental image of a shape. This develops the children's ability to work from the properties of a shape to build a picture in the imagination. It is like solving a mystery. The activity attracts and sustains the children's interest and challenges their perspectives. When the correct shape is selected the teacher uses questioning to ensure that the whole class has understood why that shape has been chosen.

Checking for accuracy

Good. Now let us check this shape you have chosen. Is the shape flat?
Yes.
Does it have four straight edges?
Yes.
Does it have four right angles?

Questioning is used to represent the thinking process.

Yes.
Is it regular?
No.
Good. Your shape seems to be the same as the one in the bag. Let us look
and see [gets the shape out of the bag]. *Do these shapes have the same*
properties? Yes. Now tell me the name of the shape. Yes, it is a rectangle.

This activity is now repeated with different shapes in the bag. The level
of difficulty will depend on the aims of the teacher. If this is continued
as a whole class activity it is important to involve all the children at
some stage. Alternatively it can be conducted as pair or group work
once the process has been established at the beginning of the episode.
At the end of the episode it is important to bring the ideas together
and summarize what has been achieved. The children can then be set
an exercise in class or for homework to reinforce this work.

Script 3: Identifying different quadrilaterals

The nature of language

It is the nature of language that objects can often be described by
different words according to particular properties. For instance, you
may describe yourself as English when talking about the country you
were born in, or you might say that you are British when discussing
nationality, or you might call yourself European when referring to the
continent you are from. Saying you are English gives me more specific
details about you than saying you are European. Being English is a
special case of being European. In the same way a shape may be
described as a square when we want to know that all its sides are
equal and all its angles are right angles. But it might be described as a
rectangle when its regular property is not an important feature, or it
might be described as a quadrilateral when all that is required is to
know that it has four edges.

> The language of maths
> is concise and precise.
> It should be used
> rigorously.

Words convey information.

All these names convey vital information about the particular shape
being discussed and are names that are in common use. It is important
to teach children the correct words to use and the properties associated
with them. The two previous episodes can be adapted to revise the
names and properties of shapes and give practice in identifying shapes
with given attributes. This script demonstrates how that knowledge
can be applied.

Resources

- Square lattice pin-boards with elastic bands

- Paper with a grid of dotted squares; pencils and rulers

Using a pin-board

The teacher uses a pin-board at the front of the class or a special
overhead projector version. If neither is available a grid of dots drawn
on the board makes a reasonable substitute. Using only a three-by-three
lattice of pins, the teacher makes a quadrilateral with an elastic band
and says:

> This activity requires
> careful demonstration
> by the teacher.

Making quadrilaterals

Deliberate demonstration

Gestures as prompts

This is a square lattice [point to the pins and count]. *One, two, three across, one two three down. There are* [count] *nine pins altogether. I am going to use these pins to make a shape* [make the shape]. *The shape has four straight edges* [trace the edges with a finger]. *It is a closed shape* [gesture with hands]. *It is a* [pause to encourage children to join in] *quadrilateral.*

The teacher writes the word 'quadrilateral' on the board. She continues by making another quadrilateral, ensuring that it is different from the first one. She asks:

Is this a quadrilateral?

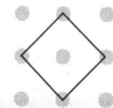

Is the shape flat? Yes. Is it closed? Yes. Does it have four straight edges? Yes. Good. So is it a quadrilateral? Yes.
Is this [pointing to the first one] *the **same** as this* [pointing to the second one]?

The teacher goes through a set of questions to establish what is the same and what is different about the two quadrilaterals.

> The words 'same' and 'different' are used in many contexts. It is important to define what is meant in this particular case.

Questions to challenge thinking

Is this shape [pointing] *bigger than this* [pointing] *shape?*
Are the angles in this one [pointing to angles in turn] *the same as the angles* [pointing] *in this one?*
Are the edges in this one [pointing] *the same length as the edges in this one* [pointing]? [And so on.]

Congruence

Finally the idea of congruence is explored by moving one shape around to see if it fits exactly on top of the other. The first shape is traced and the teacher asks:

> Congruent implies an 'identical' shape and must not be confused with 'similar'.

Teaching the technical language of maths

If I turn this one around will it fit on top of this one? [Repeat using correct mathematical term.] *If I rotate this one will it fit on top of this one?* [Try to fit shape on top by turning paper.] *No.*

If I turn this one over – if I reflect it – will it fit on top of this one? [Turn tracing paper over and try to fit on top of the second shape.] *No.*

> The teacher represents the act of thinking with verbal and non-verbal gestures.

If I slide this one along – if I translate it – will it fit on top of this one? [Slide tracing paper along.] *No.*

Let me say those last three statements again. If I rotate, reflect or translate this shape will it fit on top of this one? No.

We say: Is this shape congruent to this one? No.

Summarizing

Look at these two shapes again. They are both quadrilaterals because they are flat, they are closed, they have four straight edges. So in that way they are both the same. But this shape is bigger than that shape. Its angles and edges are different. We say that the two quadrilaterals are not congruent.

The teacher now makes a third quadrilateral that is congruent with the first one. She goes through all the questions again and establishes that the two are congruent. This reminds the children of the properties of quadrilaterals, ensures that they understand the instructions and establishes the meaning of the term 'congruent'.

Searching for different quadrilaterals

The class is now divided into groups and each group is given one pin-board. Their task is to make as many different quadrilaterals as they can (that is, quadrilaterals that are not congruent to each other) using the lattice of nine pins. The children are given a set time in which to do the task. By monitoring the groups the teacher can ensure that each child knows what a quadrilateral is and has understood what is meant by congruence.

> It is important for all the children to explore the different quadrilaterals but it is not necessary to wait for them to find all sixteen.

When the children have found a number of different quadrilaterals the teacher gets each group to make one of their shapes on her pin-board. Each time they discuss whether it is different from the others. Any of the sixteen possible quadrilaterals missed by the pupils is added to the set by the teacher.

> Four of the quadrilaterals are concave. This will need discussing.

Children should not be left to struggle.

The exercise is not a test.

All too often children are left to struggle on their own with this exploratory exercise. Children can acquire an acute sense of failure if they think that they are expected to find all the different quadrilaterals on their own and are unable to do so. The purpose of this exercise is not to test each child to see if they can discover each quadrilateral for themselves but to give them an opportunity to make a quadrilateral and inspect it to see if it is congruent to those found already. This reinforces and consolidates their knowledge of names and properties.

Developing further knowledge and understanding

The set of quadrilaterals can now be used to develop further knowledge and understanding. They can be used to revise the names of specific quadrilaterals and the grid can be used to work out the area of each shape. The children are asked to copy each shape on to paper in the order specified. This in itself is no mean feat. It may be necessary to provide the set of shapes already drawn for the pupils. The teacher has to decide how much assistance is required for this task.

Working like detectives

Once the children have a complete set of quadrilaterals they pursue their detective work.

Let us inspect this first quadrilateral. It has two right angles [point] *and a pair of parallel edges* [point]. [Invite a pupil to come and select the appropriate name from a set of cards.]

The teacher assists the inspection.

The teacher invites a child to come to the front and inspect the next quadrilateral, a parallelogram. Together they point to certain features of the quadrilateral and with the assistance of the class they describe the properties of the quadrilateral and select the appropriate name.

This is a quadrilateral. It is flat. It is closed. It has four straight edges. This edge and this edge are parallel and equal in length [point together]. *This edge and this edge are parallel and equal in length* [point together]. *The shape is a ...* [scratch head, look puzzled, take out cards one by one and select 'parallelogram'].

Practice in speaking and spelling

Each shape is named in turn and the children write the name under the appropriate shape on their sheet. This gives practice in spelling the words and speaking the names. Some of the shapes may have more than one possible name. For example, a square is also a rhombus, a rectangle, a parallelogram and a trapezium, but the maximum information about the shape is given in the name 'square'. It would be wrong to imply that any of the names are equally acceptable because mathematicians would select the word that conveys the maximum information and in this case that word is 'square'.

Maximizing opportunities for learning

There is an opportunity here to discuss whether every type of quadrilateral is represented on the grid. For example, the only type of rhombus that can be made is a square. Why is that? How does a square lattice restrict the shape? Inspect the angles. Inspect the lines. Then the area of each quadrilateral can be calculated by looking at its constituent squares and rectangles. Opportunities for further exploration are endless.

Children are frequently allowed to spend all their time on this activity finding the different shapes. The richness of the activity lies in the discussion that follows.

Lesson plan

This lesson for Year 4 pupils teaches classification of 2D shapes. It is part of the third topic in a sequence taken from the following scheme of work.

First the teacher designs a scheme of work.

1. Learning the names of shapes
2. Learning the properties of shapes
3. Identifying shapes from their properties
4. Making triangles on a square lattice
5. Making quadrilaterals on a square lattice
6. Calculating areas and perimeters of shapes
7. Generating shapes on a computer

The scheme of work is designed to enable the children to develop spatial awareness alongside the special language of maths.

Previous work

Starting with what the children know

The children have learnt the names and properties of 2D and 3D shapes and had some practice in identifying shapes from their properties.

Lesson design

Attracting children's interest

Young children love to work like detectives. This lesson is based on the script where children are asked to feel shapes in a bag and describe them to the class without using the name of the shape.

The children are set a homework in preparation for this lesson. Since the class is familiar with shapes and their properties the homework is revision. The children are given three sets of clues consisting of a description of the properties of shapes and asked to identify the shapes by name. The shapes used are a triangle, a parallelogram and an octagon.

Children present their solutions to the class.

Being well prepared

The lesson begins with the teacher inviting children to present their solutions to the homework. They are asked to describe and explain how they reached their solution. The teacher monitors the class to ensure that every child is able to do this work. She has prepared some additional examples in case she needs to demonstrate the process of identification again but normally the demonstration phase of the subsequent episode is sufficient for this purpose.

The teacher has to assist the children with their use of language and the social skills to speak in front of the class.

Preparing resources to suit the class

The teacher's resource table, prepared in advance, contains an assortment of 2D and 3D shapes, including open and closed shapes. Two sets of cards are prepared: one contains the words needed to describe shapes, such as angle, edge, straight, and the other gives the names of shapes. The shapes to be used are hidden from the children's view.

Individual children are invited to come to the front and feel shapes in the bag. They are asked to describe them using geometrical words but without giving the name. This is the demonstration phase. It is followed

Ensuring correct use of
language

Setting homework

by the modelling phase in which groups work with sets of identical
shapes. The teacher checks that the children are using the correct
geometrical language.

In the summarizing phase children are invited to come to the front to
present their group's solutions. They are asked to draw each shape,
describe it and identify it by name. For homework the children are
given sets of clues and the teacher demonstrates, with the help of the
class, how to identify the first shape.

Assisting performance
by assisting with the
language of maths

The structure and timing of the lesson

| Class | Y4 | Teacher | Miss Brown |
| Date | 5 May | Student | Jon Redway |

Lesson description	Lesson 3: Identifying 2D shapes from their properties
Learning outcomes	Discuss shapes in terms of line and angle properties. Use the correct mathematical terms to describe shapes. Use the correct names for 2D shapes. Identify shapes from their properties.
Resources	• Homework sheet • Bag for feeling shapes; selection of shapes to identify • Resource table containing various shapes • Word cards • Identical sets of shapes in bags for each group • Grid for results

Classroom framework	Time	Teacher and pupils
Summarizing ◆	5 min.	Invite children to present answers to the homework sheet. Check that all the children have understood. Ensure all pupils are facing the front and can see the board.
Demonstration ◆	20 min.	Explain to the children that the lesson is about naming geometrical shapes from their properties. Tell them that they are going to use clues and work like detectives. Invite pupils to come to the front and feel the shapes in the bag one at a time and describe them. Assist use of correct geometrical words by pointing to word cards on the board and saying the words where necessary. Invite other pupils to identify shapes on the resource table to match the description. Assist the class in naming the shapes from their descriptions.
Modelling ✵	20 min.	Arrange the class in groups and give each group a bag of shapes. Explain what the children have to do. *The shapes are numbered. Take it in turns to feel the shapes, describe them and get the rest of the group to identify them. Draw each shape in your book, describe it and name it.*
Summarizing ◆	10 min.	Bring the class back together. Ensure that all the children face the front. Get each group to describe and identify one of the shapes. Ask the children to check their answers and correct them if necessary.
Demonstration ◆	5 min.	Give out homework sheet in which clues have to be solved to identify shapes. Use the first question to demonstrate what has to be done. Explain that these questions will be summarized in the next lesson. Record the children's progress.

Practice

Practice in using the language of maths

Associating shapes with their names

Working like detectives

Children write their own descriptions.

All polygons can be dissected into triangles.

Challenging the children's thinking

Finding triangles on a pin-board

Children need plenty of practice in classifying shapes and using the language of geometry. In the modelling phase children can work in groups describing shapes and giving reasons for their choice of words, first working with real shapes and later working in the imagination.

The language of maths is often neglected in classrooms.

Following a demonstration the children can be given a set of 2D shapes and a set of cards with words that they can use to describe the shapes. These words can include: straight; edge; face; parallel; equal; angle; right angle; obtuse angle; acute angle; regular; irregular, and so on. The children take turns to select a shape, describe it using the word cards and finally to name it. Every type of assistance is available for this first practice. The children can touch the shapes, use given words and obtain help from their peers and the teacher.

In the next practice session the children can be given written descriptions of shapes. They have to inspect the words carefully, use their imagination to picture the shape and then find the shape that fits the description. They are beginning to work like detectives.

Learning to do comprehension in maths improves literacy skills.

The children can then write their own descriptions of shapes and ask other members of the group to picture them in their imagination and to find them from a set of shapes. This is more challenging because they have to consider very carefully what to write in their description. They have to think about how to describe the shapes using the minimum number of statements, yet providing sufficient information.

Similar work can be done with 3D shapes. The children will be using much of the language associated with 2D shapes in doing this work. It is for this reason that they need to become fluent in that language and confident in the knowledge of properties of 2D shapes.

All polygons can be dissected into triangles. The triangle is often used to calculate areas of more complex shapes. The right-angled triangle is used to find height, length and angles using Pythagoras' theorem and trigonometry. Children need lots of practice in working with triangles so that they are familiar with their properties and confident in identifying different types. The pin-board activity provides practice and challenges the children's thinking.

The work we do with young children should provide a platform for later work.

Following a demonstration similar to that used to identify quadrilaterals on a pin-board (see script 3 above), give each child a pin-board and a set of elastic bands. Ask the children to find as many different triangles as possible using just nine pins set out in a three-by-three square. It is crucial that the children have understood the meaning of 'different' through the demonstration activity before embarking on this investigation. Each triangle is recorded on paper with a grid of dotted squares. The children can work in pairs, helping each other to find the eight different triangles.

This pin-board activity is not easy; some of the triangles are very difficult to find. If children are left to flounder on this task they are likely to lose heart and give up. The teacher can provide assistance during the activity but the children should not be put under pressure to find all eight triangles. When the teacher judges that the children have all spent sufficient time searching for different triangles she needs to bring the class back together and select children to come to the front to present their solutions and name the triangles.

Homework

Children in Year 4 can be expected to do 15–20 minutes of maths homework twice a week. The homework can be practice of the previous lesson's work but it is even more useful if it is preparation for the next lesson. Where the children have been describing shapes and looking at properties of shapes in the lesson they will have developed the vocabulary and language needed to describe shapes. They will have written this vocabulary in their books but they should not be expected to remember all these words. For this homework a list of the words should be provided again.

> Homework provides the opportunity to practise the language of maths.

Give each child a sealed envelope containing cut-out shapes with their geometrical names written on them, like this:

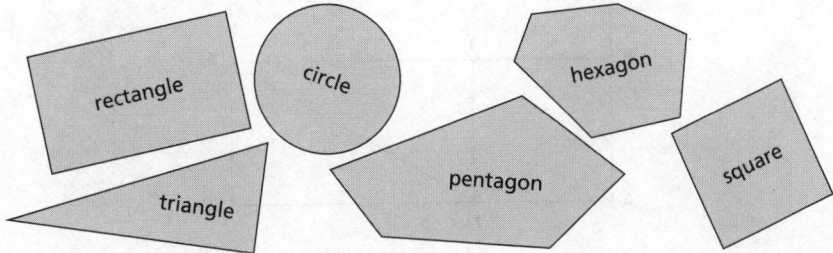

Provide instructions and a set of words for the children to use. Ask the children to write a description of each of the shapes without using their geometrical names. In the next lesson the children can work in pairs with one reading their description and their partner trying to identify the shapes from a set of shapes. The children can practise this with a member of their family in preparation for the lesson. This work also improves the children's literacy skills. Not only are they writing descriptions using given words but in the subsequent lesson they are learning how to listen, comprehend and identify something from information given.

> When we are asked not to use the mathematical name for a shape we realize how powerful its name is.

Following the pin-board activities, the children can be given a set of triangles drawn on grids and asked to identify those that are identical – that is, triangles that are congruent.

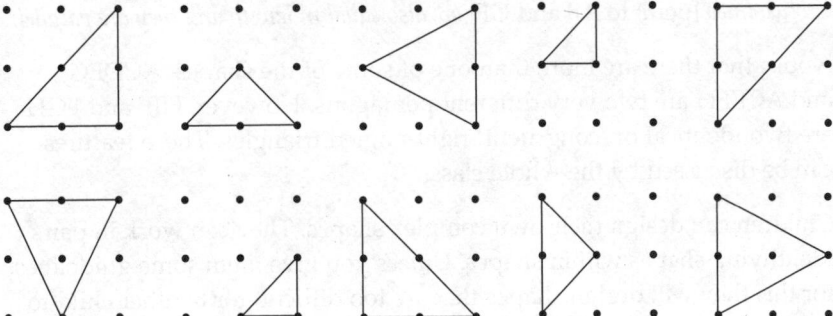

In the following lesson they will be asked to present their solutions and to explain why any two triangles are congruent. They can be given a set of phrases to use in these explanations such as 'all the edges are equal', 'all the angles are equal', 'these two angles are both right angles' and so on.

> It is the discussion following the activity that maximizes the learning opportunities.

The same set of triangles can be used for practice in naming triangles, using the names 'scalene', 'isosceles' and 'equilateral' according to edge-length properties, or the names 'right-angled', 'obtuse-angled' and 'acute-angled' according to their angle properties.

Using and applying maths

When the children have practised identifying shapes and have learnt the language associated with shape they can apply this knowledge to problems. For example, you can draw a complex shape like the one below and ask the children to identify shapes within it.

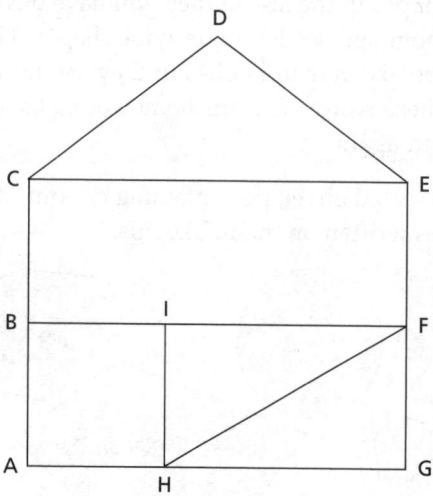

The points on the diagram are labelled to enable the children to name the shapes. Ask the children to inspect the diagram and find the following shapes:

square; rectangle; trapezium; right-angled triangle; isosceles triangle; hexagon; pentagon.

When the children have worked on this on their own invite some of them to come to the front and trace around the shapes they have found. As they trace the shape assist them to speak the letters and describe the properties of the shape. For example:

AB [trace edge AB], *BF* [trace], *FG* [trace], *GA* [trace]; *ABFG is a rectangle. It has four right angles, Here, here, here and here* [point]. *These two lines* [point to AG and BF] *are equal in length and they are parallel. These two lines* [point to AB and GF] *are also equal in length and they are parallel.*

Notice that there are more than one of some of the shapes. ACDEG and ACEFH are two very different pentagons. However, HIF and FGH are two identical or 'congruent' right-angled triangles. These features can be discussed by the whole class.

Children can design their own complex shapes. They can work in pairs identifying shapes within shapes. Unless you give them some guidelines for this they will design shapes that are too difficult for another child to work on. First you can ask them to design a shape containing a square, a rectangle and a triangle. They can then see whether in doing this they have created any other shapes. Insist that they label with letters any points where the lines meet so that shapes can be named.

You can repeat this activity with patterns and designs that occur in everyday life. You may have patterns on wall displays or markings on the playground or sports field. Children can look for patterns in books. You may find opportunities to refer to this work when doing other curriculum subjects.

Using information technology

Using LOGO

Children can apply their knowledge to create shapes using LOGO. In this discussion we use a particular version of LOGO produced by Logotron. You can adapt the ideas here to any version of LOGO that you have available.

Display a previously prepared wall chart showing the following:

REPEAT~4~[FD~100~RT~90] <return>

The character '~' is used here to represent typing a space.

This is typed into the computer by the teacher who simply says aloud: *R; E; P; E; A; T; space; four; space; square bracket; F; D; space; one; zero; zero; space; R; T; space; nine; zero; square bracket; press the return key;* at which point the class see the result of this, namely, that the computer draws a square. Individual or group use of the computer in the modelling phase is devoted simply to ensuring that each child can type in accurately, from memory, the LOGO instructions for drawing a square.

Demonstrating programs

Copying the instructions gives immediate success thus assisting motivation.

This insistence on memorizing the instructions is important. In all language learning, complex language forms are used before their structure is understood. The exposure to complex language is in many cases available in everyday speech, but this is not generally true for the language of mathematics. The LOGO instruction above is very important not only because it defines a square but because its structure invites exploration of other shapes.

Memorizing instructions

When all the children can type the instruction accurately they know it sufficiently well to begin to explore it by careful modification. What this requires from the teacher is some demonstration that certain aspects can usefully be modified and some cannot.

Modifying instructions

If I type: REPET~4~ [FD~100~RT~90] <return>, *what happens?* [The machine gives an error message.] *Why did that happen? Yes. I spelt REPEAT wrongly. What do you think would happen if I spelt it RPEAT?* [Demonstrate.] *And what if I put in FT instead of FD?* [Show in each case that an error message is given.] *And what is wrong with this?* REPEAT~4~ [FD100~RT~90] <return> [When the error message is given encourage close inspection to note that a space is missing.]

We do not wait for the children to make mistakes. We demonstrate to the whole class what happens when mistakes are made.

Inspecting for errors

The teacher then types in: REPEAT~4~[FD~150~RT~90] <return> The computer now draws a larger square and the class inspects the instruction to identify what has prompted this change. More changes are made to the instructions and changes noted.

Investigating changes

If we look at the instructions again, what other change could we make? I will try this: REPEAT~3~ [FD~100~RT~90] <return> [This draws three sides of the original square.]

This session should also include discussion of the instruction to establish that the numbers can be changed but the words must remain intact. It should also be noted that one number specifies how many operations are to be done, another number defines the length of the line drawn, and the third number specifies the angle turned.

Individual or group use of the computer in subsequent modelling phases can be devoted to an exploration of how to draw regular shapes with any number of sides. Using LOGO in addition to other investigations of shape allows formal ideas about angle to be developed as a continuation of this work.

Having established a common knowledge base, you can ask the children to create their own shapes.

Tests

There are many new geometrical words for children to learn. These words should be included in your regular spelling tests. Words such as square, isosceles and parallelogram are often misspelt.

You can test the children's knowledge of properties of shapes in the following way:

- Make sets of shape cards for all the children (include regular and irregular shapes and label each card).

- Give each child a set of cards to be put face up on the table in front of them.

- Read out the description of a shape.

- Use a prearranged signal as a cue for the children to hold up the shape you have described. (Allow sufficient time for all the children to respond.)

- Repeat with other descriptions.

> You must ensure that the children are not embarrassed if they hold up the wrong card.

Working in this way you can monitor how well the children are doing and allow every child to participate. The children are developing listening and comprehension skills when they do tasks such as this.

Another test on shape can be answered in the form of a two-way grid. Give the children a set of descriptions and ask them to tick the appropriate box. For example, you could give them these descriptions:

(a) The shape is flat. It has six edges. The edges are all equal.

(b) The shape is solid. It has six faces. All the faces are squares.

(c) The shape is solid. It has four faces. All the faces are triangles.

> This work encourages the children to read carefully and inspect the text for clues.

Properties	a	b	c
2-D	✓		
3-D		✓	✓
triangle			
square			
rectangle			
regular	✓		
pentagon			
hexagon	✓		
octagon			
cube		✓	
cuboid			
pyramid			✓
prism			

The shapes used and the level of difficulty of the test will be dependent on the aims of the teacher.

A more formal test may include the requirement to match written definitions of shapes with the geometrical names of those shapes. Whatever form the test takes, children must be sufficiently well prepared to be successful. Tests should be used to confirm what children know rather than prove what they do not know.

Properties of shapes: discussion

Language

Our everyday language is extremely rich. It provides us with the means to communicate, to convey meaning. As we listen to someone talking we hear the words and interpret them according to what we know; we experience mental images and 'see' pictures in our minds.

Suppose a friend is telling us about an event that occurred and she begins, 'Yesterday I went to visit the bank manager'. Now, we know about banks because they are a part of our culture. We read about them in the papers and hear about them on the news. Our salary is paid into our bank account and often when we buy things we use cheques or cards that the bank supplies. Sometimes we borrow money from a bank and at other times we save money in the bank. We know something about bank managers and the job they do and we have an idea what they look like because we have met some ourselves. Our friend does not have to explain these things because she knows that we will understand. We have learnt about them through everyday life. They are everyday concepts.

Two children are walking in the school playground when one of them says, 'Last night we played football for the cub team'. His friend immediately knows what he is talking about. Football is a game that is well known by most children. They see it on television; they play it at school; they talk about their favourite teams and players; they read about it in books. It does not need to be explained for the child's friend to make sense of the story that is about to be told. The 'cub team' provides a visual image of children playing for a club. In this club the children wear uniforms and meet every week for games and activities. The words used belong to the culture and are learnt through everyday life. They are everyday concepts.

The teacher tells the children to draw a parallelogram. They sit and look at her. One child puts up his hand and asks, 'What is a parallelogram?' The word 'parallelogram' is not likely to be an everyday concept. Children do not normally talk about parallelograms in the playground or at home. They do not hear them talked about on television or read stories about them in books. The idea of a parallelogram requires specific teaching. It is a schooled concept that needs to be taught. Though it is part of our culture, it belongs to that deliberately taught part of our culture, a knowledge of which schools are designed to teach. We need to meet these words frequently in order to become familiar with them and comfortable with their pronunciation, but this in itself is not sufficient for a full understanding of them.

Suppose we ask you to draw a parallelogram. What would you draw? Would it look like this?

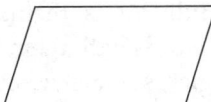

Or would you draw a square or a rectangle or a rhombus? It is highly likely that you would have drawn a shape like the one in the diagram because this represents any general parallelogram. If you drew a square, rectangle or rhombus you would not be wrong. These are parallelograms, but each is a special case of a parallelogram.

Language conveys meaning.

Everyday concepts

Words that belong to our culture

Schooled concepts

> With everyday concepts we construct images from our own experience. With schooled concepts teachers have to ensure that appropriate experience is provided in the classroom.

> Mathematical words provoke mental images. Sometimes these images are restricted to particular cases.

This reminds us of the bank manager. If we had met only one bank manager (and had not received any specific teaching about the idea of bank managers) we might think that all bank managers were men. We might expect bank managers to be tall and thin and to wear grey suits. Not until we went into our bank one day and met the new bank manager who was a woman wearing a red dress would we realize that our image was not quite right. As teachers we cannot leave things to be learnt by chance: we have to provide sufficient examples to allow children to build up visual images that encompass all possibilities.

Schooled concepts need specific teaching.

An activity to teach shape names

When we ask children to draw a parallelogram we want them to know what the shape looks like and to know the shape's properties. We also want them to know the various representations to choose from. We have to be careful not to represent a shape in only one way. It would be misleading, for instance, if we always drew squares on the board with one edge horizontal. The following activity is designed to reinforce a knowledge of the properties of shapes and to help children use mathematical language to describe and explain.

Learning a shape's name and its properties

The teacher must ensure that the children are offered the full range of possible images.

The learning outcomes of this activity are:

Learning outcomes

- to know and use the word 'parallelogram'
- to recognize and use the properties of parallelograms
- to have a visual image that can be used flexibly
- to speak the language of maths

Steps in the activity

1. Prepare a set of parallelograms (cut from card) to include rectangles, squares and rhombuses.

2. Write on the board: 'A parallelogram is a quadrilateral with two pairs of equal and parallel edges.'

Visual images to provoke mental images

The approach here is consistent with methods used in number work.

3. Give each child in the class one of the cut-out parallelograms and as you do so say: *This is a parallelogram.*

4. Write a set of words on the board, such as 'square', 'rectangle', 'rhombus', 'equal lengths', 'right angles', 'symmetrical' and so on.

5. Ask each child to draw their parallelogram in their book and to write a description of it, starting with 'This is a parallelogram. It has two pairs of equal and parallel edges' and continuing with appropriate words from those written on the board. This work is preparation for the demonstration phase and is giving the children some time to think and to draw on prior knowledge.

Using technical language

6. Select individual children to come to the front, show their shape to the class and describe it fully. Assist them. Ensure that they are successful by speaking the words with them if necessary. Encourage them to describe edges, angles, symmetry, and what the shape is not. This is the demonstration phase.

Ensuring success

7. Set the whole class the task of describing a set of parallelograms in their own books. This is the modelling phase.

8. Select individual children to present their answers. This is the summarizing phase.

Two-dimensional shapes

All real-life objects are three dimensional. They can be seen and touched. They always have thickness, no matter how small that may be. When we show a shape cut from card and say *This is a rectangle* we are actually using a three-dimensional shape (it is a rectangular prism) and effectively asking children to imagine the shape of the front face. We are asking them to look at a real object (a rectangular prism) and to work in their imagination by abstracting from it the 'rectangle-ness' of its front face. For this reason, any discussion of two-dimensional shapes is immediately mathematical. It involves working in the mind and dealing with abstract ideas. This is the nature of maths. It involves going beyond the real world.

If we want to talk to you about these two-dimensional shapes we need to have some words to describe them. These words must instantly conjure up a visual image for you. Look first at some words that describe the most general properties. Two-dimensional shapes can be composed of curved or straight edges and can be open or closed.

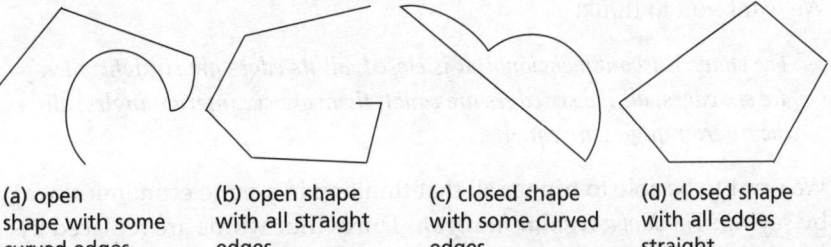

(a) open shape with some curved edges

(b) open shape with all straight edges

(c) closed shape with some curved edges

(d) closed shape with all edges straight

The two-dimensional shapes that we study most in maths are the polygons. These are closed shapes with all edges straight. When we see one of these shapes and say 'There is a polygon' we are giving its most general description. We are conveying the information:

> *The shape is two-dimensional; it is closed; all its edges are straight.*

With any particular polygon we can be more specific. We can say how many edges it has. We might say:

> *The shape is two-dimensional; it is closed; all its edges are straight; there are three edges.*

When we draw a shape that conforms to that definition (it is, of course, a triangle) we notice something that is quite remarkable. It does not matter how long we draw the edges (it still conforms to the requirements) or which way up we draw it, it always turns out to have three interior angles. Try as we might to change this, whenever we provide our shape with three straight edges, we are automatically ensuring it has three interior angles. This means that when we replace our description: *The shape is two-dimensional; it is closed; all its edges are straight; there are three edges* with *It is a triangle* we are automatically saying:

> *The shape is two-dimensional; it is closed; all its edges are straight; there are three edges; there are three interior angles.*

This is the nature of mathematical language. It carries a great deal of information that needs decoding by the listener. The special names for the polygons do just that. They invite decoding. People learning maths need assistance in how to undertake the decoding.

Margin notes (left):
- Two-dimensional shapes are imaginary.
- The nature of maths
- Using technical language
- Polygons
- The technical language of maths is economical.
- Technical words need decoding.

Margin notes (right):
- Working in two dimensions is working in the imagination.
- The language of maths provides a powerful means of communication.
- Decoding mathematical words can assist literacy skills.

There is not a special name for every polygon that it is possible to imagine. Those names used most often are listed below.

The most common polygons

3 straight edges – triangle
4 straight edges – quadrilateral
5 straight edges – pentagon
6 straight edges – hexagon
7 straight edges – heptagon
8 straight edges – octagon
9 straight edges – nonagon
10 straight edges – decagon

You can imagine each of these special shapes. You can also imagine them having some other special features. Think of a hexagon, for instance. Remember that we are asking you to think:

The shape is two-dimensional; it is closed; all its edges are straight; there are six edges; there are six interior angles.

Now we are asking you to add some extra items to your thinking. We want you to think:

The shape is two-dimensional; it is closed; all its edges are straight; there are six edges; all the six edges are equal; there are six interior angles; all the interior angles are equal.

We want to be able to trigger all that thinking in a more economical way by saying: *Think of a **regular hexagon**.* Thirty-four words are replaced by two. All that information can be conveyed in just two words.

> We must remember not to represent a shape as regular unless we are specifically told that it is so.

Triangles

When we classify triangles we often focus on the relationship between lengths of edges. A triangle with each edge of a different length is called a 'scalene triangle'. When two edges are equal the triangle is called 'isosceles'. With three edges equal (a regular triangle) it is called 'equilateral'.

> Although these names are based on line properties they also convey angle properties. The isosceles triangle has two equal angles and the equilateral triangle has all angles equal to 60°.

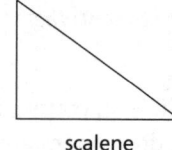
scalene

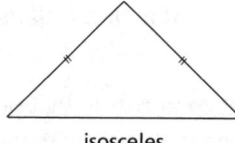
isosceles

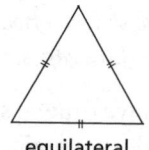
equilateral

We can also classify triangles with respect to their angle properties. If one angle is a right angle then it is a 'right-angled triangle'. It is possible to have only one right angle in a triangle because otherwise the sum of the interior angles would be greater than 180°. If one angle is obtuse it is called an 'obtuse-angled triangle' (and there can only be one obtuse angle in a triangle). It follows that any other type of triangle must have all of its angles acute and it is therefore called an 'acute-angled triangle'.

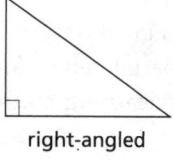
right-angled

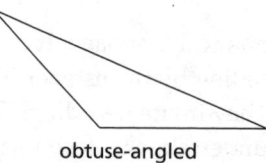
obtuse-angled

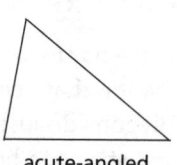
acute-angled

Side notes:
- The most common polygons
- Provoking mental images
- The technical language of maths is efficient.
- Names of shapes convey properties.
- There is more than one way of naming triangles.

Classifying
quadrilaterals

Quadrilaterals

Classifying quadrilaterals is more complicated. One classification refers to the properties of the edges.

- *If we find a pair of parallel edges then the quadrilateral is called a trapezium.*

- *If we find two pairs of equal and parallel edges then the quadrilateral is called a parallelogram.*

- *If the four edges of a parallelogram are equal to each other it is called a rhombus.*

- *If a parallelogram has four right angles then it is called a rectangle.*

- *If a parallelogram has four right angles and four equal edges then it is called a square.*

As you read through this list of properties from the beginning you can see that they become more and more specific. However, if we have inspected a shape and identified that it is a square then it also satisfies the conditions to be called a rectangle, a rhombus, a parallelogram and a trapezium. A square is just a special case of each of these. When we recognize that a shape is a square (because it satisfies the appropriate conditions) it does not prevent it from being a rectangle. It is at the same time a rectangle and a square. The conditions for being a rectangle are weaker than the conditions for being a square. This means that if a shape satisfies the strong conditions for 'square-ness' then it will always satisfy the conditions for 'rectangle-ness'.

We have now named almost all of the quadrilaterals. One last shape that we often see is the kite. This is sometimes called a 'diamond' shape although, of course, none of us would be happy at receiving a two-dimensional diamond! A kite has two pairs of adjacent edges equal. It can be thought of as two isosceles triangles joined together.

Classifying
quadrilaterals

A square is a special
case of a quadrilateral.

These words will rarely
be spoken outside the
classroom so you need
to mention them
frequently.

Concave quadrilaterals
have not been
assigned special
names although we
do sometimes use
colloquial words such
as 'arrow head'.

Identifying quadrilaterals from the properties of their diagonals

We have discussed how quadrilaterals can be classified by focusing on the properties of the edges. We can also classify quadrilaterals using the properties of their diagonals. This can be used as an interesting classroom activity. We will describe how this can be used in the classroom because this simple and elegant classification is often neglected.

Properties of
diagonals can define
quadrilaterals.

Start by drawing two lines crossing.

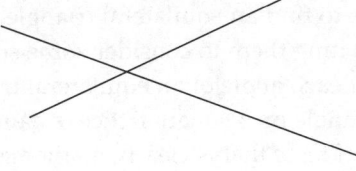

You could use two
sticks of different
length.

One diagonal is
longer than the other.

Draw straight lines joining the ends of these two lines.

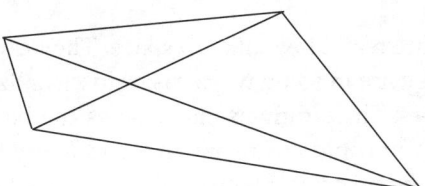

Learning outcomes

The learning outcomes of this activity are:

- to know what quadrilaterals are produced when the lengths and crossing angles of two straight lines are varied
- to know the properties of diagonals of quadrilaterals

Steps in the activity

1. Demonstrate drawing a quadrilateral by joining the ends of two lines as in the diagram above.
2. Ask a child to come to the board and draw another quadrilateral using lines of a different length and crossing at a different angle. Assist the child to do this successfully.
3. Get the class to do the same activity. This is the modelling phase. Ask them to vary the lengths and angles so that they draw all the different quadrilaterals in their books.
4. Summarize by getting children to present their answers and discuss the properties of the diagonals for each quadrilateral.

Use a board ruler to draw straight lines.

Assisting performance by helping children to achieve success

The fascinating part of this activity is the fact that defining the diagonals also defines the quadrilateral. For example, when the two diagonals are equal in length, cross at right angles and bisect each other the quadrilateral produced must be a square. When the two diagonals are different in length, cross at right angles and bisect each other we have a rhombus that is not a square. The discussion you have with the children in the summarizing phase will be rich with mathematical language. It will encourage children to describe and explain their work.

Information sufficient to define a square

Information sufficient to define a rhombus

Test markers regularly criticize children for not being able to describe and explain their maths.

More classroom activities on classification

The scripts provide more activities on classification. The activity of describing shapes that are felt but not seen requires children to work like detectives. They have to make full use of mathematical language to create a visual image. This shows how maths can become an exciting and fascinating subject.

Working like detectives

The pin-board activity can be used to find all the possible triangles on a three-by-three lattice. Children are asked to find all the triangles that are 'different'. What do we mean by 'different' in this context? In this case we are looking for triangles that are not identical, that are not congruent. The pin-board can be turned around and examined from different perspectives and this helps the children to check those triangles that are identical.

Defining 'different'

You will see that it is not possible to find an equilateral triangle. If you ask children why not, you are inviting them to consider some sort of proof which refers to the fact that each angle of an equilateral triangle is 60° and we cannot make a 60° angle on a square lattice. Again, why not? This proof involves a chain of logic that is clearly mathematical.

A mathematical chain of logic

A common error is to suppose that the diagonal of a square is equal to its edges. It is in fact about 1.4 times as big.

Three-dimensional shapes

Three-dimensional shapes are real. They take up space. They can be handled. For this reason they are in some ways easier to visualize than two-dimensional shapes. Three-dimensional shapes can be very complex in their structure. You could create one that had many faces of a wide variety of shapes, some being plane (flat) and others being

Three dimensional shapes can be complex.

curved. But the most interesting are those shapes that have some sort of regularity. These are the ones that we study in school. The most common ones are shown below.

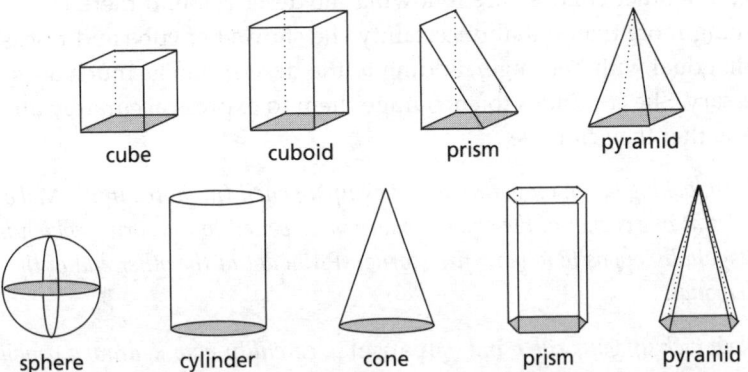

cube   cuboid   prism   pyramid

sphere   cylinder   cone   prism   pyramid

These names and their associated shapes need to be memorized.

Pyramids

Notice that the word 'pyramid' is a general name for a wide range of three-dimensional shapes with different shaped bases. We can do some mathematical work with pyramids. Think, for instance, of a pyramid on a hexagonal base, then of one on a base with, say, fifteen edges, and then several hundred edges, and more. You can imagine a pyramid on a base with so many edges that it becomes indistinguishable from a circle. Think of a pyramid on a circular base. You are thinking of a cone. A cone can be thought of as a pyramid on a base with an infinite number of edges.

A tetrahedron is a special pyramid with four faces, each an equilateral triangle.

Cones

Prisms

The word 'prism' is also a general name that summarizes a wide range of shapes. The only requirement for a prism is that it has two opposite faces which are congruent and parallel, with corresponding edges connected by parallelograms. If the ends are rectangles, the prism is known as a cuboid (and under certain conditions it could be a cube). When the ends are hexagons, we call it a hexagonal prism. Keep thinking of a prism but use the power of your mind gradually to increase the numbers of edges on its ends. Increase the number to infinity. Your prism is now a cylinder.

Cylinders

Working in the mind

School children need to be encouraged to work in the mind (they need to think mathematically). We can illustrate the type of work that can be done to promote this by looking at three-dimensional shapes. The following example shows a teacher working with her class. There is no apparatus on the children's tables. They touch nothing during the whole exercise. The teacher has prepared three-dimensional shapes which she keeps concealed and reveals only for short periods (sometimes just a few seconds) to assist children to visualize them.

Activities such as this improve children's spatial awareness.

Creating mental images

Draw a cube in your mind. Place it on the table. Stand up and look down on that cube from above. Take a bird's-eye view. Tell me what you can see.

The children probably answer by saying 'a square', although they may need to be shown a cube to see what they must picture in their mind. There will also be a labelled picture of a square on the wall so that it can be referred to if any child seems uncertain.

*Yes. It is a square. That is its name. But tell me what you can **see**.*

Using technical language

The teacher elicits, giving as much assistance as necessary, that they can see a plane shape with four straight edges; all the edges are the same length; all the angles are 90° (the corners are square). The teacher knows that previous work will enable the children to see two diagonals of the same length cutting each other in half, crossing at right angles. One child begins to describe this. The teacher monitors the extent to which the other children are following the description. If there is anything more than initial uncertainty she shows her cube and traces the diagonal with her finger, adding to the description as much as is necessary. She continues to encourage them to express accurately all aspects that they can 'see'.

Working in the imagination

> *Keep looking down on your cube. Pick up a pencil (in your mind). Make a dot at one corner of the square. Move your pencil to the corner which is diagonally opposite to your first corner. Put a dot at the other end of the diagonal.*

> *Now pick up your ruler and ... [pause] ... carefully now ... draw a pencil line to join your two dots. That's right. Draw a diagonal across that square.*

> The children have to concentrate and work hard at interpreting the words.

Visual images to create mental images

At this point the teacher shows her cube and traces the diagonal that they have just 'drawn'.

> *Place your cube on the table. Pick up a saw. Yes. You are going to cut the cube into two parts. Use the saw very carefully. Place it on the diagonal you have just drawn. Keep the saw vertical. Keep it upright. Now ... slowly ... saw down your cube. Good. Put the saw in a safe place. You have cut your cube into two parts.*

The teacher shows a prepared model of the two separated parts. But she leaves it in view for no longer than one second. The children must work from their mental image, but the teacher needs to ensure that they are confident of the picture they have in their minds.

> Assisting performance by ensuring success

Providing assistance

> *Pick up one part ... no, not both of them, just one. Look at it carefully. Tell me what you can **see**. I don't want its name. I want you to tell me what you can **see**.*

Each face is visualized.

The teacher goes on to elicit very detailed descriptions of the three-dimensional shape. It is of no interest at the moment that it is a triangular prism. The important thing is to enable the children to inspect this imaginary object and become confident in visualizing its two squares (described in detail), its two right-angled triangles and its rectangle. The children are not allowed to say only 'I can see a rectangle' but have to talk about two opposite sides being the same length and the two other sides being longer than these (but the same length as each other).

> This activity gives practice in using the language associated with two-dimensional shapes.

Challenging children's perspectives

The teacher can challenge the children further by inviting them to imagine cutting the cube in different ways. For example, they could imagine marking two points on adjacent edges of the cube and slicing off a corner. What can they 'see'? They can imagine what happens as the distance from the vertex to the points varies and so on.

Mathematical exploration

This visualization is genuine mathematical exploration, and the struggle to express in words what is being 'seen' is also genuine mathematical exploration. The teacher conducting the lesson sensitively helps the children gradually to refine what they are saying about their mental image. This is geometry.

❺ Measurement and graphs

Introduction

Measurement

Suppose I want to describe an object. I may tell you its colour or its shape but to give you more detail I would need to give you some measurements. What measurements? Its length or width? Its area or volume? Its mass or capacity? Its angles or curves? How shall I measure all these statistics? What instruments or units of measure should I use? When I answer these questions am I doing maths? Let us look at what is mathematical about measurement.

> Measurements are used for the purpose of comparison.

Reading scales

Suppose you want to know the length of an object. You need some form of measuring instrument with a standard scale marked out on it. That scale will use the counting numbers to denote whole units of measure and fractions or decimals to denote parts of those units. When you read the numbers on the scale you are doing maths.

What level of accuracy do you need? Will you give the measurement to the nearest whole unit, half unit or tenth of a unit? In making that decision you are doing maths. You may want to convert your measurement into another unit using a formula or graph, or you may want to use your measurement in a formula to calculate a different statistic. That is doing maths. When you read and manipulate the numbers associated with measurement you are doing maths.

What we need to teach.

What do we need to teach children in order that they can do this sort of maths? They need to be able to use measuring instruments and read the scales; to know the dimension they are working in and the formulae for calculating such things as area and volume; to know how to estimate measurements and give answers to an appropriate degree of accuracy. They need to know how to draw and interpret graphs. They need to know how to inspect a formula to see what dimension they are working in. All these things need careful and deliberate teaching.

> Measurement is never exact. Children need to be taught the skills to obtain the best results.

You cannot give a child a ruler, say, and expect her to know how to use it. Not all rulers are the same. They come in different lengths and are made from different materials. Some are transparent and some are not. On some the scale starts at the end whilst on others it is indented. The way you position your eye to read the scale makes a difference to the reading. Using a protractor can be even more confusing. Some are circles and others are semi-circles. Some use a rotating arm or inner circle. Scales are marked clockwise and anti-clockwise. Skills in using such measuring instruments need to be taught through demonstration.

Measuring skills need to be demonstrated.

Development in teaching measurement and graphs

Young children must be taught to use measuring instruments accurately. This is an important skill that needs to be practised regularly. We have to be careful when making a list of what has to be taught not to assume that once something has been learnt that children will automatically be able to transfer it to different contexts. The scripts in this section show how the teacher demonstrates straightforward measuring skills to children in Years 5 or 6 as she introduces a new context for measuring.

Reading scales, and in particular interpreting the marks on scales, is crucially important for all measuring activities and for constructing and interpreting graphs, yet it is often neglected. Errors made by older children can often be traced back to poor foundations in this vital skill. The ability to read scales goes hand-in-hand with an ability to deal with fractions and decimals and to relate these to units of measure.

We have linked the teaching of measurement to that of graphs because the skills required for both overlap. The emphasis placed on bar and block graphs for discrete data in the primary phase can easily distort the view that children form of graph work. It is important to introduce continuous graphs and measurement is the perfect subject for this.

Teachers should enable children to:

- *describe positions, recognize movements and combine them in simple ways*
- *compare objects using standard units of measure*
- *choose and use appropriate standard units of measure, including those associated with angles*
- *choose and use appropriate measuring instruments*
- *read and interpret scales accurately*
- *estimate measurements*
- *use co-ordinates to specify location*
- *convert one metric unit to another*
- *find perimeters of shapes including the circumference of a circle*
- *find areas and volumes*
- *represent data using appropriate graphs*
- *interpret graphs*
- *use formulae to calculate area and volume of shapes*

Demonstrating how to measure in new contexts

Introducing continuous graphs

Developing an understanding of measurement and graphs

Unless we use skills on a regular basis we forget them. Teachers must demonstrate how to measure again and again.

A sound knowledge base of measuring and reading scales must be established before moving on to graph work.

Script 1: Measuring the circumference and diameter of a circle

Demonstrating how to measure circumference and diameter

This script shows how the whole class is taught to measure the circumference and diameter of the circular cross-section of a cylindrical tin. The teacher demonstrates how to get as accurate a measurement as possible. Measuring the diameter requires the children to put two rulers alongside the tin so that they are parallel to each other. Although this is rehearsed by the teacher it is important that the children have been taught the meaning of the term 'parallel' prior to this episode. A homework is set on parallel lines in preparation for this lesson and the teacher quickly goes through the answers before starting the lesson.

Demonstrating measuring skills to the whole class is an economical use of the teacher's time.

Revision of parallel lines

Once the class has agreed the measurements for a given set of tins the data is interrogated to look for relationships. It is not immediately obvious that the circumference is about three times the diameter and other observations should be received positively and discussed.

Display the poster throughout the lesson.

Resources
- Poster showing the labelled cross-section of a circle

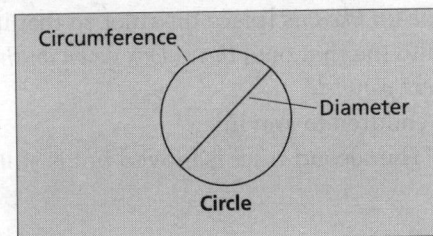

The poster should be on display throughout the teaching of this topic.

- OHP
- Small tin of shallow height (a tall tin will distort the image on the OHP)
- Two wooden rulers, one perspex ruler, one strip of acetate long enough to surround the tin
- Sufficient numbers of identical sets of tins, rulers and acetate for the class divided into groups of four children

Using tins

Learning technical terms

The teacher begins by demonstrating the method for measuring the circumference and diameter of the cross-section of a tin and ensures that the children know the terms 'diameter' and 'circumference'. The teacher shows the children the poster. It is important that the walls are not covered with other distracting posters or pictures so that the children can focus on this one poster. We frequently make use of posters in the teaching of maths and it is important that they can easily be identified and read by the children.

This is a circle [pointing to the poster] *and this* [tracing the circle] *is the* [pause; read silently, mouthing the word] *circumference of the circle. And this* [tracing the line] *is the* [pause; read silently, mouthing the word] *diameter of the circle.*

Assisting children to read

Assisting performance by assisting with the language of maths.

The teacher pauses to allow the children to read for themselves while assisting them by mouthing the words. The poster remains on the wall so that the children can refer to it throughout the lesson. The teacher then relates the diagram and words to the circular ends of a small tin.

This is a circle [pointing to the top and bottom of the tin] *and this*
[tracing the outer edge] *is* [point to the poster] *the circumference.
And this* [trace across the widest part and point again to the poster]
is its diameter. We are going to measure the circumference [tracing again]
and the diameter [tracing].

Measuring the diameter

The tin is placed on an overhead projector so that every child can see
it clearly. The teacher again refers to the circumference and diameter
whilst pointing to the tin's reflection. At first she demonstrates how to
measure the diameter. The two wooden rulers are placed alongside the
tin and the perspex ruler is used to measure. (The scale on the perspex
ruler will be visible on the OHP.)

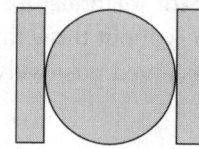

The image on the
overhead projector

If I take this ruler [take a wooden ruler] *and place it along the tin like
this and I take this ruler* [take the second wooden ruler] *and place it
along the other side of the tin like this* [place the ruler so that it is
obviously not parallel to the first one] *then I look down on them from
above, are these two rulers parallel?*
No [encourage all the children to join in].
Are they parallel now? [The second ruler is moved but is still not
parallel.]
No [all together].
Are they parallel now? [The second ruler is moved so that it looks
parallel.]
Mmm ... [pause and study the two rulers carefully] *yes, I think so.
They look parallel but we must check it out.*

Demonstrating how to
get the rulers parallel

> Alternatively the
> rulers can be placed
> alongside two identical
> tins to ensure that they
> are parallel.

The teacher has demonstrated the need to be very careful when
placing the rulers alongside the tin. As yet she has not explicitly made
the connection between placing the rulers in this way and measuring the
diameter. She will do that once she has established that the rulers are
parallel.

Demonstrating how to
measure

*I shall measure the distance between them. I shall measure here and here
and here.* [Choose three different places to measure and use the
perspex ruler to measure the distance between the wooden rulers,
adjusting the wooden rulers if necessary to ensure that all the
measurements are the same.] *This is 6.5cm and this is 6.5cm and this
is 6.5cm* [the measurement is given to the nearest millimetre]. *They
are all 6.5cm because the two rulers are parallel. The diameter* [trace an
imaginary line across the tin and point to the poster on the wall]
of the tin is 6.5cm. We write: d = 6.5cm. The diameter equals 6.5cm.

Relating the
measurement to the
diameter of a circle

> Measurements are
> taken to the nearest
> millimetre.

The teacher repeats this with a child helping and they check that the
measurement is the same. The act of making the rulers parallel is
exaggerated to emphasize the need to get as accurate a result as possible.

Measuring the circumference

I am going to measure the circumference of these circles [trace around
the ends and point to the poster]. *I am going to use this strip of acetate*

to measure around the tin like this. [Show children a strip of acetate and demonstrate wrapping it around the tin.] *I should like you to come and help me* [invite a child to come to the front]. *Now use this pen to mark the point where the end meets the strip.*

The strip is unwound and the child measures the distance from the end to the mark, using a perspex ruler on the overhead projector. Then the strip is wound around the tin again and the measurement checked.

The length of strip that just goes around the tin is 20.4cm [measured to the nearest millimetre]. *The circumference of the tin is 20.4cm. We write C = 20.4cm* [write on board]. *We say the circumference equals 20.4cm* [point to the equation while speaking].

Relating the measurement to the circumference of a circle

Teaching the technical language of maths

It is not immediately obvious to all children that the strip of acetate is measuring the length of the circumference.

Group work
The class is organized into groups and each group is given an identical set of five tins. In silence each pupil measures each of the tins and records the measurements on a given grid. The teacher monitors progress and assists children with their measuring. When most of the children have completed the task the groups are asked to discuss their measurements and to come to a group decision for each one then enter the results on a new grid.

Each child measures the same tins.

Results can only be compared if all the children measure the same set of tins.

Summarizing the work
We emphasize here the need to summarize the work done in the modelling phase of an episode of teaching. In this case the children have been modelling the measuring of the circumference and diameter of a set of tins. They have been working in groups with identical sets of tins. It is important to provide identical sets so that the summarizing phase is possible. Each group has agreed a set of measurements and these are now collected by the teacher.

Agreeing results

The teacher puts a grid on the board or the OHP with cells for each group's measurement and a column for her own measurements. She holds up the first tin and each group gives their result to the nearest millimetre. The results are inspected and compared. A child is invited to come to the front to demonstrate the group's result.

We measured the diameter like this [take the child and point to the word diameter on the poster]. *We put the two rulers either side of the tin until they were parallel and measured the distance between them. This is what we got* [point to the board]. *Then we measured the circumference like this* [point to the poster without prompting]. *We wound the acetate strip around the tin and put a mark where the end met the strip. Then we unwound the strip and measured the distance from the end to the mark. This is what we got* [point to the board].

Repeating the exercise together

The teacher and children repeat the measuring activity as reinforcement.

If there is a discrepancy in any measurements they are done again by the teacher. Each result is checked and compared with the teacher's measurement. The children are given a sheet with a complete set of correct measurements prepared by the teacher. The children are now going to inspect these results and comment upon them. For this reason they need to have the same figures in front of them. We are now moving seamlessly into another demonstration phase of teaching.

Working with the same set of results

		Tin					
	A	**B**	**C**	**D**	**E**	**F**	**G**
diameter (d) cm	6.5	7.5	8.5				
circumference (C) cm	20.4	23.6	26.7				

Interrogating the results

Inspecting results

Look at these measurements for the diameter of the circles and look at these measurements for the circumference. Inspect the numbers and comment on them.

The teacher listens to the children's responses and decides whether to accept or reject their statements. This is done sensitively and acceptable statements are recorded on the board.

'The circumference is always bigger than the diameter.' [Child's comment]

> *Let us look at this list. Is this* [pointing to a circumference measurement] *bigger than this* [pointing to its accompanying diameter measurement]*? Yes. And this* [pointing to two more]*? Yes. And this?* [Check all the results.] *Yes. In all our examples the circumference is bigger than the diameter.* [Write the statement on the board.]

> The teacher does not just accept the answer but demonstrates the thinking process to the whole class.

'If you add something to the diameter you add the same amount to the circumference.' [Child's comment]

Dealing with comments sensitively

> *Let us look at these two measurements: d = 7.5cm, C = 23.6cm and d = 8.5cm, C = 26.7cm. We have added one centimetre to the diameter. Have we added one centimetre to the circumference?* [Encourage all the children to answer.] *No. We have added 3.1cm to the circumference.*

'Yes, but if we add one more centimetre to the diameter, d = 9.5cm, C = 29.8cm, we again add 3.1cm to the circumference.' [Pupil again]

Improving statements

> *Can we make a clearer statement about that?*

> This discussion needs sensitive handling by the teacher.

'When the diameter goes up in equal steps the circumference goes up in bigger equal steps.' [Pupil]

> *Yes. That is better.* [Record the statement on the board.]

'The circumference is about three times the diameter.' [Child's comment]

Each statement is discussed. If the relationship of 'the circumference is three times the diameter' is not recognized the teacher will need to tease it out with appropriate questioning. The children then use their calculators to check this statement.

The value of the circumference found by multiplying the diameter by 3 is an approximation (it gives a result that is too low). A better approximation is obtained by multiplying by 3.1. This needs to be demonstrated by the teacher. An even better approximation is found by using 3.14 and again this will need demonstration.

Calculating circumference and diameter

Some examples are now worked through by the class to calculate the circumference or diameter of given circles. The children model this by completing a practice exercise which is then summarized by the whole class and marked and corrected by the children. A practice homework can be set to consolidate the work done in class.

> The children may need to be reminded how to do long multiplication.

Script 2: Interpreting graphs

Interrogating graphs

The work on the circumference and diameter provides excellent data for drawing and interpreting linear graphs. It is continuous data so the points on the graph can be joined and further information gleaned from the graph. Children can be invited to inspect points on the graph and use the information and their imagination to describe first of all the circles and then possible containers that could be represented by these points. This makes maths an enjoyable subject to study. The children can also use their imagination to 'inspect' points that go beyond the edges of the page and points with negative values. It is this unreal quality that makes maths so exciting.

> Working backwards is often neglected. It is this detective work that makes maths interesting.

Resources

- One large graph for display and normal size graphs for each pupil, representing the results of measuring the circumference and diameter of tins (see larger version on p.149)

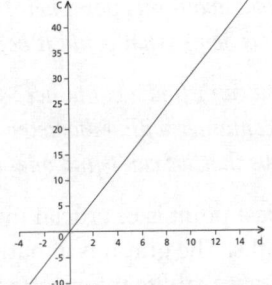

- The set of tins used in the measurement lesson and a selection of cylindrical objects

Inspecting the graph

Identifying points on the graph

The graph here is produced by the teacher so that everyone is working from an identical graph. Initially children are selected to come to the front and on the large graph to identify the relevant tins from the set of measurement data.

> *Here is the first tin we measured. Look at this grid* [original grid of measurements is displayed]. *It has a diameter of 6.5cm and a circumference of 20.4cm. Please come and show me the point on the graph representing this tin.* [Select a child and assist him to identify the point on the graph.] *Good. The tin has a diameter of 6.5cm so we go along this axis* [pointing] *until we get to 6.5 and it has a circumference of 20.4cm so we go up this axis to 20.4 and* [sliding fingers up and across the graph] *this is the point representing this tin.*

Sliding a finger along the axis to emphasize continuity

> The teacher assists the child in reading the graph.

Each tin is identified by a child in this way. The teacher then points to point q on the graph. She pauses, scratches her head and says:

> *I wonder what sort of container this point represents?*

She moves to the resource table and inspects several different containers.

> *Is it this one* [picking up a container]? *Or this one? How can we tell?* [Move back to the graph and inspect the point again.]

Interpreting points on the graph

The teacher invites a child to come to the front and together they read off the values for the diameter and the circumference. They trace out the size of the circle in the air and the child is invited to find a container to match the measurements. Now the height of the container is not given by the information in the graph so the teacher asks:

Speculating

> *Can anyone find another container to fit this data?*

She has selected the point carefully to ensure that there is more than one container to fit the data. The teacher continues to indicate points on the graph and the children work like detectives to find appropriate containers. She then moves them on to points that they cannot 'see' on the paper.

> It is important that children understand that there may be several possibilities.

Working in the imagination

Working with mental images

Speculating

> *What about this point here?* [Indicate a point way off the display. With eyes closed, say:] *It has a diameter of 32cm and a circumference of just over 100cm. What could it be?*

Suggestions such as a large plate or a concrete pipe are accepted. Several points are imagined in this way and the children suggest possible containers or objects with the given circular cross-section. Then the teacher indicates a point with negative values.

> You could also change the units to metres or kilometres. What might they represent?

> *What about this point here? It has a diameter of ⁻2cm and a circumference of ⁻6.3cm. What could it be?* [Look puzzled.]

> *You can't find a container? Oh dear! But the maths story says that there is a container with a diameter of negative two centimetres. The real-life story says that we can't find one. Maths is so much more exciting than real life!*

> See *Key ideas: The nature of maths.*

The nature of maths

This last point is of crucial importance to induct children into the nature of maths. The graph is a mathematical model that is being used to represent real-life information. But the mathematical graph of $C = 3.14\ d$ exists for any type of values of C and d, whereas the real-life equivalent cannot take negative values and it is difficult to imagine shapes with very small diameters or very large diameters.

Summary

The scripts in this section show several high-level teaching skills. The first is the demonstration of measurement using carefully selected objects and measuring instruments. The words and actions have been deliberately and meticulously planned to ensure that every child in the class can do their own measuring. Everyday objects such as food tins are selected to attract the children's interest and attention. The teacher demonstrates the care required to get as accurate a result as possible. By setting an example the teacher helps the children develop good habits.

Words and actions are deliberately planned.

> Meticulous planning and preparation are crucial to this topic.

The script then shows how the teacher uses the class to demonstrate how to inspect results and search for patterns that lead to relationships. As the children describe and explain their thinking she encourages them to think mathematically and to be rigorous in their statements. This oral work practises the use of mathematical language and terminology.

Encouraging rigour

Teasing out solutions with the whole class

It may be tempting to set the class the task of finding the relationship on their own. Although a few may chance upon the correct answer, many of the children will either make huge assumptions or find the task too daunting. By teasing out the solution as a whole class every child is being given assistance in how to think. They will have a process to replicate in future work and the confidence to try out solutions of their own. It provides an opportunity to discuss statements to ascertain their validity and to demonstrate the need to check results carefully. This is the basis for using and applying maths.

The second script focuses on interpreting graphs. We often ask children to draw graphs but rarely get them to interpret the information in a graph. The children move from the objects they used to generate the graph to other concrete objects in the classroom and then beyond that to objects in their imagination. And finally they are invited to consider points on the graph that cannot represent concrete objects. They are being inducted into the nature of maths.

Real stories to maths stories and back to real stories

Lesson plan

This lesson for Year 6 pupils teaches circumference and diameter. It is part of the second topic in a sequence taken from the following scheme of work.

First the teacher designs a scheme of work.

1. Revising the meaning of parallel
2. Measuring circumference and diameter of tins
3. Relationship between circumference and diameter
4. Working out C and d for different circles
5. Drawing graphs of relationship
6. Interpreting graphs

> The scheme of work is designed to assist development and progression.

Previous work
The children have all done work on linear measurement using rulers. They have recently covered work on parallel and intersecting lines. Work has been done on graphs using continuous data.

The teacher identifies what the children have been taught.

> The teacher knows what has been covered before but does not assume that everything will be remembered.

Lesson design
A homework will have been set to revise the children's understanding of 'parallel'. It is not the aim of the lesson to teach this concept but to draw on prior knowledge. A few minutes will be set aside at the beginning of the lesson to check the answers to the homework. Should there be any problems at this stage the lesson will have to be amended.

Revision

> The teacher has identified prerequisite knowledge.

The teacher will explain the learning outcomes of the lesson. She will move quickly from summarizing the homework to demonstrating how to measure tins. Children will be invited to assist the teacher and the method of measuring will be demonstrated carefully and deliberately. Although the children will have done linear measurement it is not always obvious to them that the circumference of a tin can be measured by wrapping something around it and then unwrapping it to measure it with a ruler. This needs careful demonstration.

Regular monitoring

The teacher will monitor the children's responses by observing the class and noting those children who are not responding to questions. When the teacher is confident that most of the class can move on she sets them the task of measuring a set of tins on their own. This is the modelling phase. Identical sets of tins are prepared so that the teacher can check the measurements easily and the whole class will later be able to compare results. It is important for all children to measure the tins for themselves to get practice in measuring and for the teacher to be able to assist those who are experiencing difficulty.

From individual work
to group work

Whole class discussion

The teacher monitors progress and when most of the children have measured all the tins she moves them on to group work so that they can compare results. She demonstrates to the whole class how they should work by collecting a small sample of results for one tin and discussing those that are close and any that are widely different. The groups are asked to agree a set of measurements for each tin.

In the summarizing phase the teacher works again with the whole class to collect and discuss the results. Final decisions are made and a copy of the correct measurements given to each child. The children are set the task of inspecting the results and commenting on them in preparation for the next lesson. The final task for the teacher is to ask the children to assess whether they can now measure the circumference and diameter of a circle and to record this in their books.

Regular monitoring is an essential feature of teaching as assisted performance.

The structure and timing of the lesson

Class	Y6	Teacher	Ms Asher
Date	4 May	Student	Ryan Saunders

Lesson description	Measuring the circumference and diameter of tins

Learning outcomes	Know the meaning of circumference and diameter. Know how to measure accurately the circumference and diameter of tins.

Resources	• Poster of circle cross-section • OHP • Sets of tins • Rulers • Acetate for measuring • Grids for results

Classroom framework	Time	Teacher and pupils
Summarizing	5 min.	Go over homework on parallel lines.
Demonstration	10 min.	Demonstrate how to use rulers and acetate to measure the circumference and diameter of tins. Select children to assist in this.
Modelling	15 min.	Children work individually measuring each tin in the set.
	10 min.	Children work in groups checking results and deciding on a group measurement for each tin. Grid of results completed by each group.
Summarizing	15 min.	Collect results for each tin. Make decisions on a single result for each tin. Class results entered on a grid and copied for each child.
Demonstration	5 min.	Explain homework. Give out copies of the grid of the correct results and ask children to inspect the results and comment on them for homework, in preparation for the next lesson.
		Record children's progress.

Practice

Practising skills

Following the demonstration on measuring, the children need practice in measuring tins for themselves. It is important that each child in the class measures the same objects so that they can compare results. It is very difficult to measure accurately and children need to learn to take care when using measuring instruments.

When the children have recognized the relationship between the circumference and the diameter they need practice in calculating the circumference given the length of the diameter and calculating the diameter given the length of the circumference. A practice exercise can be set out in a table.

Calculating the circumference requires multiplication, and calculating the diameter requires division.

diameter (d) cm	2	5	7.5	9			
circumference (C) cm					12.6	32	25.12

At first children can use the value 3 as an approximation to π. They can compare the results of their measurements of tins with their calculations. They can then go on to use better approximations such as 3.14. It is important that they compare the results that they get with different approximations. This work is best done on a calculator and will be covered again in the IT resource sheet.

Following the demonstration of interpreting the graph of circumference against diameter the children can all have a copy of the graph and use this to read off values of the circumference for given values of the diameter and values of the diameter for given values of the circumference. They can compare their readings from the graph with their calculations.

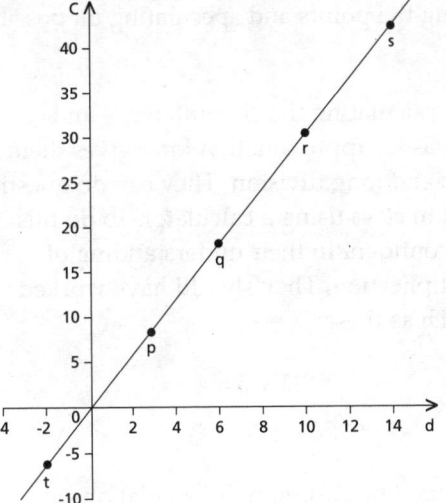

Children also need to practise interpreting the graph. Give them another copy of the graph with points marked on it. Ask the children to inspect the graph and write down the circumference and diameter of the circles identified by the points. Then ask them to speculate about possible objects whose cross-sections match the circles described.

This work will need to be summarized with the whole class.

Further practice can be set using graphs representing different relationships. You can use currency conversion graphs, such as French francs against pounds, and get the children to do conversions of prices of food, hotels and so on for a holiday. You could also use a conversion graph of the Celsius measure of temperature against the Fahrenheit measure. These two measures are often given on weather forecasts and the children can check how accurate the conversions are. These are all examples of continuous graphs that are accessible to young children.

Practising skills

Recording results methodically

Identifying points on a graph

Interpreting graphs

Speculating

Transferring skills to new contexts

Homework

Homework as practice

Children in Year 6 can be expected to do about thirty minutes of maths homework twice a week. Homework should be an integral part of the teaching programme. Children can practise work they have been doing in class and prepare for their next lesson.

Homework as preparation

When all the measurements of the tins have been collected in class give the children the set of data and ask them to inspect it and comment on it for homework. Let the children know that they will be discussing this in the next lesson. Ask them to look for any relationships between the sets of figures. Tell them that they can use their calculators to test any ideas. We sometimes pose these sorts of questions in class and get responses from a few children who have spotted the relationship during the practical work. This means that the large majority of the class who need a little more time to think do not have the opportunity to discover this for themselves. The result of this is that many children believe themselves incapable of doing maths and leave the few who answer to do the thinking for them.

Homework provides an opportunity to reflect on work done in class. All the children get the chance to inspect the results for patterns and relationships.

Providing opportunities for all children to participate

Practising measuring at home

The measuring activity can be continued for homework. Ask children to measure the circumference and diameter of circular objects in the home. Where children do not have their own measuring instruments they can mark the measurements on a strip of paper and then measure them in class the next day. They can test to see whether these objects fit the relationship discussed in class.

Take care to avoid asking children to do tasks at home which may be impossible.

Following the lesson on interpreting graphs the children can look for objects around them that could be represented by the points marked on the graph. Again, they may not have had the opportunity to offer suggestions in class and this allows them to join in the activity of looking at the graph, inspecting the points and speculating on possible objects.

Using objects in the home to speculate

Children also need to practise calculating the circumference and diameter of circles. Using 3.14 as an approximation for π gives them practice in long multiplication and long division. They can do questions for homework that they check in class using a calculator. To do this work the children need to be confident in their understanding of division as the inverse of multiplication. They should have worked extensively on calculations such as these:

Practising number work

$$3 \times 4 = 12 \qquad 12 \div 3 = 4$$

$$3.14 \times 4 = 12.56 \qquad 12.56 \div 3.14 = 4$$

Algebra is generalized arithmetic. The teacher must make the connections for the children.

Children will need to be reminded of these simple calculations as preparation for doing:

$$\pi \times d = C \qquad C \div \pi = d$$

Using algebra

It is the connection between the numerical calculations and the algebraic formulae that makes the essential link in the child's mind. This continuity with earlier work aids cognition. If we presented the algebraic formulae in a different way it would appear that we were teaching a new topic and new rules and procedures.

Using and applying maths

Almost all the work we have described concerning the circumference and diameter of circles has encompassed using and applying maths. The practical measuring and the use of everyday objects takes children through the process of starting with an everyday problem, making a conjecture and testing it. The process can be repeated using mathematical objects rather than real objects. In this case the objects are polygons with an even number of edges.

Draw several different sized squares on a sheet of paper and give every child a copy. Ask them to measure the length of the perimeter P and diagonal d for each square. You can demonstrate how to do this in a similar way to demonstrating the circle measurements. Ask the children to record their results in a table.

> Notice that we use the word 'perimeter' for the distance around most shapes but 'circumference' for the distance around a circle.

square size	perimeter (P)	diagonal (d)
4cm by 4cm	16cm	5.7cm
5cm by 5cm	20cm	7.1cm
6cm by 6cm	24cm	8.5cm
7cm by 7cm	28cm	9.9cm

Now ask them to discuss the measurements in groups and then work together as a class to obtain an agreed set of measurements. Ask for comments on the results. Add an extra column and ask the children to calculate P ÷ d = . For all the squares this division should result in a number close to 2.8.

You can then repeat the activity using regular hexagons, regular octagons and regular decagons.

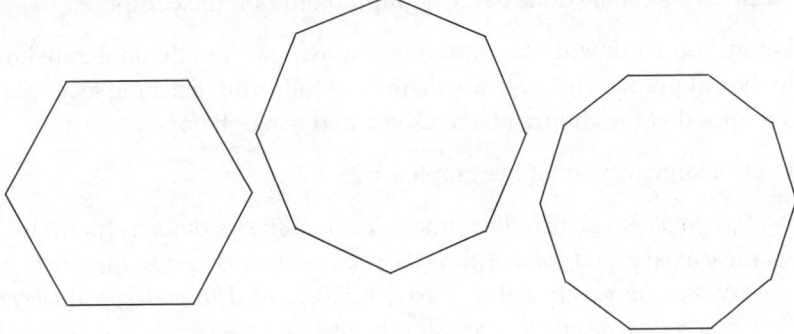

Notice that the regular polygons are all those with an even number of edges. You cannot draw the diagonal of a polygon with an odd number of edges. The relationship P ÷ d for the hexagon gives the answer 3. As the number of edges of the polygon increases so the value obtained gets closer to 3.14 or π.

> You need to exploit opportunities for demonstrating that the circle is the limiting case of a polygon.

The children can now work in their imagination.

Imagine a polygon with twelve edges. One with fourteen edges ... One with a hundred edges ... One with a thousand edges. What does it look like? Yes, it looks like a circle.

The circle is a special case of a regular polygon with lots of edges.

Using information technology

Using a calculator

Working out the circumference and diameter of circles means doing a lot of long multiplications or long divisions. Normally we would do these on a calculator. We want children to be able to estimate answers using approximations. In this case they can start by using 3 as an approximation for π. Then we want them to be able to use pencil and paper methods for calculations and they can do this by using 3.1 or 3.14 as approximations for π. For more accurate results we want children to be able to use a better approximation for π such as the one that is stored in a calculator memory. Children need to be able to use all these methods. They also need to know the most appropriate method and the most appropriate approximation for π in any given context.

Using different approximations for π

You can set questions in a way that will ensure that all methods are used. For example:

	d = 6.2	d = 4.5	d = 12	d = 16	d = 22.5
Circumference estimated using π = 3					
Circumference estimated using π = 3.14					
Circumference estimated using π as stored in calculator					

It is important to compare these results and discuss the need for accuracy in certain situations.

Comparing results

The work on circumference and diameter is a good lead into graph work. When the children have interpreted this and other similar graphs such as conversion graphs they can explore graphs of a more general nature. This can be done using a graph plotter on the computer.

Using a graph plotter

Computers and graphic calculators make graph work so easy!

Before you work with the computer you will need to demonstrate how to look at graphs and describe them. The following teaching example assumes that the children have used x and y axes before.

Draw a large display of the graph $y = 2x + 2$.

This graph is a straight line [trace]. *The line crosses this axis* [point to the y axis] *at this point. This is the point where x is zero and y is two. It crosses this axis* [point to x axis] *at this point. This is the point where x is negative one and y is zero. It is quite a steep graph.*

Do this with a few more graphs, inviting the children to join in. Then arrange the children to work in pairs at the computer. Ask them to draw the following graphs and to describe them to each other.

Investigating graphs

$y = x$	$y = x + 1$	$y = x + 2$	$y = x + 3$
$y = x - 1$	$y = x - 2$	$y = x - 3$	$y = x - 4$
$y = 2x$	$y = 3x$	$y = 4x$	$y = 0.5x$

Follow this with a class discussion drawing out the general features of linear graphs. Invite children to sketch graphs on the board showing these general features. Go back to the graph of circumference and diameter and check that it also has these features.

Tests

Checking practical skills

The work on circumference and diameter involves the children in doing lots of measuring. You can test the children's skills at measuring during the practical session. As they are working go round and check each child's work for accuracy. Record their level of skill. Note any child in the class who is experiencing difficulty with this task and provide assistance. Identify tasks in your scheme of work that require measuring skills and keep a record of the progress the children make.

Measuring skills can be tested by observation. You will need to plan carefully for this.

Written tests

You will want to test whether the children can work out circumference and diameter from given facts. This can be done informally when marking class and homework but you will also need to set a written test. The written test helps you to identify any children who are struggling with the work and confirms which children can do the work unassisted. It is vital to give the children sufficient preparation for such a test. The examples themselves should have been worked before and corrected. A test is not the time to set unusual or unexpected questions. You can assess whether a child can apply knowledge to new situations during class work.

It is important to identify what exactly is being tested. A child may be competent but unable to demonstrate this owing to a poorly constructed question.

Setting appropriate questions

The work on circumference and diameter tests not only children's understanding of the relationship but also their number skills. You will need to ensure that some of the questions can be completed without performing long multiplication or long division so that you can differentiate between these skill areas.

Testing orally

You can test the children's ability to interpret graphs during their oral presentations of their work and in their homework. You will be particularly interested in their use of language in this work. We often test children's performance in written work and neglect their oral skills. It is important to keep records of children's progress in this area.

Listening to children's use of language

Make a list of key words that you want children to learn and use in any particular topic and record their confidence in speaking them correctly and appropriately. You will need to ensure that every child has the opportunity to speak in class about their work. When this is done in the summarizing phase the children will be familiar with the language because they will have been using it extensively in the modelling phase. The activity in the modelling phase needs to be deliberately focused on developing this language.

You need to listen to children to assess their language skills.

Building confidence in oral skills

If you look at the measuring activity described in the script you will see that the children first work individually to ensure that they have all practised the task and then they have a specific focus on discussing their results in a group. The group activity gives the children the opportunity to use the words in a small public forum before being asked to speak them to the whole class. This building of confidence is an important part of developing oral skills.

Testing calculator skills

You will also want to test calculator skills and this can best be done by talking to the children as they complete the exercise described in the information technology resource. Discuss with the children the order in which they enter an operation. Ask them to estimate the answer first and to check their answers for accuracy. Again you need to keep a record of calculator skills and regularly test them in this way.

Measurement and graphs: discussion

Measurement

In 1857 Lord Kelvin said:

> *I often say that when you can measure what you are speaking about and express it in numbers you know something about it; but when you cannot measure it, when you cannot express it in numbers, your knowledge is of a meagre and unsatisfactory kind.*

Measurement is based on a need to compare.

All measurement is based on a need to compare one item with another. We may need to know whether these curtains will fit a window in our new house. Or whether the power of this engine in London is sufficient to pull those carriages in Edinburgh. In these cases it may well be rather inconvenient to carry the curtains to the new house and compare them directly (or drive the train to Scotland) and so we would resort to some indirect way of comparing the two quantities.

Choosing an arbitrary unit

These indirect methods, of course, are usually employed in measurement. How do we go about indirectly comparing the curtains with the windows? We choose some arbitrary unit, make sure that we keep a record of what that arbitrary unit looks like, and find out how many of those units correspond to the curtains and the window. For instance, we might select a favourite pen and use its length to generate a number to describe the curtains and the window. This would work quite conveniently if we were happy to visit both our existing house and our new one. But (and we forgot to mention this) we live in England at the moment and our new house is in Australia. Never mind, we can phone our Australian friends and get them to tackle the windows for us. But wait a minute – they do not remember what our favourite pen looks like.

> You may want to study the history of measurement with the children. They will see that the choice of units has been very arbitrary.

This rather silly tale is, of course, not what happens in practice. What we actually do is to compare our curtains with the arbitrary length called the metre and ask our friends to do the same with the window. This is possible because we can buy sticks that basically say: 'This is the arbitrary length that everyone has agreed to call a metre'. We can now engage in our indirect comparison.

What we are emphasizing here is that the metre is not a length defined by the gods and handed down for mortals to use. It was, in fact, invented in France and introduced at the time of the French Revolution. It was calculated as one ten-millionth of the distance from the equator to the north pole, measured along the meridian through Paris. The legal metre used to be the length of a standard platinum bar, kept in Paris. This has now been replaced by a standard based on the wavelength of a particular radiation band.

Standard units of measurement

The standard units of measurement are those of the International System of Units (SI) and those additional units that are recognized for use with SI. The decimal connection between units of different size for the same quantity in this metric system aid both memory and calculation. In the United Kingdom successive governments have been reluctant to provide legislation to complete metrication which was started in the 1960s. Some imperial measurements, which are far more arbitrary and not linked to one another, are still in common usage today.

> Although the SI system of measurement has been universally adopted, we continue to use idiosyncratic units in this country.

We can see that all measurement presupposes a well-defined attribute (like length), an agreed standard (like the metre) and instruments (like a ruler) designed to replicate that standard in relation to the objects which interest us (like curtains and windows). Some of these are summarized below.

Some typical standard
units of measurement

Attribute	Standard	Typical objects
length	metre	journeys
area	metre^2	fields
volume	metre^3	water in a lake
angle	degrees	bearings
temperature	degrees Celsius	ovens

In some cases the standard unit that has been agreed for measuring the particular attribute is rather cumbersome. The thickness of a coin, for instance, is rather small compared to a metre stick; to measure it you would need to use some related unit. The most consistent language for the related units is provided by the metric system. This system uses prefixes very consistently so that once they are learnt all other units of measurement can be understood because the logic is in the language. The prefixes are listed below, together with the abbreviations associated with the metre and the gram.

The metric system

Many British people still find it difficult to think in metric units. Tradition is persistent. For example, many of us continue to talk about our height in feet and inches.

Abbreviations

milli-	centi-	deci-	[basic unit]	deca-	hecta-	kilo-
.001 times basic unit	.01 times basic unit	.1 times basic unit		10 times basic unit	100 times basic unit	1000 times basic unit
mm	cm	dm	m	dm	hm	km
mg	cg	dg	g	dg	hg	kg

Using units of length, area and volume

Children need to become fluent in their use of the language of measurement. The units of length, area and volume that they will use most often are the cm, cm^2, cm^3. These are spoken as *centi-metre; centi-metre squared; centi-metre cubed*. Children need to be able to say these without stumbling (this is harder than you might imagine) and to relate them to other forms of the unit. The spoken language can be prompted by flash-cards like the ones in the diagram. (You will need to make a number of each card.)

Using flash cards

Relating symbolic representation to images

This is consistent with work in number.

The cards contain the symbols for the units that will be used most often in the classroom. These symbolic representations must be complemented by some physical representation. The length of 1cm can be represented by a line drawn on a sheet of paper; the area of 1cm^2 by a square of paper 1cm by 1cm; the volume of 1cm^3 by a plastic cube 1cm by 1cm by 1cm. These should be placed in different parts of the room so that they can be referred to unambiguously. The children must get used to relating these physical representations of the quantities to the appropriate spoken words and to the symbols written on the cards. This can take about 45 seconds on a daily basis, with the teacher saying:

Get ready to point; wait for the card: now [showing one of the cards, say, the 1cm²]. The class call: 'One centimetre squared' and point to the part of the room where the square piece of paper is displayed.

This is repeated for the other measurements. The same cards can be used for counting. Placing the cards on a table (in this case using the 1cm³ cards) count:

One centimetre cubed; two centimetres cubed; three centimetres cubed; four centimetres cubed; ... eight centimetres cubed. How much is there here? That's right: eight centimetres cubed.

> **Assisting performance by assisting with the language of maths.**

The same counting is applied to the use of plastic cubes. Whichever representation is used (the cards or the cubes), the objects are rearranged on the table and it is emphasized that the value is the same, but the appearance is different. The idea is that this sort of exercise is repeated with different representations, different units (cm, cm²) and different amounts so that the children appreciate that they must deal with a range of representations and that the rearrangement of the objects does not alter the value; that is, the length, area or volume is conserved. This is the key to understanding how to calculate length, area and volume of unusual shapes. Let us clarify this by looking at area.

> **The phrase 'keep the value: change the appearance' is just as relevant to measurement as to number.**

Calculation of area

The area of a rectangle which is 6cm long and 3cm wide can be found easily by imagining it filled with centimetre squares.

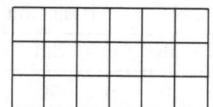

The diagram shows that each row contains 6cm² and there are three such rows. The total area is 6cm² × 3 = 18cm². Notice that we have not said that the area is 6cm × 3cm = 18cm². This is a popular way of talking about the area of a rectangle but it is contrary to the particular logic of filling the rectangle with standard units of area. You need to emphasize that we can see 6cm² in that row; 6cm² in that row; 6cm² in that row. We can see three lots of 6cm². We can see 6cm² × 3.

> **This is consistent with work in number.**

Now make the same rectangle by using eighteen pieces of card, each 1cm by 1cm. What is the area of the rectangle? 18cm². Now rearrange the eighteen squares to make a 9cm by 2cm rectangle; then some sort of L-shape; then any other shapes you can think of. On each occasion say *What is the area of that shape?* to establish each time that it is 18cm².

Display a piece of paper 6cm by 3cm. Place the eighteen pieces of card on it to ascertain that its area is 18cm². Fold the paper in half (to mark two squares) and cut the paper along the fold. Show that each piece is 9cm² by placing cardboard squares on them.

> *I have got half of 18cm² here: that is 9cm². What is the area of this? 9cm². When I cut 18cm² in half this bit has an area of 9cm².*

Now display another 6cm by 3cm rectangle. Fold it in half to mark two rectangles 6cm by 1.5cm and silently cut along the fold.

> *I have got half of 18cm² here: that is 9cm². What is the area of this? 9cm². When I cut 18cm² in half this bit has an area of 9cm². [Show the two shapes, the 1cm square and the rectangle.] Think of the area. Is this the same as this? Yes. Same value; different appearance.*

Side margin labels:

Teaching the language of maths

Visual images to create mental images

Conservation

Three rows of six centimetres squared

Conservation of area

Working towards area of a triangle

Do not place any cardboard squares on the 6cm by 1.5cm rectangle
(they do not fit). The area of this rectangle is found entirely by
calculation as half of the original rectangle. You are ascertaining that
any version of half the original rectangle has an area of 9cm². (It is
simply that different versions have an area with the same value but
a different appearance.)

It is the relationship
between the two
rectangles that is
important here.

Display another 6cm by 3cm rectangle. Silently fold it along a diagonal
then cut it along the fold. Place the two pieces together to show that
they are congruent. Discard one triangle, wave the other one and say:
This is half of 18cm². This is … ? Yes. Its area is 9cm².

The relationship
between the original
rectangle and the
triangle is the same
as the relationship
between the two
rectangles.

This way of looking at the areas of triangles is very mathematical. What,
by implication, is being said is this. We calculate area by finding out
how many 1cm² fit the shape. When they fit exactly we are dealing with
a real-world situation in which we can simply count the squares. When
we are confronted with a shape in which the 1cm² will not fit we work
with a different shape whose area has the same value but a different
appearance. When we work out the area of a triangle we are doing just
that. We are working out how many squares would be needed to make a
shape whose area has the same value but a different appearance.

Another way of looking at the area of a triangle or any other 'unhelpful'
shape is to place as many whole 1cm² inside it as possible and then
to see how many fractional bits there are to be put together. This, of
course, amounts to the same calculation as the one we have suggested
above for looking at area. But it is less helpful to the learner. The idea
that we recommend is the one that says: 'What [helpful] shape has an
area of the same value but a different appearance?' This is easier to
visualize because it links with the key idea 'Keep the value: change
the appearance' and it is consistent with the nature of maths in which
we work in the mind. It involves a construction, in the mind, of a
new shape. This is going beyond the real world. It is different from
remaining with the shape and estimating the sum of the fractional bits.

This approach to finding area uses visualization. The triangle shown
in diagram (i) is half the area of the rectangle drawn round it, (ii).

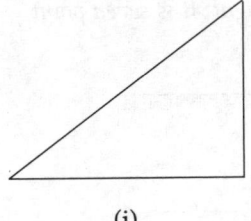
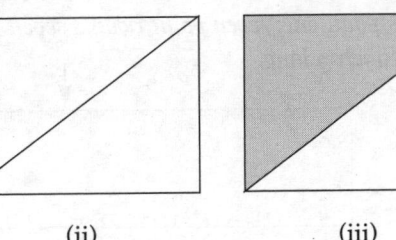

(i)   (ii)   (iii)

Now think of it as having the same area as the rectangle with the
shaded triangle removed, (iii). This is a useful visualization that involves
a change of appearance while the value of the area is kept the same. It
is especially useful when we look at the triangle in diagram (iv).

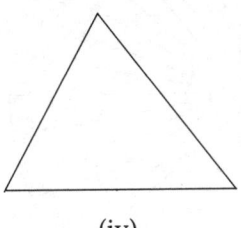
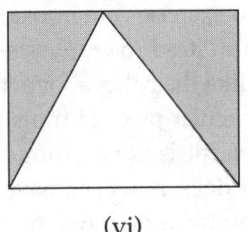

(iv)   (v)   (vi)

Demonstrating the use of measuring instruments

The ruler is a very common measuring instrument. It might seem surprising that it is often used wrongly by children. There is one mistake that is made time and time again. Many children wrongly think that the beginning of the ruler is the same thing as the extremity of the plastic (and sometimes this might be the case). They attempt to measure by lining up the edge of the plastic with the object. This difficulty can be easily overcome. You can distinguish between the piece of plastic and the ruler. Of course, most pieces of plastic sold as 'rulers' actually have two rulers drawn on them (one on each edge). Emphasize this to the children. Wave a transparent plastic 'ruler' and say: *This is a piece of plastic.* Place the piece of plastic on the screen of an overhead projector. Point to the image on the wall to show the first marking and run your finger along the edge of the ruler to the last mark. Say: *This is a ruler.* Do the same with the other edge: *This is another ruler.* Wave the plastic. *This is a piece of plastic. It is not a ruler. It has two rulers marked on it. One here* [show on OHP] *and one here* [show on OHP].

It is important to demonstrate how a ruler must be used to measure a length. Working with transparent plastic 'rulers' on the OHP makes this reasonably straightforward. Emphasize how to line up the end of the ruler (not the plastic!) with one end of an object, including closing one eye to ensure accuracy of alignment and looking at the markings from directly above them. Count centimetres by moving a pointer from the zero line to the line marked 1 and say *one centimetre* while the pointer is moving, stopping it as the word *one* is completed. Continue moving the pointer in the same way to co-ordinate with saying *two centimetres, three centimetres*, and so on. This care is necessary so that children continually see a centimetre represented as a movement or a distance, rather than as a point on the ruler.

Ensure that your demonstration includes measuring objects which are not whole numbers of centimetres. Suppose you select an object 7.8cm long. You will have counted to 7cm in the way outlined above. *Hmm. It is more than seven centimetres.* Move your pointer a further centimetre, saying, *eight centimetres. No. It is not as much as that.* Put your pointer back to the seven. *So it is seven and a bit. Quite a big bit. More than a half. It is seven point one; seven point two; ... seven point eight. It is seven point eight centimetres long.*

Similar problems arise with the use of the protractor. The first problem is the technical one of what constitutes the protractor. The second is how to exercise care in reading it. You need to emphasize that (like the ruler, above) the semi-circular piece of transparent plastic is not a protractor. It does, however, have two protractors drawn on it.

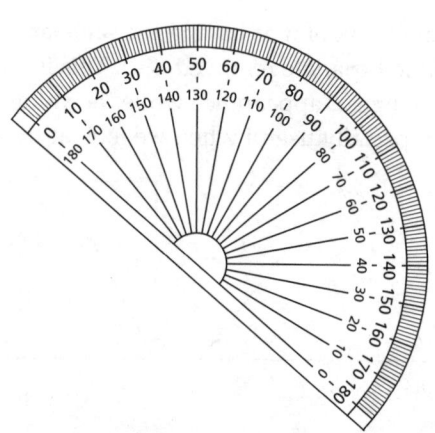

Side notes (left margin):

The ruler is the scale.

Using an overhead projector

Maximizing accuracy

Measurement in centimetres

Reading scales

The scale is the protractor.

Side notes (right margin):

When we use something on a regular basis we forget how complex it is.

This level of detail is rarely demonstrated to children.

*One protractor starts here and goes round this way. The other protractor
starts over here and goes round the other way.*

The same careful way of teaching how to use the gradations on the
ruler is also needed for the protractor. Children often do not appreciate
what they are measuring with a protractor. They do not understand
what an angle is. Important ideas are discussed below.

(You may come across a different instrument, called an angle measurer,
that consists of a full circle with a rotating arrow fixed to it.)

An angle measurer is a full circle.

Angle as turn

The single most important feature in establishing ideas about *angle*
is that it is a measure of *turn*. This is persuasively demonstrated by
being contrasted with the more commonly met measurement of length.
Follow the teacher in this classroom who has a number of metre sticks
on the floor in the centre of the classroom, with the class sitting around
the edge of the room. With three metre sticks placed end to end, the
teacher walks along the line of the sticks:

*I am going to start here and finish here. Have I moved? Yes, of course
I have. How far have I moved? That's right. Three metres. What if I do
this –* [place two sticks in line, pointing in a different direction] *start
here; finish here? Have I moved? Yes, two metres.* [Do this a number of
times, using half metres, revising centimetres and decimetres as
appropriate, and with new alignments.]

If I start here and finish here [stay on the starting point but twist one
full turn] *how far have I moved? That's right: I have moved no metres.
I have moved zero metres. But have I moved? Yes, I have, but it is not
the sort of movement we measure with metres. We say I have moved
through **one full turn**.* [Demonstrate this by holding a large pointer
with a clear arrowhead on one end.] *If I start like this, and move like
this, I say I have moved through one full turn.* [Do this several times,
each time clearly start by looking in a different direction.]

Note the emphasis on turning *through* an angle because this is an
important notion in later work and needs to become a part of normal
vocabulary.

This demonstration is taken further by introducing a half of a full turn
and a quarter of a full turn, as well as two full turns, three full turns,
two and a half full turns, and so on. Additionally, a full turn is defined
as 360 degrees, with the consequent 180 degrees and 90 degrees for
half and quarter turns, and the range of turns are expressed in terms
of both full turns and degrees.

This next demonstration is vitally important. The teacher now moves
about the room, tracing out a distance as well as turning through
an angle and asks the class to observe how much has been turned.
This emphasizes that turn can be measured even when the 'turner'
moves forward. It is important that the children understand that
moving forward (or backwards) does not in some way muddle up
the measurement of turn. The classroom demonstration outlined below
is now accessible.

An angle is a measure of turn.

Distance as movement

Angle as turning

Fractions of turns

Measuring in degrees

Children often describe angles as the distance between two lines!

The physical action of turning is used to demonstrate the definition of an angle.

A turn is not always about one point.

The sum of the exterior angles of a polygon

The teacher again works with the whole class. The children sit around the edge of the room, leaving a demonstration space in the centre of the floor. There are a number of long canes available so that geometrical shapes can be formed fairly rapidly (several different lengths are in use to avoid accidental emphasis on regular figures). The session starts with a pentagon formed with canes on the floor.

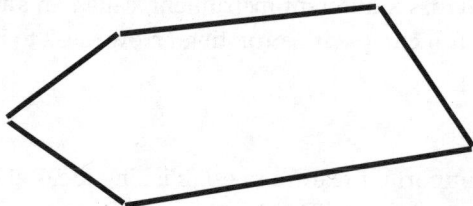

The teacher walks round the pentagon, marking the starting point and the starting direction (*I will start here, facing this way*) with a cardboard pointer. At each vertex, the teacher emphasizes *I am facing this way* [and places a short cane to extend the line of the side just walked] *and I am turning through this angle* [turning to face along the next side to be walked].

In this way the five exterior angles of the pentagon are indicated when the teacher returns to the starting position.

> *How many full turns have I made? Yes, one full turn, that is 360 degrees. I turned through this angle* [indicate first marked angle] *and this angle* [indicate second marked angle] *and this angle* [indicate third marked angle] ... [and so on]. *So when I turned through this angle and this angle and this angle and this angle and this angle, altogether I turned through one full turn – altogether I turned through 360 degrees.*

This process of finding the total turn when travelling round a pentagon, turning through the exterior angle at each vertex, can be repeated with all the other plane shapes (triangle, quadrilateral, hexagon, heptagon, octagon and so on). In each case, the total turn of these exterior angles is 360 degrees, a result which is initially surprising and then increasingly obvious.

The special result that children respond to enthusiastically is the idea of applying the method to a shape with, say, a thousand very short sides, or ten thousand very short sides, or a hundred thousand sides, and realizing that we are in fact thinking about a circle (which, technically, has an infinite number of edges). This kind of realization is truly mathematical.

The reason for the emphasis on the phrase *turning through* becomes clear when we look at the interior angles. The same techniques are used as before, but this time at each vertex *turning through* the interior angle requires that we alternately face forwards and backwards. With the interior angles, the total turn in each case is different depending on the number of sides of the shape.

Graphs

If you study the script about teaching circumference and diameter you will notice an important use of graphs. They record information, certainly, but they enable us to 'go beyond the information given'. In

---

Sidebar notes (left column):

Visual images to create mental images

One full turn

Walking around any polygon is equal to one full turn.

A polygon with an infinite number of sides

Interior angles

Going beyond the information given

Sidebar notes (right column):

This activity is particularly useful before using LOGO to draw shapes.

The result is obvious when acted out in this way.

Once again the opportunity has arisen to demonstrate that a circle is the limiting case of a polygon with an infinite number of edges.

the discussion about circumference and diameter it was possible not only to read the information that was recorded about the tins we measured but also to know something about tins that had not been part of the activity. Reading graphs for information beyond the actual experience is very mathematical.

'Going beyond the information given' is used when dealing with graphs far more often than is appreciated. (It is used implicitly.) Let us take an example. Using the Celsius scale, the freezing and boiling points of water are 0°C and 100°C. Using the Fahrenheit scale they are 32°F and 212°F (same value: different appearance). We can think of the equivalent freezing temperatures as the point (0, 32) and the equivalent boiling temperatures as the point (100, 212). When these are plotted on a pair of axes and the points connected with a straight line, we have a graph which gives us much more information than was initially available.

> The reason we can be confident that the graph is a straight line is that both scales are linear.

Temperature conversion graph

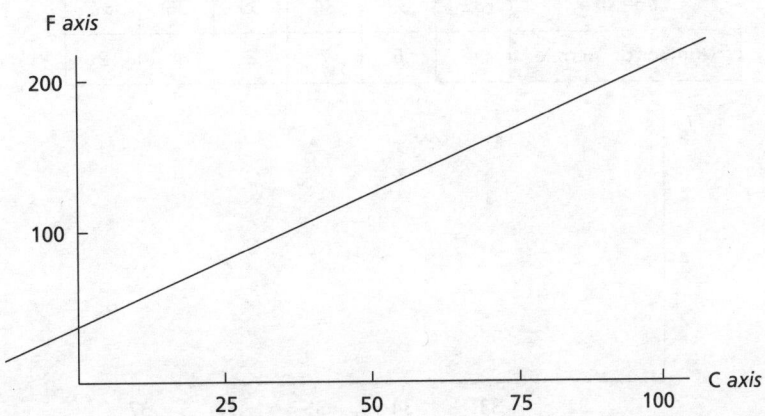

We drew the graph by knowing that 0°C is equivalent to 32°F and that 100°C is equivalent to 212°F. We can now use the graph to find an infinite number of equivalent Fahrenheit and Celsius temperatures, none of which we have actually measured or were available when we drew the graph.

An infinite number of points on the graph

Drawing the straight line to join the two points was an easy thing to do but it has a number of implications. First, because we have drawn a continuous line, it implies that we are convinced that all temperatures exist between freezing and boiling points. Is this reasonable? Yes, it is. It seems unlikely that at some stage the possibility of measuring the temperature disappears. It is not likely that you could be sitting comfortably enjoying a temperature of 24°C and, turning up the fire a bit, have to say, 'Whoops. The temperature has disappeared!' The implication of drawing a continuous line in this case is very sensible. It is consistent with common sense.

Temperature scale is continuous.

Notice that we have drawn a line that is not only continuous but also straight. This implies that we are convinced that a rise in temperature from, say, 34°C to 35°C is the same 'size' as a rise in temperature from, say, 76°C to 77°C. Again, this seems sensible. It would be rather strange if the measurement of temperature went up in steps that were not equal.

Linear relationships

> The idea of continuity is important in maths. We should not join points on a graph with straight lines unless we are certain of continuity.

The data we have dealt with in our discussion is *continuous data*. The measurement of temperature in both degrees Celsius and degrees Fahrenheit is continuous. It is because they are both continuous (because they can both take any value on a number line) that we were justified in drawing a continuous line on the graph.

Suppose now that we think about measuring feet. If we tell you the size of the foot we have just measured it is possible for it to be any number (between certain limits). You cannot expect only whole numbers, or only numbers with just one figure after the decimal point. It is conceivable that the number we give you could appear anywhere on the number line. The measurement of feet is continuous data. On the other hand, if we tell you the size of shoe that each foot is wearing we are limited in the types of number we can choose from. If we are working in the continental measurement we can only use the whole numbers. The shoe sizes are not continuous data. They are separate, individual numbers which do not allow the numbers in between to be used. This is *discrete data*. We want to emphasize this point by considering how we could construct a graph to represent the following information collected in a small survey.

Length is a continuous measurement.

Shoe sizes are discrete data.

> We normally represent this information in a bar graph.

Shoe size	32	33	34	35	36	37
Number of people	4	6	7	8	4	2

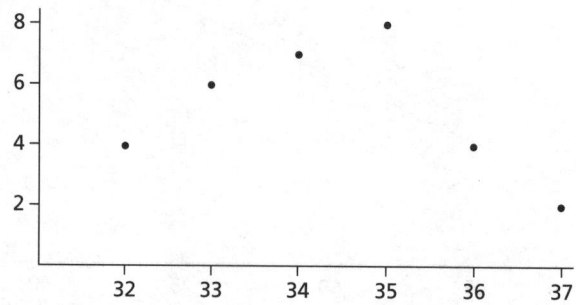

The graph represents this data. It would be wrong to join the dots with straight lines, curved lines or any line at all. Joining the dots with lines would imply, for instance, that a shoe size of 32.4 exists and that just over four people were found to wear this size shoe. This is clearly not the case.

Points representing discrete data cannot be joined.

When children learn to draw graphs they tend to join all points with straight lines. They do not distinguish between discrete and continuous data. It is not appropriate to teach them some sort of rule that specifies when they are allowed to join the dots. What is important is that they are assisted to work out whether or not it makes sense to do so. They must be enabled to provide some sort of justification for joining the dots or not joining the dots. When they do this they are engaging in a mathematical proof. They are proving, say, that it makes sense to join the dots. In order to do this a lot of work is needed in relation to reading the 'story' of a graph. This is discussed further in the final topic in this book, 'Handling Data'.

Mathematical proof

> It is important to make the distinction between discrete and continuous data and to use the correct language in doing so.

Our interest here is in continuous data: the kind of data you collect when you measure things (like foot length) rather than when you count things (like the number of people) or assign numbers to things (like shoe sizes).

When we discussed the temperature scales we were dealing with continuous data and the possibility of 'going beyond the information given'. The graph shown here is another example of continuous data. It represents the journey of a train from Rochdale and the axes show distance plotted against time.

Distance-time graphs

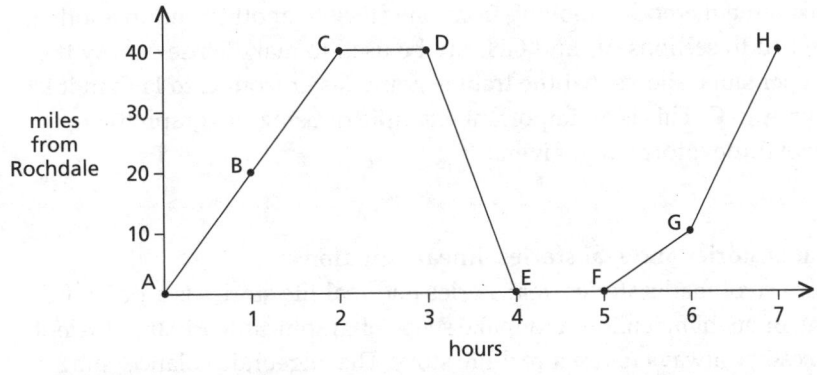

A discussion with children about this graph should make the following points.

Making sense of the graph

> Look at the section AB of the graph. When the journey starts the train is 0 miles from Rochdale. One hour later it is 20 miles from Rochdale. How far has it gone? 20 miles. How long has it taken? 1 hour. It has travelled 20 miles in 1 hour. Its speed is 20 miles per hour. Look at the section BC of the journey. When the train travels from B to C it goes a distance of 20 miles. It takes 1 hour to do this. Its speed is 20 miles per hour. For the journey from A to C the train has been travelling at the same speed all the time. We can look at the journey from A to C in one go. How far has the train travelled? 40 miles. How long has it taken? 2 hours. What is its speed? Well, it does 40 miles in 2 hours so it does 20 miles in one hour. Its speed is 20 miles per hour.

Maths stories and real-life stories

Remember that we are looking at a maths story and translating it into a real-life story. We can assist children to understand this relationship by discussing a real story that links them. Use some object to represent the train (it could be a toy train or a chocolate box). Mark the position of Rochdale on a table and place markers at distances of 20 miles, 40 miles, 60 miles and 80 miles. (*These are not really miles. They represent miles.*) Show the train moving, punctuating its journey with the words: *ten minutes; twenty minutes; … one hour.* Then use the same words and move a pointer on the graph. Repeat the real story on the table, emphasizing that this is a speed of 20 miles per hour. Show the train continuing at the same rate until it is 40 miles from Rochdale. *Look how far it is from Rochdale now. Let's look at this on the graph.*

This process of working between the real-life story, the real story and the maths story needs to be continued for each section of the graph. This is especially important for the section CD and the section EF. Leave the train on the table at the point 40 miles from Rochdale. Count: *ten minutes; twenty minutes, … one hour.* Punctuate this counting with the same question each time: *How far is the train from Rochdale now?* Elicit the same answer each time: 40 miles. Move to the real-life story. Why is the train standing still? The graph does not answer this question. We can speculate about possible answers: *It is at a station. There is a signal failure. The driver has gone on strike. A passenger has pulled the emergency handle.* This speculation is useful for helping children to make sense of the graph but it must be made clear that we can only *know* the answer by studying further data. We need to make the distinction between fact and fiction, between known data and speculation. Move to the maths story (the graph). *Show me where the train is standing still. Prove to me that the graph tells us it is standing still.*

Questioning to tease out information

Speculation

A common error is to interpret this graph as 'going up a hill, going along, going down hill', etc. The axes need careful inspection before interpreting the graph.

Writing stories to match the graphs helps to reinforce their meaning.

It is important to distinguish between true facts as represented by the graph and speculation that requires further information.

This same method of moving from one story to another and to another, applied to sections AC and GH, can be used to make sense of why the steeper slope shows that the train is going faster from G to H than it is from A to C. This is an important example of using the graph to go beyond the information given.

Maths stories and real stories: linear equations

Our use of maths stories, real stories and real-life stories is a powerful way of enabling children to make sense of graphical work, but it is not necessary always to use a real-life story. The 'algebraic balance' shown in the diagram, commonly used in the classroom, can be employed in close connection with graphical work.

The algebraic balance

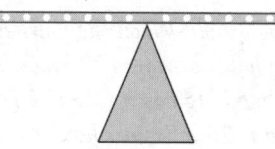

The balance provides a visual image of a mathematical concept.

Demonstrate to the class how a ring hung on the 6 on one side will balance a ring on the 6 on the other side. Show also how a ring at 6 on the right-hand side will balance two rings on the left-hand side (one at 4 and one at 2).

Relating the real story to the maths story

Display a poster showing '$x + y = 10$' clearly written for all to see.

Questioning to provoke thinking

Get the class to focus on the meaning of the equation: *What does this mean?* This question is prompted by asking: *Which parts of it do we recognize? What kinds of thing would we normally put here and here* [pointing to the x and the y]? *Can we put just any numbers? What connection has it got with this apparatus* [indicating the algebraic balance]?

Ask some of the children to make sketches on the board of all possible 'balance situations' that conform to the equation. Display a poster showing all the possible solutions, then select children to place rings on the algebraic balance to correspond to each picture.

Linear equations and linear graphs

Display a poster with graphs of each of the linear equations shown below.

Alternatively you could use a computer graph plotter or graphics calculator.

| $x + y = 12$ | $x + y = 1$ | $x + y = 10$ | $x + y = 9$ | $x + y = 8$ |
| $x + y = 7$ | $x + y = 6$ | $x + y = 5$ | $x + y = 4$ | $x + y = 3$ |

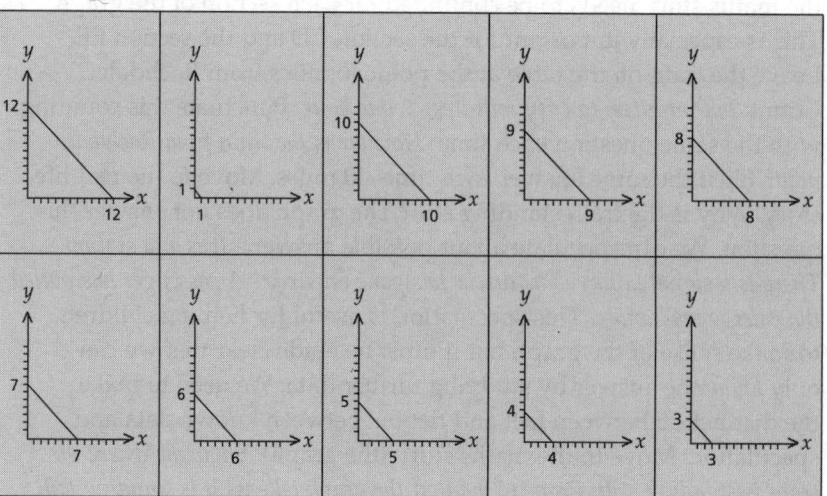

Maths stories and real stories

Working in the imagination

The language of maths

Making connections

Point to the graph of $x + y = 10$. Read: $x + y = 10$. Point to the dot that is at (7, 3). Say: *This is not me putting rings on the balance. It is not a picture of rings on the balance. It is a hint about one of the balances, with some rings, that I am thinking of. Can you put rings on the balance to show the one I am thinking of?*

Put a dot at (3.5, 6.5) and repeat the words above. Discuss the idea that it is a balance that makes sense, we can imagine it, but we do not actually have one that has pegs at the 'halves'. Do this with several others that use halves.

In this work there is a distinctive emphasis not only on using algebra ($x + y = 10$) as the language of maths but also on using language to make sense of the algebra. It is here that pupils can begin to recognize that language, even when it is as unfamiliar as $x + y = 10$, can be explored for its meaning, and that further sense can be made by relating it to other experience. It is the case here, of course, that those experiences have been deliberately set up and represented in ways that invite the making of connections. That, of course, is in the nature of teaching and planning for teaching. The reference to the dots on the graph at (3.5, 6.5) is an example in early maths work to utilize symbolic representation ($x + y = 10$) in order to suggest something about an object that has not been explicitly referred to ($3.5 + 6.5 = 10$, which cannot be represented on the balance).

We introduced these linear graphs with the algebraic balance. This real story allows us only to use discrete data (we can only hang rings on pegs labelled 1, 2, 3, and so on). When we draw a graph and draw a continuous line we are expressing the fact that we know it makes sense to extend this discrete data to become continuous data. The use of continuous data on the graph is an immediate recognition that we can sensibly move from a real world to an imaginary world (in which there is implicitly an infinite number of pegs on the algebraic balance).

> This can be linked to work on number bonds.

> Going beyond the information given is the nature of maths.

6 Handling data

Introduction

A world rich in data

We live in a world that is rich in data. What does this mean? It means that we have available to us a massive amount of figures and pictures and diagrams that relate to the world we live in. Could we therefore say that we live in a world that is rich in information? Not necessarily. The data does not become information until we see how it relates to the real world. We have to undertake some kind of interpretation of the data before we can call it information. We need to teach young children how to collect data, how to choose the most appropriate way to represent that data and how to interpret the data so that it becomes information. The mathematical term for this work is 'statistics'. You are using statistics successfully when they give you a 'feel' for the story behind the figures and diagrams.

We often hear people claim that 'there is so much information on the Internet'. There is certainly a mass of data but until we make sense of that data it is not information.

Statistics

Although handling data does not appear as a separate heading in the Key Stage 1 programme of study of the National Curriculum, much of what the children do in Number, Measures and Using and Applying Maths in that key stage is directly related to working with data. When children sort objects, classify them using criteria, record results in tables and lists, and represent information in simple diagrams or charts they are handling data; they are doing statistics.

Working across the curriculum

Handling data is one area of maths that can be applied right across the curriculum. Children gather information, order it and try to make sense of it in almost every subject. It is in maths that they learn how to represent and interpret the data and how to do certain calculations that will help them to make better sense of it.

Interpreting data

The first script in this section shows how the teacher can assist the children to interpret data that is represented in different forms. The second script demonstrates the teaching of calculating the mean. You will see in this script how calculating statistics requires a particular mathematical viewpoint.

It is the interpretation of data that turns it into information.

Selecting appropriate representations

An over-emphasis on collecting and representing discrete data at Key Stage 2 can lead to children making errors at later key stages. Children spend far too much time colouring in block graphs or bar charts on such things as their favourite TV programmes or favourite pets. They sometimes come to believe that a block graph is the only type of graph available. Children need to learn how to select the most appropriate representation for various types of data and how to interpret diagrams and graphs. It is important to distinguish between discrete and continuous data from an early age.

Development in teaching the handling of data

Early work in handling data overlaps with work in shape and number. As the children work with plane shapes they learn to sort and classify them according to certain criteria such as the number of straight edges or the number of angles. As they work with numbers they learn to sort them according to size, odds, evens, squares and so on. In other areas of the curriculum they learn to classify plants, trees and animals and to order historical events.

Children are constantly working with data that they are sorting, classifying and turning into information. In maths they learn the most appropriate ways of representing data and how to interpret that data. They also learn certain mathematical methods of summarizing data in meaningful ways so that comparisons can be made between sets of data.

Teachers should enable children to:

- *sort objects and classify them, demonstrating the criterion they have used*

- *formulate questions that will require the collection of data*

- *collect appropriate data*

- *record data in tables, block graphs and diagrams*

- *interpret tables, block graphs and diagrams*

- *tell stories using tables, block graphs and diagrams*

- *interpret tables used in everyday life*

- *collect data and record it in frequency tables, including those for grouped data*

- *represent discrete data appropriately, using a range of graphs and diagrams, including frequency graphs, line graphs and pie charts*

- *use computers as a source of data and as a tool for representing data*

- *calculate summary statistics such as mean, median, mode and range*

- *draw conclusions from statistics and graphs, and recognize why some conclusions can be uncertain or misleading*

- *develop an understanding of probability and the language associated with it*

- *know that the probability of an event lies between 0 and 1*

- *recognize situations where probabilities can be based on equally likely outcomes, and others where estimates must be based on experimental evidence*

Sorting and classifying

Developing a knowledge of statistics and probability

Every subject in the curriculum presents data that needs interpreting.

Even in early years children are learning how to handle data by sorting objects.

Recognizing misleading information is a life skill.

167

Script 1: Inspecting and interpreting data

Interpreting data

In this script we look at how the teacher demonstrates how to inspect and interpret data and its representation. The context is one that the children are all familiar with so that a rich discussion can take place. Before looking at the diagrams representing three surveys the teacher can ask the children about their own preferred forms of travel and can conduct a small survey in the class.

The idea of 'inspecting' is a recurring theme in maths.

Resources

- Three posters (or overhead projector transparencies) of the following surveys, and scaled-down individual copies for the children.

Survey 1: Survey of preferred form of travel

Form of travel	bus	train	walk	car	bicycle
Number of people	1200	400	300	200	300

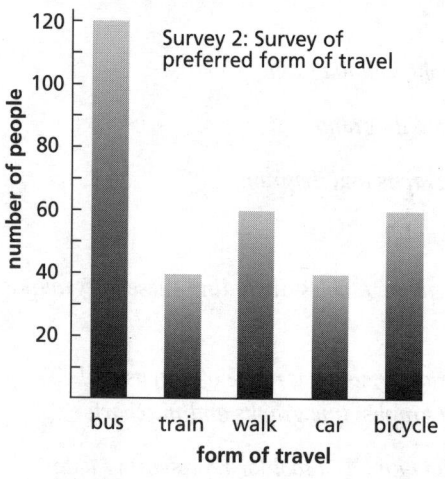

Survey 2: Survey of preferred form of travel

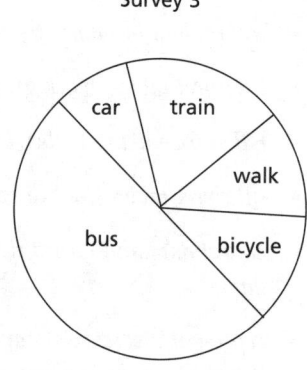

Survey 3

Inspecting the diagrams

Demonstrating how to inspect diagrams

The teacher begins by looking at the table for survey 1.

Let us read this table together. This first row [point] *tells us about the form of travel. These are bus, train, walk, car and bicycle.*

This second row tells us about the number of people who prefer to travel in a certain way. This first number [point to 1200] *tells us that twelve hundred people prefer to travel by bus. The second number tells us – what?* [Invite the children to respond.] *Yes, that four hundred people prefer to travel by train. And ...*

Reading together is not only done in literacy work.

Each number is carefully inspected and interpreted. The teacher now elicits what other information can be gained from the table.

Teasing out information

Does this table tell us anything else? It does not tell us the date or time of year when the survey was carried out. It does not tell us the ages of the people in the survey. [Invite the children to add to the list of what it does not tell us.] *Can we work out how many people took part in the survey? Yes. If we add all the numbers in this second row we can work out that two thousand four hundred people took part in the survey. We are assuming, of course, that each person was allowed only one choice and that everyone responded.*

The teacher can now demonstrate that a simple table like this can provide further information.

Questioning to provoke thinking

What is the most popular form of travel in this survey? [Invite response.] *Yes, the bus is the most popular. And what is the least popular form of travel? Yes, the car. Are there any forms of travel that are equally popular? Yes, walking and cycling.*

> The children have to explain how they know which is the most popular form of travel.

Comparing sets of data

If the children have learnt how to calculate percentages they can also work out the percentage of the total sample who preferred each form of travel in the survey. This information will be helpful in comparing sets of data with different sample sizes.

Constructing fictional stories

It must be emphasized that we have now extracted all the possible information from this table of data. The table itself does not provide anything further. However, we could construct a story to fit the data. This would be fiction. The act of telling a story is useful in helping us to make sense of the data but we must always be clear about what is fact and what is fiction. This story-telling can be done before moving on to the next survey.

> Making incorrect inferences from data is a common mistake often seen in newspaper reports.

This is another survey about people's preferred form of travel. This time the data has been presented in a bar chart. Let us read this together. Look along this axis [point to the horizontal axis and the words 'form of travel']. *The first bar represents those who prefer to travel by ...* [invite response] *bus, the second bar ...* [and so on].

Reading axes

Now look at this axis. There are equally spaced marks representing numbers on this axis. The numbers represent the number of people [point to the words 'number of people']. *This first mark* [point] *represents – what?* [Invite response.] *Yes, ten people. And the second? Yes, twenty people. And that number is labelled. And ...*

The teacher then moves on to interpret the information in the chart.

Look again at the first bar. How many people prefer to travel by bus? [Invite response.] *Yes, one hundred and twenty. How many prefer the train? Yes, forty. How many ... ?*

Demonstrating how to interpret diagrams

Each bar is carefully interpreted before moving on to look at further information. As a first question the teachers asks about the total number of people in the survey. Working this out is not immediately obvious. Unlike the first table where the numbers were clearly stated, here they have to be carefully extracted from the chart and recorded in order to be added correctly.

> It is important to demonstrate how to interpret bar charts.

Extracting information

Can we tell from this chart how many people took part in the survey? Look at this first bar [point]. *There are one hundred and twenty people here* [write down 120] *and* [point to second bar] *forty people here* [write down 40] *and* [point to third bar] *sixty people here and ...* [Add up all the numbers recorded.] *That makes three hundred and twenty altogether.*

Information on the most popular form of travel is more accessible from this chart. It is immediately obvious that the tallest bar represents the most popular form of travel. However, there is no bar that is the shortest. The chart shows that there are two bars of equal height, showing that the train and car are equal in being the least popular forms of travel. We are now beginning to be able to compare the two

> Even the most obvious facts need to be explained to some children.

surveys. However, the sample size in each survey is different. There are ten times as many people who prefer to travel by bus in the first survey compared with the second survey but that does not necessarily reflect how the two surveys compare. It is only when we work this out as a percentage that we can accurately compare the sets of data. In the first survey 50% of respondents preferred the bus compared with 37.5% in the second.

The third survey is represented as a pie chart. The title is missing from this chart (a common mistake made by children), as is any reference to numbers of people. The teacher demonstrates how some information can be gleaned from the chart.

> *Look at this pie chart* [point]. *This sector* [point] *of the circle represents something about a bus. This sector* [point] *something about a car. This sector ...* [and so on]. *They all represent something about travel. This chart does not have a title so we can only guess that the sectors represent preferred forms of travel.*
>
> *Can we tell how many people took part in the survey? No. We can only see the fraction of the total in each sector.*
>
> *Can we tell which form of travel occurs most often? Yes. The bus is represented by the biggest sector.*
>
> *Can we work out the percentage of the total sample that is represented by each sector? Yes. We can measure the angle at the centre, work that out as a fraction of 360 and write the answer as a percentage. It will only be approximate because we are measuring.*

The teacher can now discuss whether the pie chart could represent the data in either of the other two surveys. The percentage figures are the same as those for the first survey but not the second.

This careful demonstration of how to interpret data can now be followed by a session where the pupils work in groups with similar sets of data. They can answer questions about the data and write stories to help them make sense of the data.

| You can spend some time discussing graphs and charts with information missing. |

| This calculation needs to be worked through with the class. |

Script 2: Calculating summary statistics

The purpose of this demonstration is to show the children the difference between descriptive statistics (those things that can be 'seen' from the data) and summary statistics (those things that can be calculated from the data). It shows how we can do things in maths that we cannot do in real life. This is the nature of maths.

This way of introducing summary statistics is important for later work. In the discussion section we shall show how these ideas are crucial in the teaching of standard deviation. We should always keep an eye on the way that mathematical ideas develop so that we can prepare the ground for later work.

| It is important to maintain consistency of approach. |

Resources
- Coloured linking bricks
- Two sets of data that can be represented by bricks – for example:

	Height in metres				
Sample set A	2	6	7	10	10
Sample set B	2	5	6	7	10

Carefully selected samples

Calculating the mean

The teacher makes up sets of bricks to represent each sample using a random mixture of colours. She begins by holding up five bricks joined together and says:

This is a person. This person is five metres tall.

Now this is a rather silly story. People are not that tall. The children are being invited to join in with an imaginary story for the purpose of doing maths. They will be used to this idea from their work with negative numbers. If we used real heights we would not be able to represent them easily with bricks.

Stories are powerful learning tools.

The teacher puts away the five bricks. She then displays the set of bricks for Sample A and invites the children to describe what they can see. She writes their statements on the board.

Descriptive statistics

There are five people in the sample.
The smallest person is 2 metres tall.
The tallest person is 10 metres tall
One person is 6 metres tall. One person is 7 metres tall. One person is 10 metres tall.

> Describing the set of people in this way is laborious. It demonstrates the need to summarize.

The teacher does not allow the children to make statements about averages at this stage. She insists that they must be able to see what they are describing.

Describing what can be seen

This is a good description of what you can see. Each statement is a description. Each statement tells me something about the people in the sample. 'There are five people' obviously tells us how many people there are altogether. 'The smallest person is 2 metres' tells us something about one of the people and that all the others are taller. 'One person is 6 metres' tells me about one of the people. And so on. Because you are telling me how many people you are talking about and giving numerical data about those people you are doing statistics. You have given me a statistical description of the sample.

Notice that this sample was rather small: there were only five people. Imagine if I had given you a sample with a million people in and asked you to describe it. You might say:

The teacher now writes some possible statements on the board to demonstrate that when the sample is large it is not a good idea to describe it in this way.

Describing a large sample

There are one million people in the sample.
The smallest is 2 metres.
The tallest is 10 metres.
One person is 5 metres. Another person is 5 metres. Another person is 5 metres. Another person is 5 metres. Another person is ...

> Acting out this lengthy description emphasizes the need to summarize.

She goes on speaking and pretending to write the many statements to indicate the tedious nature of the activity. She looks at the statements written on the board and, pointing to the first one, says:

Demonstrating the need for summary statistics

This one is all right [underline the first statement]. *It tells us something about the whole sample. It tells us that there are a million people in the sample. The second and third statements are also all right* [underline them] *because they tell us that everybody in the sample is two metres or more and ten metres or less. They give us information about the whole sample. However, statements like these* [pointing to the fourth row] *only tell us about individuals and it would take a long time to tell you about everyone in the sample.*

The ones I have underlined are useful: they are summary statistics [emphasize by writing 'summary statistics' on the board]. *They summarize what the sample is like. They give us an idea what the sample is like without going on and on about each person one by one. So what we do in statistics is to find ways of giving other people a good idea of what a sample looks like without actually talking about each person one by one.*

This demonstration has established the difference between descriptive and summary statistics. The teacher now displays the bricks that represent Sample B. She asks the children to describe this sample using summary statistics and writes their statements on the board.

The samples have been carefully constructed to demonstrate the need to look for further information.

Summary statistics

There are five people in the sample.
The smallest person is 2 metres tall.
The tallest person is 10 metres tall.

Using summary statistics to compare two samples

A comparison of Sample A and Sample B using only summary statistics implies that the two samples are the same. But we know that they are not. The teacher discusses this with the children and explains that they will need to use some summary statistics that they can work out rather than just what they can see.

She displays the bricks for Sample A again.

Visual images to provoke mental images

We can work out that if we chopped the heads off the tall people and put them on the small people [slowly take bricks off the tallest and put them on the smallest, continuing until all the piles of bricks are the same height] *we could make all the people the same size.*

This representation of the mean improves understanding.

The heights of the people in the samples have been carefully chosen so that this is possible without cutting up the bricks.

The nature of maths

We cannot do this in real life; we cannot chop people's heads off in real life, and we certainly cannot put them on top of other people to make them bigger. But in maths we can. We can do experiments in our minds. That is what we are doing now. We are saying: let us pretend we can chop off heads and put them on smaller people, and see what height they would be if we could make them all the same height. [Put bricks back to show original sample.] *Well, we can see that these taller people can help the smaller people to become ...* [shift bricks around to equalize the heights, then count the bricks] *they are all seven metres tall.*

The teacher now returns to the list of summary statistics and goes to add this new statistic. Before writing she reads:

There are five people.
The smallest is two metres.
The tallest is ten metres.

Then she says:

Calculating the mean

If we could make them all the same height they would all be 7 metres tall. We can write this in a shorter way by saying 'The mean height is 7 metres' [write this on the board]. When we read 'The mean height is 7 metres' we know that it is telling us that if we could make them all the same height they would all be 7 metres.

The teacher repeats this several times to ensure that the children understand the definition of the word 'mean'. She then does the same activity of moving the bricks to equalize the heights on Sample B. The mean height of this sample is 6 metres. They can now compare the two samples by looking at the mean heights.

The samples could have been constructed to demonstrate the need to find even more information such as standard deviation.

Having established how to work out the mean using bricks, the teacher now returns to the original set of data.

Repeating the exercise with bricks

Look at this first set of data and look at the bricks that represent them. Let us take all the bricks apart. How much is there here? Yes, there are 35 bricks. That represents 35 metres. If I move them around like this how much is there here? Still 35 metres. If I build the bricks like this [build the bricks to look like the data set] how much is here? Still 35 metres. If I build the bricks like this [build the bricks into five equal blocks] how much is here? Still 35 metres. How much is in each block? [Counts the bricks in one block.] 7 metres.

The concept of 'Keep the value: change the appearance' is employed once again.

Now the teacher moves back to the numbers in the data set.

Repeating with numbers

How much is there here? [Add up the numbers in the data set.] Yes, 35 metres. If I share them out equally amongst all the people in the set how much will each person get? [Mime sharing them out.] Yes, 7 metres. So to work out the mean we have to add up all the numbers in the set and divide by the number of members of the set. We add up these numbers to get 35 and divide by 5, the number of people in the set.

Repeating with a second sample

She then repeats this exercise with Sample B, inviting the children to do the calculations with her. The children can now work on similar sample sets, working out the total number in the set, the smallest, the tallest and the mean.

Notice how the samples for this exercise were carefully chosen to allow the teacher to demonstrate a mathematical method using equipment without the distraction of large numbers, decimals or fractions. Once the method has been understood and practised the teacher can move on to look at larger samples that will result in more complicated calculations.

Calculating the median and mode

Statistics are used to compare.

Median and mode

The previous activity could have been conducted with one sample set but there would not have been a purpose for doing the calculation. It is when we want to compare sets of data that summary statistics become important. Bricks can be used in a similar way to demonstrate how to work out the median and mode of sets of data. In these cases you would want to start with larger samples. The blocks of bricks can be displayed in order of height so that you can identify the one in the middle for the median height. If you have an even number of members in the set you will have to demonstrate how the median is midway between the two middle heights.

Statistics are measurements used for comparison.

Choosing the most
appropriate statistic

Similarly you can demonstrate the mode by ordering the blocks of bricks and looking for the most common height – the mode. You can then discuss with the children the most appropriate 'average' to represent the sets of data. For example, the most frequent height may, like Sample set A, be the two tallest in the sample. This is not very representative of the heights of the sample. However, the median and the mean for this sample coincide. In Sample set B there is no mode and once again the median and the mean coincide. You will have to check your samples carefully to ensure that the averages you are finding are meaningful.

Lesson plan

First the teacher
designs a scheme of
work.

This lesson for Year 3 pupils teaches interpreting graphs and covers the first three topics in the following scheme of work.

1. Interpreting tables, bar charts and pictograms
2. Working out most, least and number in sample
3. Comparing sets of data
4. Collecting data from members of the class
5. Using tables to organize data
6. Storing data in a computer database
7. Representing data, using bar charts and pictograms

The scheme of work begins with interpreting and moves on to representing.

Selecting an
appropriate order of
teaching

Previous work
Contrary to the practice often seen in schemes of work on handling data, we recommend that the collection and representation of data is postponed until the children have practised interpreting data. We believe that the holistic view of data representation given in this lesson provides the basis for developing an understanding of the subject.

Lesson design

Class organization

The teacher has prepared two large bar charts showing people's preferred forms of travel. The room is organized so that every child can see the board and the pupils are seated so that they can work in pairs. The lesson begins with a demonstration of how to read the bar charts. The teacher reads the title and the labels on the axes of the first bar chart with the children.

Working in pairs ensures that all the children have the opportunity to interpret the bar charts.

Working with the
whole class

Each bar is interpreted in turn, the teacher inviting children to help in reading and interpreting the bars. She provides sufficient assistance to ensure that this is successful. She poses questions on the most, the least and the sample size and helps children find the answers. The second bar chart is then displayed and interpreted jointly by the teacher and children. The class compare the two sets of data.

Children working in
pairs

The modelling phase of the lesson will consist of the children repeating this activity. The teacher gives out sets of two bar charts to each pair of children. She has prepared three different sets on the same theme of preferred travel. She explains clearly that each child will take a bar chart and describe what they see to their partner. She asks the children to compare what they see. During this activity the teacher assists the children in reading the words and interpreting the data. As she does so she monitors progress.

Explaining and giving reasons

In the summarizing phase the children are invited to come to the front and interpret their bar charts. The teacher has prepared overhead transparencies of the bar charts to use in this phase. When the children have compared the pairs of bar charts, the teacher helps them to compare all six bar charts that have been used.

The teacher then prepares the children for a homework. She gives each child a sheet containing two bar charts on a different theme. She reads through the title and labels with them and asks them to describe and compare what they see to someone at home. She does not ask them to write this down for homework because that would be too difficult for some children. She wants them to practise speaking the words at this stage. She will summarize this work in the next lesson and write a summary for the children to copy into their books.

Homework to practise the language of maths

Presenting answers to the class improves the children's use of mathematical language.

The structure and timing of the lesson

Class	Y3	Teacher	Miss Lowe
Date	24 February	Student	Melissa Cann

Lesson description	Interpreting bar charts
Learning outcomes	Know how to read the axes of bar charts. Know how to read the most and the least values. Know how to work out the sample size.
Resources	• Two large bar charts on forms of travel for demonstration • Three different sets (two in each set) of bar charts on forms of travel for children to use • OHT versions of children's bar charts • Bar charts on favourite foods for homework

Classroom framework	Time	Teacher and pupils
Demonstration	15 min.	Display first bar chart. Select a child to come to the front to help demonstrate how to read axes. Provide full assistance. Inspect bar chart and extract information by asking questions and showing how to find answers. Work out the form of travel preferred by the most and the least, and the sample size. Display second bar chart and invite children to join in its interpretation. Compare the information extracted from the two bar charts.
Modelling	20 min.	Children work in pairs. Each pair is given a set of two bar charts (also on travel). There are three different sets being used in the class. Ask the children to record the most and the least popular forms of travel and the sample size for each bar chart. Each child interprets one of the bar charts to her partner. They compare the information extracted from the bar charts.
Summarizing	20 min.	Select children to present their bar chart and explain what they have found out. Use the OHT version for all the class to see. Assist where necessary.
Demonstration	5 min.	Give out two bar charts to each child (identical ones for all). Ask the children to describe these charts to someone at home in preparation for the next lesson. Record the children's progress.

Practice

Comparing sets of data

When the children hav% learnt how to read the information represented in tables, bar charts and pictograms they need to practise using this information to answer questions about the data. In particular they need practice in comparing sets of data. The collection, representation and interpretation of data should always serve a purpose. We want children to ask: 'Why is this data being collected? What questions are we asking? Who wants to know? What are we comparing?'. Questions such as these will help children decide on the best ways of representing the data and what summary statistics need to be calculated.

Making sense of the context

Let us look again at the bar charts representing preferred forms of travel. Why has this information been collected? First we need to know who the people are who have been questioned. Suppose the people all live in two villages and a company wants to know whether it is worth putting on a bus service to the nearest town. We can inspect the two bar charts and attempt to find an answer. Perhaps we need more or different information. Maybe the data represents children travelling to school and the local authority wants to know whether to run a school bus. Perhaps a company is thinking of setting up a cycle shop and wants to find out which town would be the most profitable place for it.

> It is important to discuss the purpose of handling data.

Recognizing the purpose of the exercise

When children practise interpreting diagrams and graphs they need to be given questions to answer that will help them see the purpose of the exercise. The diagrams and graphs are maths stories. We can describe what we see and work out summary statistics from the data but the maths stories represent real-life stories and the questions and comparisons arise from real-life contexts.

Telling a maths story

Relating maths to the real world

Give the children three bar charts on children's preferred lunchtime food. They can describe the bar charts and compare the most popular food and the least popular food. By reading and describing the bar charts they are telling the maths story. You can then tell the children that the data was collected from three classes in a school to help the caterers decide on lunchtime menus. They can now inspect the data to see how they may answer the caterers' questions and suggest possible menus. This is the real-life story. They must be careful not to speculate and use only the information given. This work provides an opportunity to discuss the distinction between making decisions based purely on statistical information and using that information as a part of a wider debate. The children could consider what else the caterers should take into account before deciding on menus, such as nutritional information, parents' preferences for their children, cost and so on.

> When the children are set meaningful tasks they are more likely to be motivated to learn.

Practice in interpreting data before collecting their own data

It is important that the children have plenty of practice in interpreting diagrams and graphs before they collect data for themselves. They will gain a wider perspective of the purpose of doing such a collection. Following the interpretation of the diagrams above, they can collect similar data from their own school and compare the results. They can ask questions about the difference between food preferences of children at different ages, that of boys and girls, how this compares with the given data and so on. They can compare children's preferences to actual menus. Doing the work in this order gives the children a reason for collecting and representing data and makes the work more interesting.

Homework

Homework as practice

Homework as preparation

Children in Year 3 can be expected to do 15–20 minutes of maths homework twice a week. Homework should be an integral part of the teaching programme. Tasks set for homework should be part of the modelling phase, giving practice in work demonstrated in class in preparation for the summarizing phase in the next lesson. It should be an opportunity for children to talk to their parents about their work. All the tasks set should have been well rehearsed in class. We want children to be successful in the work they do at home so that they can gain in confidence.

Telling a maths story

When the children have practised reading and describing diagrams and graphs in class they can usefully practise repeating the exercise at home with their parents. Give the children copies of bar charts and ask them to use the information to tell a maths story. This is an opportunity for children to use and become familiar with the language of maths. In the next lesson the children can be invited to tell their stories to the whole class.

> Explaining the diagram to another person aids understanding.

Collecting data

Once the children are confident in interpreting diagrams and graphs they can collect data themselves and draw their own diagrams. Ask the children to collect data for homework and record it in a table. This task needs to be well organized and focused. The data to be collected should be specified and not left for the child to decide. For example, data can be collected on preferred foods or preferred forms of travel following the class activities described earlier. The data can then be collated by the teacher and used to compare results with the class-based or school-based data already gathered.

Drawing diagrams

When data has been collected the children will want to draw their own diagrams. They can begin these in class and spend time at home completing them. They can then spend as much time as they like making these diagrams look attractive. However, care needs to be taken to ensure that the art work does not detract from the purpose of the diagram in conveying information. This will need some discussion with the children before they start on the task.

> Far too much time in school is spent drawing pictures and colouring in.

Using real-life data

Another task that can be set for homework is that of collecting examples of data representation. Most children will be able to find diagrams and charts in newspapers or magazines that they have at home. Many of these will be of a type not yet met by the children, so make it clear that they are to look for a bar chart or pictogram that they can describe to someone else. In the following lesson the children can work in pairs, describing what they have found to a partner. Be prepared with some examples of your own for those children who have forgotten or been unable to find anything suitable at home. Children should not feel at a disadvantage if they have been unable to complete a homework. The summarizing phase is an opportunity for children who have been successful to present their work and at the same time an opportunity for others to take part in that success and learn from their peers.

Involving parents

Handling data is a topic that most children enjoy and are able to do. It is also a topic that most parents feel sufficiently confident in to discuss with their children. Homework tasks set in this area of maths can encourage parents to take a more active role in their children's learning.

Using and applying maths

Data handling is all about using and applying maths. Whenever we interpret diagrams and graphs we are applying maths to real-life data. In class teachers extract the necessary data from a problem so that it can be used to teach a particular skill. They also decide what data needs to be collected and what information is needed to answer a specific question. We want children to be able to extract that information for themselves when it is presented as we normally see it in real life.

Extracting information is comprehension.

Extracting information in this way is comprehension. When we read a story we want children to read and comprehend. When we read a story that includes numerical data we also want them to be able to comprehend that data and they need to learn the skills to do this from demonstration by the teacher. We can use stories to teach these skills.

Work in maths can assist literacy skills.

Reading with the whole class

You can start by writing a newspaper story, using vocabulary that the children can read, and include numerical data. Read the story with the whole class. Discuss what the story is about. Now carefully inspect each of the numbers in the story and discuss what they represent. Write the numbers on the board in words and figures. Discuss what kinds of numbers they are. Collect the numbers together in a table and consider ways of representing the data.

Getting information from text

This work is not suitable for group or individual work. It requires the teacher to tease out the information from the text and this needs deliberate and meticulous demonstration. We often expect children to be able to do this for themselves without teaching them the necessary skills. The following example is the first paragraph of a newspaper story:

Gill Sweet from Wide Creek School won the 800 metre race at the county athletics meeting. This was the first time the school had ever won that event. There were 230 competitors taking part on Saturday. Altogether Wide Creek won eight gold medals, six silver and four bronze. They were only two gold medals behind the overall winner. This was a great improvement on last year when they only managed to collect seven medals in total.

Making sense of the numerical data

Read the story and extract all the numerical data. Write the numbers on the board. How far is 800 metres? Where would you be if you were 800 metres from the school door? How many is 230? How does this compare with the number of children in the school? How many medals did the school win altogether? Draw a bar chart to show the number of each type of medal won. How many medals did the winners get? Draw a bar chart showing this. How many more medals than last year did the school win this year?

You can read the story together to improve reading skills.

Following on from this exercise you can provide another story which you read together with the class. This time provide a choice of diagrams and ask the children to select those diagrams that match the data in the story. Now they have to inspect the story and inspect the diagrams and check the figures and words to find a match.

Matching text to diagrams

You can give groups of children a set of short stories and a set of diagrams and ask them to match the stories to the diagrams. The children can read the stories together, extract the data and find the matching diagram. In the summarizing phase they can present their answers and explain how they made their decisions.

Using information technology

Handling large sets of
data

Using a database

Discrete data

Continuous data

Misleading diagrams

When we demonstrate methods and skills in handling data we normally select small samples of data. We often start by collecting data from the children in the class and this gives us a sample size of about thirty. This is manageable. We then compare the data we have collected with that from other classes. We are beginning to handle larger sets of data. As we move on to using larger data sets our methods of recording become less reliable. We all make mistakes when we count large numbers. It is more sensible to enter the data on to a computer database. This data can then be saved and used at a future date in comparisons with other data sets.

You can set up a database for the class and ask children to record certain statistics about themselves. This can be done in advance of any work on handling data so that it is available for use. You have to be sensitive about which statistics to collect. Also remember that if you are asking children to provide data that can be counted, such as their favourite food or something such as shoe size, this is discrete data. It can be represented in bar charts, pictograms and pie charts. If you collect measurements such as heights then you are collecting continuous data and this requires a knowledge of histograms or line graphs for its representation. These will not have been taught to children in Year 3.

One of the problems in using computer software is that it will often do whatever you tell it to do even if it is mathematically incorrect. If you tell it to draw a bar chart using continuous data it will probably do so. Computer-generated diagrams can be very useful but the user must be careful to select appropriate representations for the data recorded.

Some computer software will draw attractive three-dimensional pictures to represent information. This can be misleading, as we mentioned earlier. Again take care with your selection. You can use these misleading diagrams to demonstrate to children how easy it is to misrepresent results. You can alter the scales on both the axes to exaggerate particular features.

Display the following bar charts on the board.

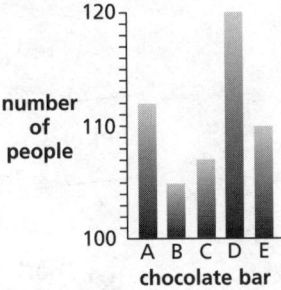
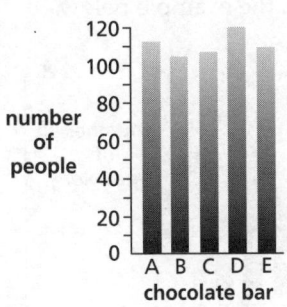

Inspecting diagrams

Ask the children to tell the story of each bar chart. Look at the first one. Read the numbers carefully. What is the favourite chocolate bar? Is it much more popular than bar B? By how much is it more popular? Look at the second bar chart. Does this give the same information? Read the numbers and compare them with the first bar chart. Which is the most popular chocolate bar? Is it much more popular than bar B? Discuss the different images you get with each diagram. This work will emphasize the need to inspect diagrams closely before drawing conclusions. At a later date the children will check for accuracy of representation by calculating the percentage of the sample in each bar.

> Children should be competent handling small sets of data before they move on to using a computer.

> Teachers must be clear in their own minds about the distinction between discrete and continuous data.

> Demonstrate thinking by asking appropriate questions.

Tests

Most of the work described in handling data for Year 3 is oral in nature. It follows that the monitoring and assessment of this work should also be predominantly oral. The children should be regularly invited to give presentations of their work to the whole class. It is vital that every child is given the opportunity to do this. As the children give their presentations you can record their progress in certain skill areas.

You will want to record the progress that the children are making in their use of mathematical language. Make a note of the words that you want the children to learn and record their confidence levels. For example, you will want the children to use the terms 'bar chart' and 'pictogram' without hesitation. You will also want them to be able to say 'the most popular ...', 'the least popular ...' and 'the number in the sample is ...'. As you listen to the children describe the diagrams, assess their use of language. In this way you can evaluate their readiness to move on to the next stage of learning. This is formative assessment at its very best. It is also diagnostic in that you can immediately identify any children who are struggling with the language and who need more assistance.

When the children are working in groups matching diagrams to stories you can monitor reading and comprehension skills. You may need to repeat the whole class activity if the children are struggling. Ask pupils to read the stories aloud to each other, giving assistance if necessary.

The representation of data can be tested by setting the children the task of producing a poster to compare two sets of data. They can select the appropriate representation for themselves. This also assesses their ability to use and apply maths. Once the posters have been completed, the children can be invited to present their work and describe their diagrams. Once again you can check their use of language.

It is not appropriate to set much in the way of written tests at this stage. One form of written test would be to give the children a set of word cards and ask them to use the words to complete a story about a diagram, as in the example below.

> Monitoring children's progress can often be achieved by listening to them.

> Assessment can take many forms. When you plan lessons you need to consider what opportunities there are for assessment.

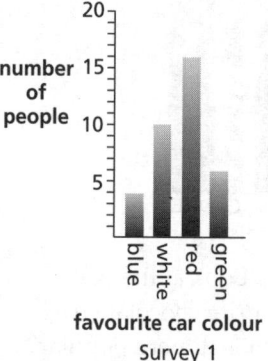

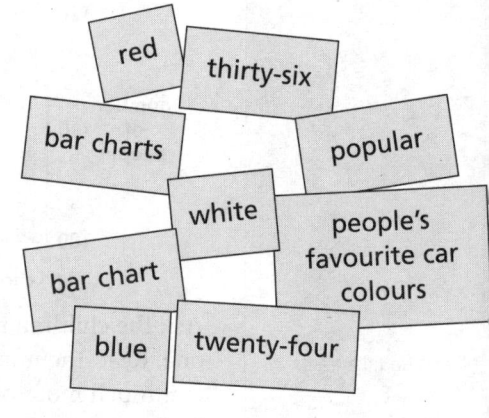

These two diagrams are called _____. They are all about _____ _____. In the first _____ the most _____ car colour is _____. The least _____ car colour is _____. In the second _____ the most _____ car colour is also _____ and the least _____ car colour is _____. In the first survey there were _____ people. In the second survey there were _____ people.

Handling data: discussion

Making sense of data

Useful information

Discrete data

Continuous data

Grouping data

Distinguish between counting and measuring.

Introduction

As we have said earlier, we live in a world that is rich in data. School maths includes teaching children how to handle that data so that they can make sense of it. And in enabling them to make sense of the data we are helping them to make sense of the world around them.

What exactly is data? Data is a set of facts or observations normally given in numerical form resulting from counting or measurement of some kind. In their raw form these data are not terribly useful. When they are ordered, organized and recorded in tables or diagrams they begin to become more useful. When they are reported in ways that allow them to be compared they are becoming useful information.

Suppose we are told that Fred ran a 100 metre race in fifteen seconds. This sounds quite fast to us but it does not tell us much about how fast this is compared to other runners. When we know how fast everyone else ran that particular race and how this compares with similar races it begins to become meaningful. If we are also given the country or world records for the 100 metre race we can make an even better comparison. It would not be helpful to have data on the 1000 metre race or the 100 metre hurdles because we would not be comparing like quantities. We must therefore be very careful that our comparisons are valid.

> We are bombarded with data all the time. Data has become a part of our everyday life.

Discrete and continuous data

Data can be categorized as discrete data or continuous data. Discrete data refers to quantities that can only take a limited number of values, usually integer values. They are normally found by counting. Examples of discrete data are 'the number of people who prefer a certain type of travel' or 'the number of red cars in the car park' and these are integers. However, another example of discrete data is the scoring system for ice-skating which is represented on a decimal scale but which can only take specific values such as 5.8, 5.9, and not 5.843.

Continuous data refers to quantities that can take an infinite number of values within a given range. These are mostly concerned with measurement, such as of length or time. It is crucial to distinguish between discrete and continuous data when we consider methods for representing data.

On the whole the distinction between discrete and continuous data is obvious. If the collection of data involved counting it is discrete. If it involved measuring it is continuous. However, some data such as test results are not so easy to categorize. It is true that a score out of, say, 20 cannot take any value between 0 and 20. There may have been half marks awarded but not values such as 14.23. The raw data is therefore discrete. However, we do not usually represent this raw data. Instead, we normally group the data in class intervals of, say, five marks and treat the grouped data as though it were continuous. We often group data in this way and treat it as continuous.

> Statistics is such a young subject that even the experts disagree about the terminology and representation. Text books often contradict each other.

When you are teaching children how to collect data you need to make them aware of when they are *counting* and when they are *measuring* so that they gain an understanding of the difference between discrete and continuous data from an early age.

Different representations

Representing discrete data

Consider the data described in the first teaching script. This concerns people's preferred forms of travel. It is discrete data. It has been represented in three different ways: as a table, a bar chart and a pie chart. The table records the numbers of people next to their preferred form of transport. The bar chart has separate bars, each labelled with the respective mode of transport and the height proportional to the number of people who preferred that mode of travel. There is a space between each bar to show that they each represent something different. The pie chart uses sectors of a circle proportional to the number of people who preferred each mode of transport. The data could also have been represented by a pictogram such as this:

The different forms of representation provide different visual images.

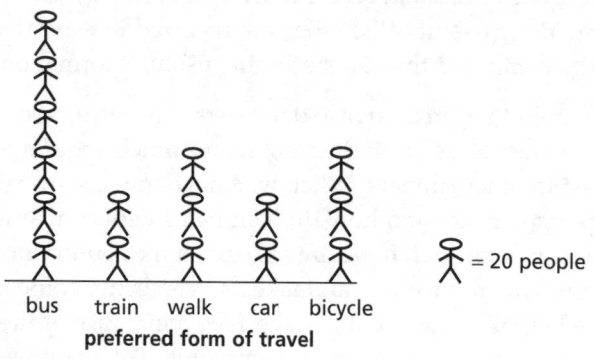

bus   train   walk   car   bicycle
preferred form of travel

🧍 = 20 people

Although children draw their own diagrams and charts they find interpretation difficult.

Representing continuous data

Consider the following data.

The heights in cm of 50 pupils at Exford School									
132	140	148	143	150	153	131	142	146	154
145	135	146	150	149	159	145	146	156	147
152	149	142	136	149	149	143	146	148	140
145	131	141	147	145	137	148	155	135	151
139	138	142	143	162	142	147	148	144	152

These are measurements and are therefore continuous data. The first thing we have to do with this data to make it useful is to reorganize it into some sensible order. We can construct a frequency table with the data grouped into class intervals of 5cm.

Reorganizing data

The first task is to organize the data and record it systematically.

Height in cm	Tally	Frequency
130–	111	3
135–	𝟙𝟙𝟙𝟙 1	6
140–	𝟙𝟙𝟙𝟙 𝟙𝟙𝟙𝟙 1	11
145–	𝟙𝟙𝟙𝟙 𝟙𝟙𝟙𝟙 𝟙𝟙𝟙𝟙 1111	19
150–	𝟙𝟙𝟙𝟙 11	7
155–	111	3
160–	1	1
	total	50

A frequency table

At first we have recorded each height with a tally mark next to the appropriate group. Then we have counted the tallies and recorded the frequency. This frequency table already provides us with some useful information. We can see that the most common height is between 145cm and 150cm. We say that the modal group is 145cm to 150cm. We can see that only one pupil is over 160cm.

Since the heights are presented in order we can see that the 25th and 26th children, the two in the middle, are in the group 145cm to 150cm. We can represent this information in a histogram.

Histograms

A histogram looks much the same as a block graph but it has some important distinguishing features because it represents continuous data. First of all the horizontal scale is a continuous scale. It is not the rectangular blocks that are labelled but the marks on the scale. The scale begins at 130cm at the far left-hand side and finishes at 165cm at the far right-hand side. It is not the height that is proportional to the frequency but the area of the block. In this case each class interval is equal in size so the blocks are of equal width. This may not always be the case.

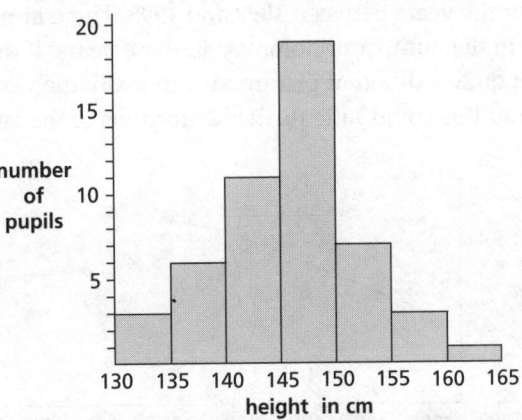

Note how the horizontal axis is labelled with a continuous scale.

This continuous data can also be represented by a frequency polygon. You can construct a frequency polygon by joining the midpoints of the tops of the rectangles of the histogram. When the class intervals are equal, as they are in this case, the frequency polygon encloses the same area as the histogram, but has a smoother form, and so it may provide a better picture of the data.

Misrepresenting data

Diagrams and graphs are normally used to represent data in such a way as to inform the reader of the particular characteristics of that data. They are part of the process of turning data into information. They tell us a story. However, great care must be taken in selecting appropriate representations in order not to misrepresent those characteristics. For example, incorrect use of scales can change the storyline altogether.

Visual images can easily fool us. We must take care to inspect diagrams and graphs carefully before interpreting data.

The vertical axis

First let us look at what happens when we exaggerate the vertical scale and instead of starting at zero we begin at a point well up on the scale. Suppose the figures represent the sales of a toy.

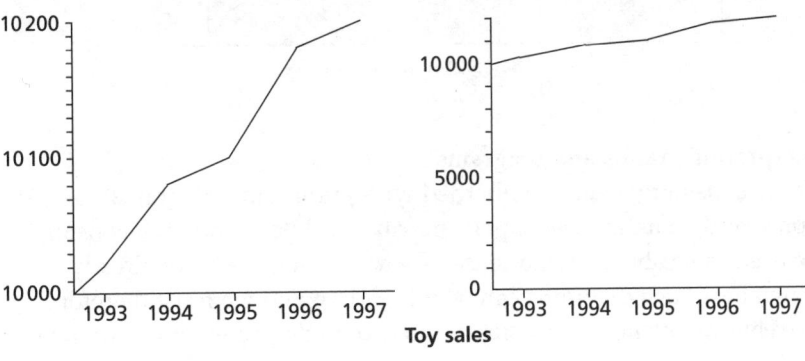

It is easy to give a false impression using diagrams and graphs.

Toy sales

183

The first diagram implies a remarkable increase in sales from 1993 to 1997. The company seems to be doing very well indeed. Perhaps this graph has been produced by the sales personnel who are hoping for a pay rise. The second diagram implies that sales have been fairly constant over the four years. If we look at the percentage increase in sales we can see that the second diagram is a better representation of the data. The vertical axis can be used to distort information.

The horizontal axis

The horizontal scale can also be used to misrepresent data. Look at the following diagrams concerning the number of homeless in a city between 1990 and 1998. Notice how the horizontal scale is not evenly spaced. There is no data for the years between 1992 and 1998. There appears to be a dramatic rise in the number of homeless in these years. If the scale is corrected we get quite a different picture. Additionally the vertical axis has no scale and this could hide further distortions of the facts.

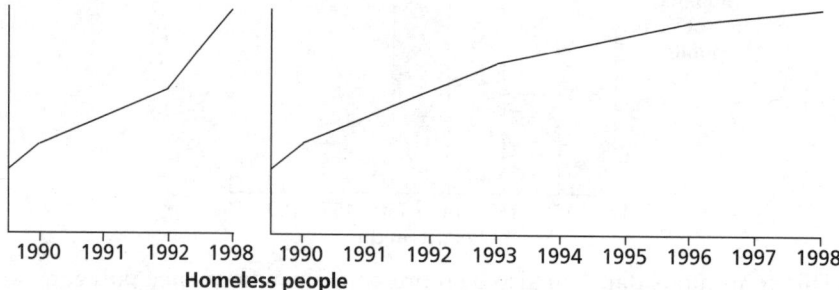

The scale distorts the information.

Homeless people

Using 2D and 3D diagrams

Another way of misrepresenting data is to use two- or three-dimensional diagrams. Suppose we have the sales of houses doubling in two successive years. A bar chart correctly represents the sales with the height of the bars being proportional to the sales. The second bar is twice the height of the first. A two-dimensional picture of a house may be more attractive but enlarging the house by a scale factor of two has increased the area by a factor of four, implying a fourfold increase in sales. A three-dimensional picture of a house exaggerates the increase even more by magnifying the volume by a scale factor of eight.

It is tempting to use the most attractive diagram instead of the most accurate.

The visual image distorts the information.

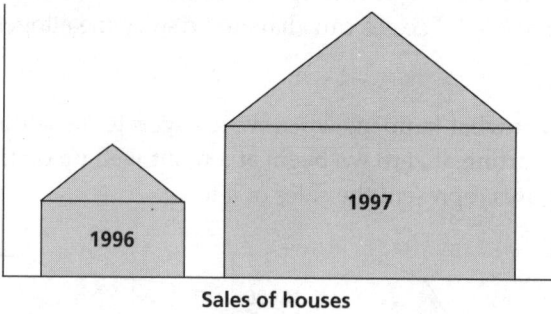

Sales of houses

Interpreting graphs and diagrams

We are constantly being bombarded with graphs and diagrams representing data in newspapers, magazines, books and on television. We need to be able to make sense of what we see. We have already shown how such diagrams can be misleading and we must therefore give children plenty of practice in interpreting representations of data.

The teacher displays the following pie charts on an overhead projector and says: *I wonder what stories these pie charts tell us?*

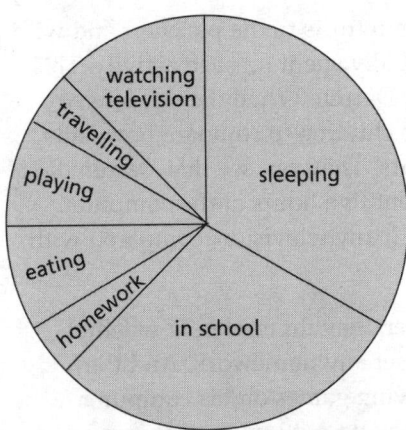

How Sally spent the last 24 hours

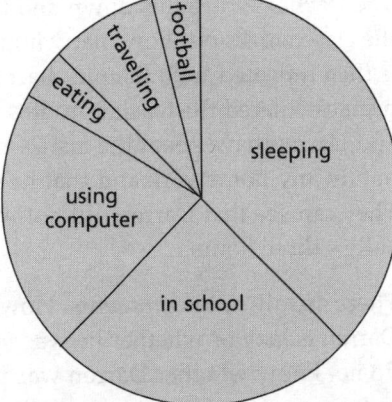

How Darren spent the last 24 hours

Pie charts

> You can use the pie charts to tell stories.

The teacher demonstrates how to inspect the pie charts and extract the information. First she inspects each sector and carefully reads out what the sector represents.

Extracting information

> *Look at this pie chart* [inspect the first pie chart]. *This sector* [point] *shows us how much time Sally spent sleeping in the last twenty-four hours. And this* [point] *shows us how much time she spent in school. And this shows ...*

Before doing any calculations she looks at the chart to see what general impressions can be gained from it.

Demonstrating how to inspect diagrams

> *This sector* [point to sleeping] *and this sector* [point to school] *are the biggest sectors. This means that Sally spends quite a lot of her day sleeping and going to school. This sector* [point to homework] *and this sector* [point to travelling] *are the smallest sectors. This means that Sally does not spend much time doing her homework or travelling. We can say* [point to remaining sectors] *that she spends some of her day watching television, eating and playing. We want to know exactly how much time Sally spent doing all these things.*

> This general description should precede interpretation by measuring sector angles.

The teacher removes the pie chart from the OHP and replaces it with a circle (of the same radius as the pie chart) with 360 degrees marked out. She places it so that 360 and 0 are both at the top and the numbers are marked clockwise.

Interpreting the sectors of a circle

> *This circle represents 24 hours* [trace around the circle]. *It is like a 24-hour clock. You turn through 360 degrees if you go all around the circle. How many hours is this* [point to bottom point of circle]? *Yes, 12 hours. How many degrees have you turned in 12 hours? Yes, 180 degrees. How many hours is this* [point to right-hand quarter]? *Yes, 6 hours. How many degrees have you turned in 6 hours? Yes, 90 degrees. How many ...* [continue to point to various places around the circle]. *How many hours is this* [point to 15 degrees]? *Yes, 1 hour. How many degrees have you turned in 1 hour? Yes, 15 degrees. Three hundred and sixty divided by twenty-four is fifteen.*

> The example has been chosen because the circle can be seen as a clock with hands turning.

The teacher now places the circle marked in degrees over the pie chart, ensuring that one of the division lines coincides with zero.

> *Now we can see how many hours Sally spent sleeping. Let us count in fifteens* [trace around the sector for sleeping]. *Fifteen, thirty, forty-five,*

sixty, ... one hundred and twenty. That is eight fifteens. Sally spent eight hours sleeping.

The teacher writes this down and then returns to the pie chart and with the class works out how many hours Sally spent on each activity. This is then repeated with the pie chart for Darren. When the times have been calculated the teacher invites the children to compare how Sally and Darren have spent the last 24 hours. They can see that Darren did not do any homework and that he spent five hours at the computer. They can see that Darren did not watch any television, compared with Sally's three hours.

These are all valid comments. However, they do not know whether Darren is lazy or whether he was not set any homework. And they do not know whether Darren was playing games on his computer or learning from an encyclopaedia. They do not know what sort of programmes Sally watched on TV. It is important at this stage to be clear about what can be gleaned from the pie charts as certain facts and what is speculation.

The children can now be organized in groups and each group given their own copies of the two pie charts. They will also need a transparent circle marked in degrees to measure the sectors (unless they are proficient in using a protractor). First they have to work out what they definitely know about the two children represented by their pie charts. They can then be asked to write a fictional story about the two children. Each group can be invited to tell their story to the class, using the pie charts to indicate the facts that they can be certain about. The children can be encouraged to say 'This is fact' and 'This is fiction'.

This way of demonstrating how to interpret diagrams and graphs should be repeated with bar charts, line graphs, pictograms and so on. Each time be clear about what can be read from these various representations and what is only speculation.

Matching stories to diagrams and graphs

Children love to work with stories and bringing story-telling into maths makes it more exciting. They also love to work like detectives and you can bring these two activities together in handling data. You can give the children a short story to read. Then show them six different diagrams and graphs and ask them to match the story with the correct representation. You can make the task more challenging by leaving the graphs untitled or not labelling the axes.

When the children have read the story to themselves you can read it together as a whole class and search for data. Whenever you find a piece of data ask a child to come and write it on the board. Collect together all the data and then inspect each diagram and graph to see if there is a match. There may be more than one that matches. For each one that is rejected a reason must be given.

When this has been demonstrated to the whole class the children can work in groups with several different stories and a selection of diagrams and graphs. Each group can be given the same set of materials to work on so that they can compare their results in the summarizing phase of the lesson.

Comparing data

Speculation

Using data to tell a story

Matching text to diagrams

A common mistake is to make incorrect inferences from data representation.

Work in maths can assist the children's literacy skills.

The mean	**Summary statistics**

Summary statistics

In the scripts you saw how the teacher demonstrated how to look at a sample set of data and describe what can be seen (descriptive statistics) and how to work out the mean (a summary statistic). Now suppose the two sample sets had been:

> Sample set A: 2, 5, 6, 7, 10
> Sample set B: 2, 2, 6, 10, 10

> *Because we are working with small sample sets we can immediately see that the two sets are different.*

We are using two small sample sets here for the purpose of illustration, though summary statistics are primarily designed to provide information about large sets of data.

Comparing sets of data

In both of these sample sets the smallest number is 2, the greatest number is 10. Hence the range for both is 8. The mean for both sets is 6. If you did not have the raw data in front of you but were given the summary 'The range is 8 and the mean is 6', you might be led to believe that the two samples were identical. However, when you look at the raw data you see that this is clearly not the case.

What is it that is different about the two samples? If you make up the two samples with bricks as described in the script and place each sample on a number line you will see that Sample set B is much more spread out than Sample set A. How can we describe this 'spreadoutness'?

Deviations from the mean

Let us inspect the data again and look at how each number differs from the mean. In other words, let us see how each number 'deviates' from the mean. We can work this out for Sample set A. The mean is 6 so the deviations from the mean are: ⁻4, ⁻1, 0, 1, 4. If we add these up we get zero. Oh dear! That is not very helpful. However, statisticians decided that they would overcome this little problem by squaring each of these differences to get rid of the negative numbers. The squares of the differences are: 16, 1, 0, 1, 16. So the total of these is 34. If we share this among every member in the sample (divide by 5) we get 6.8. Now, because we squared all the deviations earlier we are not working in the correct units, so we must now take the square root of this number to get 2.6. We call this number the standard deviation of the sample set.

> *The word 'difference' is used in maths to mean the positive result of subtraction. The word 'deviation' requires us to subtract each number from the mean.*

Standard deviation

Let us summarize this.
- Work out the deviation from the mean for each member of the set.
- Square the deviations.
- Find the total of the squared deviations.
- Divide by the number of members in the set.
- Find the square root of the answer to get the standard deviation.

> *This is an algorithm for calculating the standard deviation. It can be written as an algebraic formula.*

Using standard deviation to compare sets of data

On its own the standard deviation is fairly meaningless. However, if we now work out the standard deviation for the other sample set we can compare these measures of spread. In fact, the standard deviation for Set B is 3.6 and you can see that this tells us that Set B is more spread out than Set A. We have a way of comparing the two sets.

Making links and connections

We are not suggesting that you teach this to young children. We have described this work to illustrate why it is important to work with young children in ways that can be developed later. Building the necessary foundations for later work to provide for continuity and coherence is crucial. The work on calculating the mean, as seen in the scripts, leads naturally into the work on calculating the standard deviation. Making these links and connections is the key to effective teaching.

Probability

There are many words used in probability, such as 'certain', 'likely' and 'chance', that are also used in our everyday language. The day-to-day familiarity with these words can lead to incorrect use and misconceptions in maths. Teachers need to demonstrate how these words are used correctly in maths and show how the words carry with them numerical quantities. For example, the word 'impossible' means a probability of zero, whereas 'certain' means a probability of one.

The language of probability

Quantifying probability

Defining the two extremes of probability as 0 and 1 means that all other probabilities must lie between 0 and 1. Expressing probability as a number brings together all the different forms of representing numbers. For example, if we toss a coin we may say that the probability of getting a tail is a half (fractional form), or 0.5 (decimal form) or 50% (percentage form) or that the chance of getting a head or a tail is 50 : 50 (ratio form). Unless children's understanding of the language and fluency of number is good they may have difficulty in recognizing these different forms.

Children will need to recognize these different forms of number to be able to quantify probability.

We can introduce young children to the language associated with probability by getting them to place events that they are familiar with in order of 'likelihood', using words such as 'impossible', 'very unlikely', 'unlikely', 'evens', 'likely', 'very likely', 'certain'. Write a set of events on cards and ask children to come to the board and put them in order of probability, starting with 'impossible'. Get the children to explain how they made their decisions about where to place events. When doing this activity it is important to choose events that can be placed in order from what is known about them. When the children have ordered events using language they can place these events on a probability scale from 0 to 1. Use cardboard arrows to indicate the positions on the scale.

This is by no means a simple task for many children.

Writing probability in different forms

The probability scale should be written variously in fractions, decimals and percentages. Children need to be able to move flexibly between these forms of writing probability. In particular they need to recognize that 100% is equivalent to 1 (it has the same value but a different appearance).

Theoretical probability

There are some theoretical probabilities that need careful introduction. We can look at a coin and see that provided it is perfectly symmetrical it is equally likely to fall on its head or tail when tossed. We can *calculate* that the probability that it will fall on its head is a half. The reason we can say this is because there are exactly two possible equally likely outcomes and one of those is a head. That does not mean that if we toss a coin several times it will come up heads, tails, heads, tails ... and so on. It does mean that if we toss a coin many, many times about half of the times we shall get a head and the other half tails (and the fraction gets closer to being a half the more throws we try).

These are sophisticated ideas. Events in real life are rarely equally likely to happen.

Equally likely outcomes

Similarly if we throw a fair die we can calculate the probability of getting the number 4 as one sixth. There are six equally likely outcomes and one of them is a 4. The probability of getting an even number is a half because three of the six possible outcomes are even. Again this does not mean that if we throw a die six times we will get three even numbers. It is only when we throw the die lots of times that we begin to get about half of the results being even. When we can calculate probability from knowledge about equally likely events we are stating a theoretical probability.

In situations in which each of the possible outcomes is equally likely:

$$\text{Probability of an outcome} = \frac{\text{number of favourable outcomes}}{\text{number of possible outcomes}}$$

When children have seen how to calculate theoretical probability they need to carry out experiments to verify their results. When they toss a coin a hundred times, how close do they get to achieving an equal number of heads and tails? What about a thousand times? How can they organize the work to make large numbers of trials possible?

Children are often surprised when their experiments produce results close to the theoretical answers.

Estimating probability

Using statistical data to estimate probability

We do not often encounter events that are equally likely in real life. We normally have to collect data over a period of time or carry out experiments in order to estimate probability. For example, the weather can be predicted from probabilities that have been estimated using statistical data collected over many years. In industry, samples are checked on a regular basis to estimate the probability of a product being faulty. You can see that there is a distinction to be made between experimental probability and theoretical probability. Weather forecasters make some estimate of the probability of a certain pattern of weather by considering their records and relating these to current weather conditions. This is experimental probability. When we deal with packs of cards and dice our discussion of probability is based on the fact of certain events being equally likely. When we are interested in seeing a 'six' turn up, there is no reason to contemplate previous experience of getting sixes. The probability of getting a six is entirely related to the symmetry of the dice. Our calculation of probability is theoretical.

Common misconceptions

One of the most common misconceptions held by children concerns games of chance. When playing such games the children can see that there are two possible outcomes: win or lose. What they do not see is that these two outcomes may not be equally likely. The result of this misconception is to think that there is always a 50:50 chance of winning or losing one of these games. This often follows people into adulthood, as demonstrated by those people who buy lottery tickets believing that they have an even chance of winning!

If people were to stop and calculate their chances of winning they would not be so keen to gamble.

Games of chance

Children need experience of playing games where winning has a low probability. An example would be a win achieved by throwing two dice and getting a total of 10. There are thirty-six possible outcomes when throwing two dice and only three of these give a total of 10. The probability of winning is therefore three thirty-sixths or one twelfth.

Further reading

The nature of critical reflection

Papers can be found at the Letts web site.

A detailed knowledge of psychology can be used to examine pedagogy.

The writings of Vygotsky

The nature of explanation

The nature of instructional representation

Introduction

Teaching is a complex and intellectual activity. In this book we provide a framework for understanding its complexity. This framework has been developed from a principled analysis of theoretical ideas, empirical research and developmental work in classrooms with teachers and children. This is the nature of critical reflection. The background work to this book is contained in a number of papers which can be found at the Letts web site (www.lettsed.co.uk).

There are many papers at this site. Below we provide a brief description of the ten most relevant to the ideas in this book and list a further five useful titles. The papers themselves also suggest additional reading.

Ten principal papers

• *Introduction to psychology*

Most people find reading about psychology difficult and tend to deny its relevance to teaching. In fact, as a teacher you should have a detailed knowledge of psychology which you can use to examine your pedagogy. This paper provides an introduction to the psychology associated with teaching and learning. When you read this paper keep trying to relate it to the scripts and discussions in this book.

All too often methods of teaching are selected to satisfy immediate needs rather than a long-term view of how children learn.

• *Activity theory*

Activity theory, *Explanation* and *Instructional representation* are the three papers which have been crucial to the development of this book. *Activity theory* deals with epistemology (the nature of knowledge) and offers a discussion which is essential reading for professional teachers. Activity theory has its roots in the writings of Vygotsky, which are currently popular, and develops this work further.

• *Explanation*

This paper provides a detailed discussion of the nature of explanation and clarifies why an understanding of this is essential for every classroom practitioner.

• *Instructional representation*

You will have noticed that in our work we persistently refer to maths stories, real stories and real-life stories. As you read this paper cast your mind back over the scripts and discussion in this book to see how they relate to the idea of instructional representation. Everyone teaching maths should have the clearest possible idea of the nature of instructional representation and how it relates to subject knowledge.

- *The nature of maths*

This paper complements the *Key ideas* both in this book and in *Mathematics for Primary Teachers: An Audit and Self-study Guide*. A thorough understanding of the nature of maths is vital to all maths teachers.

See *Key ideas* in this book (pp.10–21) and in *Mathematics for Primary Teachers: An Audit and Self-study Guide* (pp.80–91).

- *Assessment*

This paper provides a background to the purpose and nature of assessment in the national curriculum for pupils.

The purpose and nature of assessment

- *Context versus concepts*

As you read this paper try to relate the ideas it contains to those of instructional representation. In recent years it has been popular to claim that all maths should be taught in context, i.e. that it should be made relevant. This is not appropriate to the effective teaching of maths. This paper demonstrates once again how teachers need to plan their use of maths stories, real stories and real-life stories.

Maths stories, real stories and real-life stories

- *Cognitive apprenticeship*

A description of how trainee teachers can be enabled to access the craft-knowledge of experts, this paper is included here because it has direct relevance to the way all teachers need to work with their pupils. As you read this paper relate it to our *Framework for teaching maths* and especially to the idea of assisted performance.

- *Supervisory conferences*

This paper describes the importance of articulating to another person what has been learnt. You will see that supervisory conferences are an important feature of learning to teach. As you read this paper connect the idea of articulation to the essential features of the summarizing phase of a teaching episode. You should increasingly see that children learn maths through the medium of language in the same sophisticated way that you are learning to teach.

Describing, explaining and justifying are the crucial constituents of a convincing argument.

Making connections between learning to teach and learning maths

- *A discussion of teaching*

Recent government initiatives have provoked substantial changes to the way in which maths is taught. This paper offers a detailed critique of what was previously common practice and contributes to the professional debate about what is involved in teaching maths effectively. The paper also shows how the ideas in this book take account of the work of the psychologist Jerome Bruner and its relationship to instructional representation.

You can look at examples of students' work to see how they have used all these papers in examining their own understanding of teaching.

How the ideas in this book developed

Five further papers
Discussion in the maths classroom
Numeracy
How children learn maths
Attitudes towards maths
Algebra

You can also find scripts and their analysis at the Letts web site.